INFRASPECIFIC CHEMICAL TAXA
OF MEDICINAL PLANTS

ABBREVIATIONS

Organs

Ba	bark
Bu	bulb
Fl	inflorescence
Fr	fruit
Lf	leaf
My	mycelium
Pl	peel
Rh	rhizome
Rt	root
Sc	sclerotium
Sd	seed
Sh	shoot
Sp	sporophyte
St	stem
Tb	terminal branchlet
Th	thallus
Tu	tuber
Tw	twig
Wd	wood
Wp	whole plant above ground

Indication of physical condition

E-O	essential oil
J	juice
LX	latex
OR	oleoresin
PS	press-sap
TP	turpentine

Chemical taxa

A	acid
Abs.	absent
Ac	acetate
Ch.	chemical
CHAR	character(s)
CORR	correlation
D	difference(s)
DEP	dependent
IDP	independent
IND	individual
ISP	infraspecific
MA	main alkaloid
MC	main component
MP	morphological
OG	ontogenetical
PHYS	physiological
Pst.	present
Tr.	traces
VAR	variation(s)

INFRASPECIFIC CHEMICAL TAXA OF MEDICINAL PLANTS

BY

PÉTER TÉTÉNYI D. Sc. (Biol.)

DIRECTOR OF RESEARCH INSTITUTE FOR MEDICINAL PLANTS, BUDAPEST

CHEMICAL PUBLISHING CO., INC.
200 PARK AVENUE SOUTH NEW YORK, N.Y.

General Part translated by István Finály

Special Part translated by Péter Tétényi

TO MY WIFE
DR. MAGDOLNA E. TÉTÉNYI

CONTENTS

INTRODUCTION

Medicinal plants* belong to the earliest plants collected and cultivated by man. However, it was only in the course of the 19th century that the very nature of their usefulness was elucidated, as a consequence of the development of chemical and pharmacological sciences. Since then the earlier, purely empirical use of medicinal plants has been replaced by a scientific application of medicinal plants based on knowledge of the active substances present in these plants, and on deliberately inducing the effects. From this date, research into medicinal plants was undertaken with the scope of isolating the active substance detected in a plant species and from other ones too, and of establishing the composition (main ingredient and accessory substances) of the active substance of the species and of detecting the corresponding and pharmacologically differing effects.

Meanwhile, infraspecific differences in the active substance remained undetected because, quite obviously, the investigation of average samples obtained on macroscale by scientists could not disclose any infraspecific distinctions. The botanical-morphological classification of subspecific systematic categories resulted in their chemical-pharmacological investigation at the end of the 19th century. Obviously this happened only in the case of species which had already been studied to a satisfactory extent. By the beginning of the third decade of the 20th century, however, phytochemical processes had evolved (in place of average samples and) for analyzing microsamples. In this way, it became possible to detect infraspecific individual chemical differences, quite independently of morphological ones.

By extending the range of observations, the existence, within the species, of so-called "chemical races", "biochemical varieties", or "physiological forms", could be established, proving the occurrence of deviations at a taxonic level. The existence of these infraspecific chemical taxa affects not only pharmacognosy but also botany, biochemistry, genetics and their practical applications, namely the breeding and production of medicinal plants. Thus e.g. the detection of the chemical differentiation of spontaneously occurring medicinal plants results in discovering the sites of the infraspecific taxon yielding material of superior quality and in car-

---

* Both here and in the following discussions the concept of medicinal plants is interpreted in a rather broad sense. The term medicinal plant comprises all collected and cultivated plants whether employed directly for their curative power, or utilized as raw materials in pharmaceutical or essential oil industry, or used as spices.

rying out the collection there. Similarly, in cultivating new species of medicinal plants, the production of a regional variety containing the adequate active substance only is preferable. In the case of drug standards and pharmacopeian specifications the definitions of the level of plant species generally used up to the present appear to be frequently unsatisfactory. More accurate infraspecific definitions are needed, with respect to possible deviations in therapeutic effects.

The infraspecific chemical differences in the processing of medicinal plants are of no less importance. The technique of processing a variety containing only a sole alkaloid or a sole glycoside may deviate widely from that required for isolating one or two therapeutically useful components from a complexity of active substances present in other plant varieties. This is even more complicated by the presence of possible accompanying substances which are likewise due to the chemical nature of the given variety. These directly affect the processing of the herb, as well as the costs of processing.

The breeding of medicinal plants, similarly to that of other cultivated plants, earlier was based on morphological characters. Evaluation and selection on the basis of microchemical, individual analysis to an appropriate extent took place only in later periods of the history of breeding. Still, there were no trends of evolving chemical taxa and no deliberate directions were perceivable in the breeding of medicinal plants.

The theoretical aspects of research into infraspecific chemical taxa are of no less significance. Studying the inheritance of differences in the contents of active substances may facilitate more detailed information on inherited properties, while the detection of the existence of chemically differentiated infraspecific taxa may promote the determination of the interrelations of the species and its varieties.

Though the literature of infraspecific chemical taxa is fairly abundant,* up to now no attempts have been made to prepare a comprehensive survey of this field from either the Hungarian or worldwide aspects. The scope of the present work is merely to offer a tentative critical review. This survey, the first of its kind in this field, must be limited to a rough presentation of problems with an emphasis

* The more important milestones in the development of our knowledge on infraspecific chemical taxa are indicated as follows.

1882 — Moens discriminated *Cinchona ledgeriana* var. *chinidinifera* from var. *cinchonidinifera;*

1906 — Stapf distinguished the "Physiological races" of *Andropogon nardus* L.;

1921 — Klein defined the "Chemische Rassen" of *Galium mollugo* L.;

1937 — *Problems of Inheritable Chemical Characters.* Discussions. Academy of Sciences USSR, Moscow;

1957 — *Chemical Races of Medicinal and Useful Plants.* Conference. Nederl. Verg. Geneeskr. Wageningen,

1960 — *Infraspecific Chemical Differentiation.* Symposium. FIP Med. Plant's Sect. Copenhagen.

1963 — *Chemically Characterized Infraspecific Units of Medicinal Plants.* Conference. Germ. Soc. Med. Plant Research. Zurich.

on facts considered of prominent importance, but should be regarded, at the same time, as a preparatory work for gathering a more thorough knowledge of the theme.

The author wishes to express his thanks for the aid given by the Ministry of Agriculture, Ministry of Heavy Industry, Biological Section of the Hungarian Academy of Sciences, and for the helpful assistance received from the personnel of the Research Institute for Medicinal Plants and the Publishing House of the Hungarian Academy of Sciences and the Academy Press; herewith he would like to acknowledge his particular indebtedness to Professor R. Soó, who has been most obliging in revising the manuscript of this work.

GENERAL PART

1. INFRASPECIFIC DIFFERENTIATION

1.1. INFRASPECIFIC DIFFERENCES AND THEIR POSSIBLE CAUSES

A species represents a definite phase of the evolution process (Komarov, 1940), i.e. a state of specific quality of the living substance which is defined, besides the common origin and separation from other living organisms *(hiatus)*, rather by a complexity of intrinsic and external characters. Despite the homogeneity of this quality, the diversity of the individua in a species, the occurrence of infraspecific differences cannot escape our attention. It is just for this reason that most of the recent scientific treatises search for an interpretation of the concept of species and evolution in the intrinsic conditions of the species.[*]

Infraspecific varieties as deviations from the species had already been described by Linné (1751), but Adanson (1763) was the first to study these varieties experimentally, drawing some conclusions for certain plants (barley, strawberries, etc.) which proved to be valid even today. Based precisely on cultivated varieties, Darwin (1955) detected the existence of infraspecific varieties occurring in nature and deduced a multitude of wild varieties from the conditions of spreading and the evolution of species, i.e. with "predominance". Darwin distinguishes between infraspecific varieties which being transitory ones may serve as bases for the development of a new species. The interest raised by the publication of the "Origin of Species" induced also De Candolle (1872) to investigate the infraspecific conditions. He found that the plants grown from seeds from different sites within the area of the species have different vegetation periods (*Trifolium repens* L., *Senecio vulgaris* L. etc.).

Most of the Darwinian, evolutionist authors (e.g. Jurjev, 1952) even today hold the view that the infraspecific systematical units represent transitions to new taxa. According to Stebbins (1950), the races and subspecies are the initial substances of the development of a new species. Vasiljchenko (1958) considers the varieties to be deviations from the average. According to this opinion, the infraspecific taxa are actually the representatives of a gradual transition: they are already steps leading to the new species.

This recognition of the differentiated quality and its extension over the limits of the species deprive the species of its real existence. In fact, the infraspecific

---

[*] Distinction is made, on the one hand, between macrosystematics where research on and into the order of the species is undertaken, and, on the other hand, microevolution and microsystematics, respectively, dealing with infraspecific development and changes (Timofejev-Ressovsky, 1958). The use of the more correct and internationally accepted term infraspecific (*infraspécifique* in French and *внутривидовая* in Russian) systematics is to be preferred to the above-cited terms.

taxa are not deviations from the species but rather components constituting the species in their complexity, and this is the opinion generally accepted by modern descriptive systems (e.g. Willis, 1940, Lamprecht, 1959) because variety is no "alternation" (Soó, 1964).

The species is the sum total of the varieties, while the differentiated infraspecific groups are realizations of the species under various conditions. Consequently, the differentiated varieties, i.e. the forms of existence of the species can be determined on the basis of their conditions of existence rather than on their deviations from the generalized criteria. Diversity and the great number of varieties are guarantees and proofs of the prosperity of the species.

If the *cultivated taxa* as results of human activity are added to the infraspecific differences spontaneously evolved in nature, it is clearly evident that infraspecific diversity can be raised to great extent. For example according to Zhukovski (1950), 2,000 varieties of *Malus domestica* Borkh. and 3,000 varieties of *Triticum aestivum* L. are known, and these cultivated species are not the only ones in that respect! Human activity, agriculture, crop production represent altered conditions which can be utilized by the plants and to which the plants must adapt themselves. Thus, breeding in combination with the effects of natural conditions develop the cultivated taxa.

According to Juzepchuk (1948), the cultivated species do not correspond to the concept of wild species since they are frequently of a polyphyletic and heterotypic character which otherwise occurs also in the case of wild species. Owing to their diversity, which is doubtlessly a result of differentiation due to their being cultivated and to the weakening of solid heredity, they can prosper even under diverse ecological conditions and are well capable of adapting themselves to the respective regional environment.

The taxon which has undergone an adaptation of this kind and which has become more stable in respect to the quantity and quality of yield, has been denoted by Konstantinov (1946) as agroecotype. The diminished solidity of inheritance leads to the drawback that the species do not always adequately retain their characteristic properties. For that, human interference is necessary. Though the crossings and other direct deteriorations can be avoided in this way, the species nevertheless becomes sooner or later aged, and is omitted from cultivation.

In contrast to natural selection, plant breeding results in a continuous, unbroken "line of development" (Jirásek, 1958); however, individua with less favourable biological properties may be retained if so required by the needs of the breeders. That is, the natural propagation methods of plants become superfluous or even unfavourable from the aspect of collecting the yield of seeds (e.g. spontaneous drop of seeds).

According to Darwin, the differences in the same species, under natural and other conditions, are to be attributed to causes such as diversity, possibility of securing advantages, infraspecific battle, and natural selection. Of the great number of representatives of this opinion, Jirásek can be mentioned, who considers natural selection as a primary cause and who understands by the natural limits of infraspecific taxa (and taxa above these) the hiatus caused by natural selection itself.

The development of infraspecific units may be correlated with the changing external conditions and with the (intrinsic) reaction of the living. This intrinsic possibility is, in an organism which has attained any of the steps of phylogeny, directly connected with metabolism, with the chemism of the living. The opinion of Souèges (1938) is quite correct in that the differentiation of species is fundamentally a chemical problem. This earlier statement has been supported also by molecular biology (Straub, 1965), a new field of science developed in the course of the evolution of biochemistry. Biological phenomena are closely related to the chemical and physical properties of macromolecules occurring in living organisms. The characteristics of living organisms may be attributed to the alterations which continuously occur in these organisms, to the specified enzymes which control these alterations, and to the different nature, ratio and activity of these enzymes, depending on well-defined conditions. This so-called enzyme stock can be traced back to the proteins of cells, to their composition and structure which are in fact the fundamentals of all inherited properties. According to Blagoveshchenski (1960), the fundamental differences appearing in the course of phylogeny manifest themselves mainly in the differences of proteins present in the organisms and, in connection with that, in differences of the ferment systems. All other differences (morphological, anatomical) are only the consequences of these.

Törő (1966) considers that the basis of differentiating cells can be found in chemo-differentiation at a molecular level.

On investigating the rise of chemical taxa from the numerous aspects of molecular biology, the biochemical process of metabolism and its genetic control are of particular interest. According to Mothes (1957), "real genetics of metabolism began only when the genetical analysis of a larger collection of races chemically differing from each other became possible". Though genetical research was primarily directed to the synthesis of proteins and to the role of DNA-RNA in this process, there are also data on the genetically determined being, synthesis and control of the so-called "secondary" metabolites.

Thus, it has been proved by Mothes et al. (1955) and later by Steinegger (1958) that it is impossible to produce alkaloid-free individua of alkaloid-bearing species by irradiation. The production and accumulation of alkaloids to a limited extent is an indispensable part of plant metabolism because the variants with low alkaloid contents sooner or later die out. It is likely that the other, more complicated mechanism reported by Chakravarty (1963) is already characteristic of chemical taxa. Namely, the four taxa of *Trifolium repens*. L., differ from each other in that they contain lotaustralin and the enzyme linamarase which hydrolyses lotaustralin, or only the glycoside or enzyme, respectively, or containing neither the enzyme nor the substrate. The analysis of the F_2 of crossing by groups indicated that the control of cyanogenesis and linamarase synthesis is quite independent of each other. However, the occurrence of hybrids which appear in a striking variability and in

2

quite unexpected compositions point to the possible role of modificators in the examined genetical system.

The above-mentioned two independent examples of the absence of active substances and of the control of their synthesis have been combined in experiments by Micke (1962). In order to select coumarin-free varieties of sweet clover, hybrids of *Melilotus albus* Desr. ap. Lam. and *M. dentatus* (W. et K.) Pers. were produced. On recrossing a strain free of O-coumaric acid glycoside by another, containing coumarin, a medium level was observed in F_1 generation, while a so-called "semi-dominant monofactorial" segregation was experienced in the later generations. This is already a transition to the hybrid investigations carried out with the genus *Baptisia* (Alston and Turner, 1963). According to this, polyphenols afford more authentic data for introgression than the morphological features with spontaneous hybrids.

The recent interpretation of the detected *unity* of the living organisms and their environment, and the extension of this interpretation to their substances (Straub, 1965) point to their close correlation, on which the characters of the living, including their metabolism and their differentiation, depend. Namely, metabolism may also take place in the same way as that of the direct ancestors, though it is possible for the organism to deviate from that of the ancestors, in order to secure its viability under conditions deviating from the earlier ones, and to alter its inheritance. The intrinsic contradiction of the species consists, as stated by Soó (1953), in being constant (with inheritable characters) and at the same time alterable (producing new taxa). The intrinsic possibility, i.e. variability, prevailed (and still prevails today) since the start of phylogeny, up to the development of the present forms of existence, and this is just the biological aspect of the general evolution rule of the material world. Changes in ecological-geographical (biological) conditions are directly or indirectly reflected in the rise of infraspecific taxa, by their number and nature. It has been established by Soó (1926) that stable biotypes emerge from populations of primeval forms, on the selecting effect of coenological factors, particularly on that of the habitat. According to Heslop-Harrison (1960), immediately detectable variation differences are induced in the population by an unusual environment. This does not mean that "latent genetical variation" manifests itself, due to the influence of conditions of temperature, light, etc. but rather that the living react actively, quite in accordance with their inheritance.

A number of authors are of the opinion that alterations which take place on account of climatic, soil and other ecological-geographical factors are only temporary modifications, and this is certainly true in some cases. However, it may be presumed as well that prolonged environmental effects may cause inheritable changes. This was considered to be the case by Linné and Darwin, and by contemporary botanists: Rothmaler (1950), Soó (1956), Zhukovski (1949) also held this view. Keller (1952), the founder of the evolutionist trend in plant ecology, and Shakhov (1952, 1959) accept the inheritance of changes induced by ecological effects and their important role in phylogeny, as proved by their experiments. The British "experimental botanist" Heslop-Harrison (1960) came to the conclusion that "the acquired characteristics become genetically assimilated". According to the theory of the "ecologically directed adaptation mechanism" evolved by Hegnauer (1959), under various ecological-geographical conditions, different local plant populations and ecotypes* (which summarize them, respectively) are developed, due to the adaptability of plants. Ecotypes, according to Hegnauer, are the "raw material" of evolution, and if, owing to certain causes, hybridization is inhibited in some directions or it becomes entirely impossible (e.g. owing to geographical limits; to differences of floral-biology and periods of flowering; to intersterility), ecotypes may develop into species–ecospecies or into series of species–species aggregates. This dynamic Darwinian interpretation of the "little species" theory of Jordan (1873) and of the "ecotype" theory of Turesson is undoubtedly a positive feature of the concepts of Hegnauer.

The ecotype is, in turn, rather the result of natural selection (Zhukovski, 1949) instead of being the "raw material" of further evolution. The forms of existence of the species, even if taxa exceeding the limits of species are formed from them, are just proofs of the unity and viability of the species and not that of "self-liqui-dation" mechanism or forerunners for extinguishing the species. It appears to be more correct, on investigating this phenomenon, similarly to Jurjev (1952), as regards agricultural production and plant breeding, to consider this biotype (or these biotypes) as ecotypes which have been formed on the creating effect of plant habitat, and which are characterized by specific inheritable properties e.g. in re-spect to the vegetation period and stages of development. Just for this reason we cannot accept the attempt of Hegnauer to assign certain ecological categories in an obligatory way to systematic categories, even if such a procedure is complete-ly justified facultatively in certain cases (cf. Soó, 1964). Another feature of Hegnauer's concept which can be criticized is that he considers the changes taking place on ecological effects as those which gradually all lead automatically to new species. It is more likely that these changes occur after a preparatory period of accumulation, more or less combined with each other, rather simul-taneously, and this is why a hiatus is raised. This sudden change based on the accumulation of effects is defined as mutation by classical genetics. Subsequently, the adequately adapted plant individua and taxa, respectively, emerge from these mutants on the effect of natural selection, and of the drift (Brehm, 1966).

However, some authors, in contrast with the above-mentioned considerations, derive infraspecific (chemical) differences from the spontaneous crossing of species (Nikolaev et al., 1961) and from introgression, respectively (Dillemann, 1957, 1960; Mirov, 1956, 1961; Taylor, 1963, etc.), the term introgression was suggested by Andersen (1953). Still, this spectacular theory which is based according to Bobrov (1961) on the formal genetical concept, may explain only the direct rea-son and not how the concerned character transferable by introgression came into existence. Thus, though the route of introgression, and hybridization is important

---

* Ecotype is a term coined by Turesson (1922). Within the ecotype, Sennikov (1953) dis-tinguishes climato-type, edapho-type and coenotype.

from practical and technical aspects, it can be considered theoretically only as a primary, empirical explanation. For example, the variation in *Juniperus virginiana* L. long thought to be due to widespread hybridization between that species and the allopatric *J. ashei* Buchh. In fact, there was no chemical evidence of introgression to be found anywhere. More recent investigations have shown that the populational structuring is one of clinal intergradation (Flake et al., 1968). Although Hall (1952) ascribed its origin as due to introgression, it seems rather that the variation may be attributed to parallel selective influences as was first suggested by Barber and Jackson (1957).

1.2. INFRASPECIFIC DIFFERENCES IN CHEMISM AND THEIR CAUSES

The nature of the plant is in fact the characteristic structure together with the typical metabolism. This latter refers to a reaction complex, to the operation of a ferment system (Oparin, 1937) consisting of processes running in defined main directions and linked to each other in time. The chemical composition characteristic of the given plant is formed as a result of all these. Though processes of the same type may also occur in different plant species or in different infraspecific taxa, these always possess some concrete specificity. Blagoveshchenski (1950) is thus quite right in stating that within the species, each variety preserves its own biochemical characteristics, even if the natural conditions are altered to a great extent (e.g. the sour and the sweet apple varieties). Still, infraspecific differences even if they are defined, are not great, and we find generally greater differences only at the level of species or families. This also supports biochemically the Darwinian theory of divergence.

It is the merit of Ivanov (1915) of being the first to recognise the effect of external conditions on the chemical composition of plants. He succeeded in proving that the examined plant species were chemically variable within the area; in the centre of the area they show an average content while moving away from the centre, the contents of active substances become more and more different. The experimental evidence of this concept was only later (1926) supplied by Ivanov and confirmed also by McNair (1929). This connection between the active substances and external conditions has been substantiated by botanists (Komarov, 1940), and proved by Baranov (1940) by his experiments carried out on the Pamir plateau.

The correlation between the geographical distribution and metabolism of plants has been thoroughly studied by Doroganevskaja (1953). She proved that the geographical variability of plants was based on variations in their metabolism which, in turn, are due to alterations in the external environmental conditions. Investigating the effect of certain ecological, but mainly climatical factors on the part reactions making up plant metabolism, she published some observations on medicinal plants too. Moreover it has been pointed out by her that linalool, the main component of the essential oil of coriander is present in the plant to varying degrees, depending on the climatic-soil conditions. Opium-bearing poppy in the cen-

20

tral territories of the U.S.S.R. is much poorer in alkaloids than the varieties in Central Asia. Analogous results were obtained by Rubin (1953) who found that *Dictamnus albus* L. growing in Central Asia is toxic while that growing near Moscow is not toxic. Hegnauer (1954) showed that among the tropical representatives, are the scopolamine producing species *Solanaceae* which produce alkaloids with a tropane skeleton. Presumably, these are the most primordial phylogenetically. The extratropical species growing in the cooler regions of the family area, produce hyoscyamine. Ilinskaya and Yosifova (1956), on investigating the variability of the total alkaloid contents of opium obtained from poppy, arrived at conclusions identical with that of Doroganevskaja. In their experiments these authors proved that the ratios of the alkaloid components to each other varied, and this points to a biochemical variability depending on ecological conditions.

Variations in the contents of active substances of medicinal plants due to environmental effects were the subject discussed at the Wageningen Conference. Subsequent to an introduction by Flück (1957), a number of complementary experimental data were given by Cuzin (1957) in respect to tobacco, by Schratz (1957) and Rovesti (1957) on essential oil bearing plants, and by Dillemann (1957) on cyanogenetic glycosids bearing plants. Later, Kirjalov and Konovalov (1959) dealt with the natural regularities controlling the storage of substances economically valuable in plants.

In general, infraspecific chemical differentiation can be attributed mainly to these ecological-geographical factors. At the Wageningen Conference Mothes

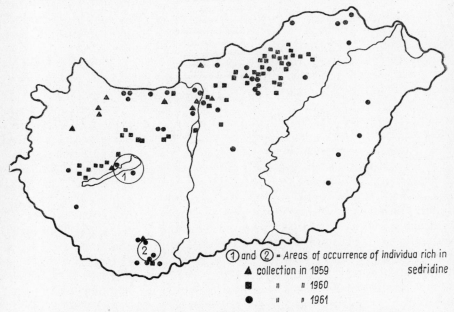

Fig. 1. Sites of spontaneous occurrence of *Sedum acre* L. in Hungary

(1957) stated that "chemical races" frequently occur as geographical races (e.g. *Claviceps, Duboisia* etc.). In the discussion of this theme, Bolshunov emphasized that chemical races occurring in nature can be considered as differentiated systematical units only when they meet the Vavilovian conditions, i.e. when they can

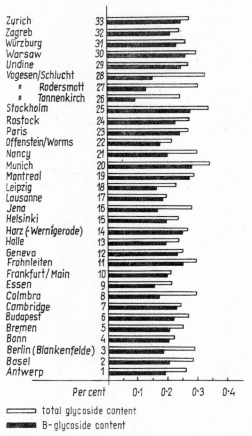

Fig. 2. Total glycoside and B-glycoside contents of *Digitalis purpurea* L. populations of various origin (Wirth, 1961). 1—33 = places of origin

be limited also from a geographical aspect. Our collections of *Sedum acre* L. from their spontaneous sites in Hungary proved that plant individua rich in sedridine occurred in two defined areas, in a region which climatically mostly approached the Mediterranean character (Priszter and Tétényi, 1963, Fig. 1). Similarly, differences were observed in the populations of *Digitalis purpurea* L. collected to compare the contents of total glycosides and B-glycoside from mainly European (and from a Canadian) gardens and grown in the same environment (Wirth, 1961, Fig. 2).

According to the observations of Rovesti (1957), essential oil bearing plants react in various ways, by regulating their osmotic pressure, to various ecological and soil alterations. Namely, the more severe the xerophil conditions become, the greater the extent that the simpler components of essential oils are converted into oxidized compounds which vigorously reduce the transpiration of the plants (in connection with their tension). This conversion promotes the drought resistance of the plant, i.e. it represents an "ecological advantage" (Jaminet, 1960). Investigating the components of the essential oil of *Thymus serrulatus* Hochst., Rovesti (1958) found that in Eritrea in the presence of a sufficient amount of soil moisture, the level of its linalool content may attain 20 per cent while under arid conditions it decreases to 3—5 per cent.

There is also experimental evidence in respect to the effect of climatic-edaphic conditions on alterations in the composition of plants. In the polar botanical gardens of the USSR, alterations of plant colour were observed by Shavrov (1961) on the effect of the environment over a period of 10—15 years. Thus, the originally golden yellow flowers of *Erigeron aurantiacus* RGL. in the second generation appeared in a diversity of colours, from white through yellow to dark brown and violet. Colour changes were also observed in the flowers of second generations of *Rhodiola linearifolia* A. Bor. and *Pyrethrum carneum* M. B.

It has been pointed out by Kirjalov (1939) that *Pycnanthemum lanceolatum* Pursh., a plant indigenous in the U.S.A. and containing carvacrol in its essential oil, did not produce any carvacrol after being introduced and after having multiplied in the U.S.S.R. The principal components of the essential oil of the variety grown in the U.S.S.R. were menthone and pulegone. Junusov (1950) reported that the plant *Cocculus laurifolius* DC. growing in Japan and containing the alkaloid coclaurine, was completely free of coclaurine when grown in the botanical gardens of Batumi. This latter variety, in turn, contained cocculine and cocculidine, two alkaloids of entirely different structure. According to the experiences of Woodward and Smith (1962), *Hyoscyamus muticus* L. grown along the upper course of the Nile contains 1·8 per cent alkaloid while the alkaloid content of the plants grown in the Nile delta is only around 0·1 per cent. The species *Ammi visnaga* L. in the Mediterranean basin contains much coumarin and cromone. In North America (Arizona), in turn, these compounds are present in the plant in just detectable traces.

The experiences of Daday (1954) of the differences in the active substance contents of spontaneously occurring *Trifolium repens* L. are very interesting. This species in many regions of Europe contains some cyanogenetic-glycoside while at other sites this is entirely absent. In Northeastern Europe and in the Alps at higher altitudes only populations free of glycoside occur, while in the Mediterranean basin and in Western Europe populations bearing cyanogenetic glycoside are widespread. It has been observed by Daday that the dividing line of cyanogen-bearing and free populations coincides with the course of the 0° median temperature isotherm of January (Fig. 3). Plants of this species contain cyanogenetic-glycoside when grown in warmer areas while those grown in cool areas are free of glycoside.

23

Thus, in respect to the areas of occurrence, the two chemically differentiated plant groups are geographically sharply separated. They may be described even as sub-species because morphological differentiation (e.g. white spots on the leaflets,

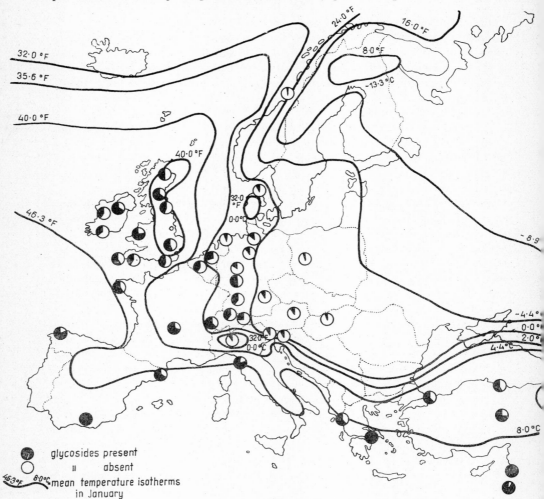

glycosides present
   "   absent
mean temperature isotherms
   in January

Fig. 3. Distribution of cyanogenetic glycoside-bearing and free *Trifolium repens* L. populations
(Daday, 1954)

deviating lengths of the flower headed inflorescence) was observed in the analysed spontaneous populations.

Jaminet and Böcher (1960), in the course of the discussions in Copenhagen, considered "chemical races" to be developed due to the influence of the environment. It has been definitely stated by Hegnauer (1959) that adaptation to ecologi-

24

cal-geographical conditions may be combined with biochemical alterations, with differentiations in active substances. Hanover (1966) could separate the part played by heredity and by environmental effects in the appearance of a chemical character determining the heritability factor.

The question arises whether infraspecific chemical differentiation occurs just as easily in nature as in cultivated conditions. In the opinion of Hegnauer (1957), "chemical races" are separated in nature, with greater difficulty than in cultivated conditions, owing to intercrossing. Woody plants with a long individual life span which are capable of transferring chemically different characters to their progeny over several years, and developing a population, are exceptions to this generalization. In contrast to natural conditions, "chemical races" can be readily selected and maintained separately in the course of cultivation and breeding.

Metabolism is to a certain extent defined by the infraspecific biochemical differences, making possible the interpretation of the existence of chemical taxa. Rubin is quite right in stating (1937) that the direction of the metabolism-ferment system is in fact the basis of the species of cultivated plants.

It is an established fact as well, that chemical characters are developed similarly to other characters (Mothes, 1957) and that they are of an identical hereditary value (Doroganevskaja, 1953). According to the latter's arrangement, the special substances developed on account of the biochemical characters cannot be classified into the group of formative or intermediary or reserve substances. In her opinion, the occurrence of these substances depends, in addition to external environmental effects, on the chemical characteristics and on the nature of the plants.

However, the biological role of the formation of special metabolites in plant life is still not cleared up. As regards the explanation of the character of essential oil, formation three interpretations (transpiration substances; reserve substances; protecting substances) were discussed at the Wageningen Conference without finally solving this problem. Hegnauer (1962), though emphasizing the technological character of the concept of essential oils, refers to the chemical aspects (mono- and sesquiterpenes, phenylpropane derivatives and aliphatic compounds), the concept of plant physiological excreta (anatomically differentiated storage areas, oil cells, channels etc.), and the completely deviating physiological role and localization of the heterosides with scented aglycons, and lastly the homologous nature of the odour substances of mushrooms.

Zolotnickaja's (1953) opinion on the correlation of the life forms of plants and of alkaloid production is of interest. According to her, plant alkaloids are not excreta but rather important biologically active complexes (acting as sensitizing agents against light effects of various spectral ranges). Later, it was proved by Mothes and his school *in vitro* that the presence of alkaloids is indispensable for the growth of tobacco plants. But as regards this, one cannot generalize.

In the radiation treatment of medicinal plants, attempts were made by some authors to produce plants free of active substances. Thus, in the case of the species *Datura stramonium* L. the alterations to the X_3 generation were examined by Mothes (1954) and by Mothes et al. (1955). No alkaloid-free plants were detected

25

among the obtained individuals. Far-reaching conclusions were drawn from this observation by stating that the presence of the alkaloid was indispensable for the normal life activity of the plant and that, if its ability for producing the alkaloid was suppressed on the effect of irradiation, the plant lost its viability and dies. This conclusion has been confirmed by the experiment of Steinegger (1958) which proved that in plant individua poor in alkaloids, earlier or later physiological disturbances followed by decay occur during ontogenesis.

Though the physiological role of the active substances of medicinal plants has not been elucidated thus far; Zenk (1967) shows their necessity in the synthesis of vitamin Q and of methionine as an example demonstrating enzymic regulation, compartmentability and the repeated use of specific substances, and rejects the theory to their being excreted or final products of metabolism. It is clear that these substances are in fact the products of specialised processes pertaining to the entity of metabolism. In a broader sense metabolism is the complexity of all the processes taking place in the plants, comprising both the fundamental and the specialized characteristics.

1.3. ESSENCE OF INFRASPECIFIC CHEMICAL DIFFERENTIATION; ONTOGENETIC HYPOTHESIS

In general, chemical taxa are differentiated within the species in the same way as the units segregating in other aspects, i.e. according to the ecological-geographical differences of the area of the species. The special chemical characteristics, the deviations, are manifest in the chemical character of differentiation, in the chemical features of taxa deviating from each other from qualitative and quantitative aspects, i.e. in *polychemism*, a term coined by Gurvich (1960).

Polychemism is apparently an arbitrarily chosen term since it refers to a plant product selected on the basis of the anthropomorphic principle. Namely, it means that the active substance of the plant is not homogeneous at the date when collection or harvesting is judged as most useful from an economic point of view. Though primarily the concept of polychemism is limited to the end product, all literature agrees that polychemism is in fact a final result, a consequence of the differences in the whole life processes of the plant. This is denoted e.g. by Culberson (1961) by the term *résumé biologique* in the case of lichens.

Polychemism, just as any other differentiation, is a characteristic which makes it necessary to determine the conditions of its formation, giving rise to its existence. Essentially, the chemical features do not deviate from other characters, their formation being linked to a determined moment of the metabolism of the living.

Up to the present, Schratz (1960, 1963) is the only author who published his opinion in respect to the connection between the infraspecific chemical taxa of the species of medicinal plants and the physiological phenomena. His papers deal mainly with the physiological reactions and effects which are to be neglected on establishing chemical differentiation. Among these factors, he mentioned the diurnal changes, the effect of environment and age, and, respectively, the combination of all these factors. However, he failed to emphasize the interrelations of physiological and genetical phenomena. Differentiation can be explained only by finding the physiological grounds for inheritance.

The formation of momentary values of the active substance levels and of the components of the composition depends on a number of external and internal factors, without rendering any possibility for a direct determination of their correlation with infraspecific differentiation. In practical research great attention has been paid to the level and composition of active substances varying in medicinal plants. These have been examined in relation to the age of plants, as well as the optimum dates, or optimum hours, of the day for harvesting, which were determined accordingly.

Though the present actual effect of the exogenic and endogenic factors may be practically speaking of great importance, it does not give any explanations or physiological reasons as regards the formation of chemical taxa in the past. The phylogenetic conditions, in turn, the changes of which are taking place again in an accelerated form during ontogenesis, may be considered as true fundamentals of inherited characters. However, the occurrence of ontogenetic changes is not in itself an explanation for the differentiation, for the genetical differences of taxa.

Ontogeny, however, as a particular reflection of phylogeny, cannot be homogeneous. Instead, it consists in stepwise qualitative changes (Lysenko, 1928), in distinct phases of development. These alterations affect not only the morphological characters of the plant but they are also related to intrinsic changes, i.e. those of metabolism. It has been accepted already by Komarov (1940) that ontogenetic alterations occur in chemism, while evidence proving the phasic nature was supplied by chemical methods employed by Sisakian and Filipovich (1951), by Rubin (1958) and by others.

Nilov (1934—1936) was the first to demonstrate that the formation of essential oils occurs in different ways, depending on the nature of the vegetation process. By the example of *Carum copticum* Link he succeeded in proving that in the course of the development of this plant, at first α-terpinene then p-cymene and lastly thymol accumulates, and all the other characteristics of the essential oil alter according to the changes in the main component. Qualitative alterations during the development of the individual were proved later by Nilov (1937, 1938) in *Thymus* species and coriander, as well as the ratio of anethol to esdragol in sweet fennel. Changes in the components of essential oil caused by individual development have been reported by Berry et al. (1937) as well.

On investigating the flower and fruit organs of dill, Kalitzki (1954) and Ihloff (1956) found that the initial phellandrene content has been stepwise replaced, quite in accordance with the ontogenetic process, by carvone in that at first carvone began to be synthesized and later the carvone contents predominated. Changes in the ratio of menthone to menthol as components of peppermint, parallel with the phases of ontogenesis have been confirmed by Kalitzki and later by Lemli (1955).

27

Their observations were corroborated by Gurvich (1958) who stated that, instead of presuming the direct conversion of menthone into menthol, menthol is formed directly from menthofurane and menthene, the contents of the former attain according to Lemli sometimes even 29 per cent. In young individua of *Carum carvi* L. and *Oenanthe aquatica* L., linalool has been found by Luyendijk (1956) but in later stages of development, this component was not detectable.

Ontogenetic chemical changes are characteristic not only of plant species bearing essential oils but also of those which contain other active substances. Thus, according to James (1950) and later to Hegnauer (1951), in the species *Datura stramonium* L., *Hyoscyamus niger* L., *Atropa belladonna* L., and later also (1954) in *Datura metel* L., *D. meteloides* DC., *Scopolia lurida* (Link et Otto) Dun., scopolamine predominates (with hyosciamine as accompanying alkaloid) in the germination-sprouting phase, while in the period of flowering hyosciamine is the major component (in the foliage). In contrast with this, the plants of the species *Mandragora officinalis* L. contain already in the germination phase more hyosciamine and less scopolamine while in the flowering period a third, so far unknown base becomes predominant.

Ontogenetic differences are also those detected by Rabinin and Ilina (1951). The plant *Smirnovia turkestana* Bge. *(Fabaceae)* in May contains smirnovine, while in August smirnovinine and sphaerophysine alkaloids. According to the investigations of Arendaruk (1953), in *Thesium minkwitzianum* B. Fedtsch. *(Santalaceae)* the alkaloids thesine and thesenine are present in the flowering period while the plant contains only thesine at the end of the vegetation period.

Cuscohygrine has been isolated by Reinouts van Haga (1956) as first alkaloid of *Atropa*. However, in the flowering period of this species, the sprout formations already contain hyosciamine as the predominant alkaloid (Evans and Partridge, 1953). Rowson (1958) reports that 8 per cent of the hyosciamine contents of the leaves collected at the beginning of flowering consist of scopolamine. In the experiments of Albors-Yoldi (1958), the maximum level of scopolamine coincided with the maximum contents of total alkaloids, in August and September, it attained 10 to 25 per cent. Ontogenetic changes are summarized by Nowinski (1957), and by Mothes and Romeike (1958) too. It was proved by Essery et al. (1962) in individua of *Medicago sativa* L. aged 3 weeks that, owing to a reaction of another route, no formation of ornithine-stachydrine takes place, and that actually the biosynthesis of the alkaloid is realized only at the age of 5 to 6 months.

It has been pointed out by Marker and Lopez (1947) that in young plants of the species *Agave* different sapogenins are present than in aged plants. Thus e.g. young individua of *A. funkiana* C. Koch et Bouché contain mexo- and samogenin while only the steroid smilagenin is present in the flowering period.

With respect to all that has been said above, Plouvier's (1962) opinion can be accepted, which states that the correlation of biogenesis with chemical characteristics is the same as that of embryology with morphological characteristics.

Hegnauer (1954) cites examples for the correlation between ontogenetic alterations of chemism and differentiation occurring in the course of phylogeny. He

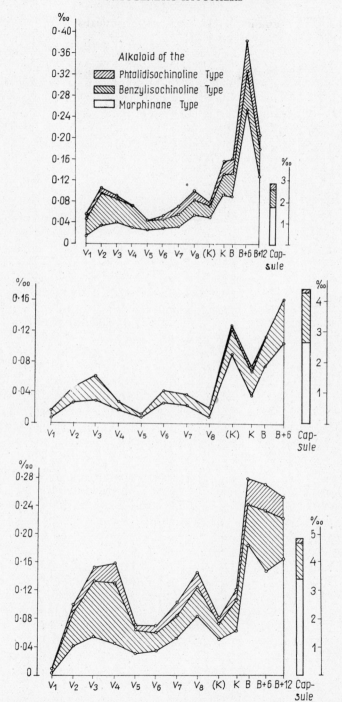

Fig. 4. Changes in alkaloid content and alkaloid composition of three *Papaver somniferum* L. taxa during ontogeny. Samples collected: $V_1 - V_8$ = during vegetative stage; (K), K = during bud stage; B — B + 12 = during ripe fruit stage

considers that, the young individua of the extratropical species of the *Solanaceae* family characterized by a content of alkaloids with a tropane skeleton contain, in general, scopolamine, i.e. the same alkaloid which is present in older individua of the tropical species of this plant family.

Similar observations were made also by McNair (1945) as regards the composition of the essential oil of certain phylogenetically younger and more ancient species of the genus *Eucalyptus* in that the essential oil of the seedlings of younger species was characterized by the presence of pinene which was however replaced by cineol at 2 to 3 years. This ontogenetic feature is quite in accordance with phylogenesis because the more ancient species of the genus *Eucalyptus* are characterized when fully developed just by pinene content while the content of cineol, a more complicated compound, is a characteristic feature of the younger species.

Even the above-cited small number of data of literature confirm that the presence and composition of active substances are characteristics of a rather varying type in the course of the ontogeny of plants. It is presumable however that certain biological-genetical connections exist, on the one hand, between the ontogenetic chemical alterations occurring on the effect of changes in metabolism and rising from qualitative differences, and, on the other hand, infraspecific chemical differentiation. The presumed existence of this correlation induced me to evolve the *ontogenetic hypothesis* of the genesis and existence of chemical taxa (Tétényi, 1962, 1964). This hypothesis was proved in respect to *Sedum acre* L. and *Papaver somniferum* L. (Tétényi, 1963, Tétényi and Vágújfalvi, 1965). The ontogenetic differences of three poppy taxa are presented in Fig. 4.

The life of the species evolves in time and space, i.e. under definite living conditions. Since life conditions are highly variable, differentiated infraspecific taxa have emerged by adapting themselves to different conditions of life. This phylogenetical process holds also in the case of chemical taxa, and it may be reflected in the ontogeny and, respectively, in the ontogenetic qualitative changes of metabolism as well.

According to this hypothesis, some alterations of ontogenetical metabolistic changes of individual development may have occurred in certain phases characteristic of the given plant species, due to external and intrinsic interrelations: to the degree the metabolism of the phase deviated from the genetically given one, the course of metabolism became differentiated and so polychemism took place. If this deviation was of a durable nature and it again occurred in the corresponding phases of ontogenesis of the progeny, and also other (e.g. reproduction biological, geographical etc.) factors participated, a group of plants would be differentiated from biochemical-physiological aspects, i.e. a chemical taxon would be formed.

The special type of metabolism of this taxon is fundamentally characteristic of the species though it deviates in a certain phase of development. The intensity of certain biochemical reactions of metabolism alternates and the equilibrium of reactions shifts in another direction; the formed reaction products are present in other ratios or also new reactions occur. Possibly also new substances participate in the reactions, and novel compounds not present in the original metabolism may appear among the reaction products. However, the essence of the chemical taxon is never the accumulation of a differing chemical product but this differentiated physiological process the course of which deviates from the mode character- izing all the other taxa of the species and which results in the production of the differentiated product. Taxonic differences are thus based on the fact that, subsequent to a phase of development in which the active substance (and its composition, respectively) is identical, such phases follow in which already a

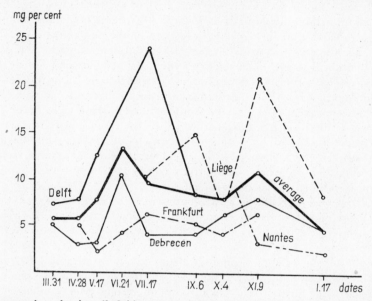

Fig. 5. Changes in sedamine-alkaloid content of *Sedum acre* L. clones from March 31, 1961 to January 17, 1962

different taxonic quality of active substance becomes characteristic. This differen- tiated phase: the turning of metabolism into diversity as a defined phase of onto- genesis is in fact the physiological basis of chemical taxa.

However, the ontogenetic hypothesis would be rather one-sided if one would not take into account the quantitative aspects of the alterations, not in the sense of the course of the accumulations of active substance but in respect to the *inten- sity* of this accumulation. Namely, a given species is characterized by the phase or by the phases of its vegetation cycle, its ontogenesis in which the secondary metabolites are accumulated (or decomposed to a smaller extent). Within this framework, the specific character of taxa is the extent of the accumulation (de- composition) in the single phases. The intensity of producing or decomposing the active substances of a taxon during the entire ontogenesis may deviate from those of other taxa belonging to the same species in a positive or negative sense.

31

This is however an extreme case which may be detected most readily. More frequent is the case when secondary metabolites are produced and decomposed, respectively, by a taxon in one phase of development to a smaller extent while in another phase to a greater extent and with higher intensity. This, therefore, is the basic reason for the existence of infraspecific taxa with quantitative deviations (e.g. Fig. 5).

On summarizing what has been said above we can state that the phasic nature of the metabolism of ontogenesis may be directly connected with the existence of chemical taxa. Namely, if the phases characteristic of the metabolism of a species are diverse in certain individua or in certain infraspecific taxonomic units because the active substance and the metabolic indices of the same phase are quantitatively or qualitatively various from each other, differentiation takes place in that phase. Differences in the intensity or in the quality of metabolism in the single phases may be inherited, becoming taxonic characteristics, and thus establishing the physiological bases of the existence of chemical taxa. Just this differentiated phase of development, the deviating biochemical-physiological process, i.e. the physiological validity of the biogenetical rule is the essence of infraspecific chemical taxa, which is not only the symptom serving purely for distinction as presumed by Bate-Smith (1959). The evolution of chemical characteristics is connected in this way with the ontogenetic qualitative changes of metabolism, proving also the biochemical validity of the biogenetical rule.

The ontogenetic hypothesis as a theoretical, physiological explanation of the essence of chemical taxa has been cited by Davis and Heywood (1963) as an accepted view, while according to Soó (1964), the application of the theories of Severcov and Takhtadzhyan (1955) for the specific case of chemical taxa is essentially valid also for the formation of morphological taxa. In the opinion of Kozma (1964), the hypothesis is of importance in the study of the evolution of the plant kingdom and as regards the further development of plant species. Merxmüller (1967) agreeing with this, reminds us of the hypothesis as follows: we can judge the progression and her tendencies in accordance with the possibility or impossibility of the steps of synthesis and not by the substances present or absent. Thus we can approach micro-evolution by a more accessible way.

Otherwise, changes in the various stages of development are characterized by their localized nature. Is there any evidence for the localization of qualitative differences of metabolism in connection with the existence of chemical taxa? This question can be answered in the positive because the above-mentioned two realizations of the biogenetical rule serve as examples of localization as well. That is, it has been observed by McNair (1945) that on the strong new sprouts of *Eucalyptus* plants rejuvenated by pruning, the composition of essential oils of the foliage corresponded to that of an earlier phase of ontogeny, in that the contents of pinene exceeded that of the foliage of seedlings of the same age. Hegnauer (1954) reported an observation of the same sense: the new shoots grown after pruning of *Atropa bella-donna* L. synthesized hyoscine, instead of producing predominantly hyoscyamine as did plants of the same age. The shift in the nature of the secondary metabolism in favour of hyoscine synthesis was in accordance with the capability of the plant to produce alkaloid in the seedling age. A third example is furnished by Klishev (1961): the shoots grown after the deep pruning of *Anabasis aphylla* L. plants contained three times as much alkaloid as the unpruned plants. Also the composition of alkaloids altered in that instead of anabasine, aphylline was present as the main alkaloid.

This composition of the new shoots formed after pruning points to the fact that the plant parts in the younger stage preserved the character of their secondary metabolism, that the nature of metabolism characteristic of an earlier stage had been localized. Taking into account this circumstance, a connection can be established not only between the qualitative changes in metabolism and the chemical taxa but also between the taxa and the quality of the active substance formed in the various phases of development in the same or in different plant organs. However, recapitulation manifests itself not only in the morphological characteristics but also generally in the different biosyntheses of the single leaves of a shoot (Trinkler, 1962).

The connection between ontogenesis and infraspecific chemical taxa is proved by the fact that long-life woody plant species disclose the highest number of spontaneous "chemical races" (Hegnauer, 1957). This can be explained partly by the fact that the change can be localized due to a lasting environmental effect, and, on the other hand, that the altered individua are capable of reproduction and of taxon formation with the seed progeny of altered metabolism.

Still, the question emerges on the connection of ontogenesis with the rise of plants free of active substances. In other words, lack of the active substance or lack of a characteristic component of the active substance can be experienced in a great number of species. Taking into account the biogenetical rule and on the basis of the ontogenetical hypothesis, the metabolism of these chemical taxa during ontogeny is in one or several phases identical with that of the other taxa of the species. If a phase free of active substance occurs in the ontogenesis of the other taxa and this phase precedes the other phases of development, then the taxon free of active substance must be considered as the more ancient initial taxon from which the taxa bearing active substance have been differentiated in a secondary way. If however no such active-substance-free phase of development can be detected in the ontogenesis of the otherwise active substance bearing chemical taxa, the chemical taxon deficient in active substance must be considered as a derivative from the aspect of phylogeny. This, owing to the cumulative effect of some external or intrinsic factors, has lost its ability to produce active substances, or it is inhibited from producing active substances by some new factor (which promotes the decomposition of the produced active substance).

Though theoretically, both possibilities exist, according to our investigations the second alternative is realized more frequently in practice. Thus e.g. from the beginning of the formation of essential oils in the plants yarrow and chamomile, an early phase, free of prochamazulene should actually have existed in the individual development of prochamazulene-bearing taxa. However, no such phase

3

could be detected. Thus, in the case of taxa free of the active substance, the majority of evidence is in favour of the second alternative.

Several authors share this view in respect to analogous cases of phylogenesis. Thus, according to Jaretzky (1925), in the *Euacetosa* section of the genus *Rumex*, the species free of anthraquinone are to be considered as younger ones. In the opinion of Hohmann (1936), in turn, the saponin free genera of the family *Scrophulariaceae* must have developed later in the course of phylogeny. These opinions are to a certain extent in accordance with the view of Blagoveshchensky (1950) according to which the taxa with specialized metabolism are the more ancient ones. Now we have the first experimental proof too: Bőhm (unpublished) could restore the alpinigenine production by feeding tetrahydropalmatine to his *Papaver bracteatum* Lindl. plants, which lose this ability during ontogenesis.

On the basis of the ontogenetic hypothesis of chemical taxa, it is possible to set new aims. The essentials of the phenomenon must be investigated in a way to disclose the phase which is being differentiated and which is derived from the alterations in the quality and intensity of metabolism, serving as the basis of the existence of infraspecific chemical taxa. The essentials of two or more deviating chemical taxa of a given plant species can be considered as completely elucidated if we know the connection between the chemical characteristic and the phase of deviating chemism, i.e. if we have cleared up that phase of ontogenesis in which polychemism was formed (and eventually localized). The respective data will be given in the detailed discussion of the single species in the Special Part.

1.4. CONNECTION OF FORM AND FUNCTION IN INFRASPECIFIC CHEMICAL TAXA

From the fact of infraspecific chemical differentiation the question as to how and to what extent the intrinsic physiological-chemical characteristics are connected with the external formal (morphological) ones follows.

On the basis of the investigation of plants with a special metabolism, the authors are almost unanimous in considering that the primary characteristic is the type of metabolism while the secondary one the morphological character. According to Komarov (1940) "biochemical differences can be observed even if the classification of plants is based on the morphological features. The plant is a biochemical combination connected with a morphological process affording defined forms". In the opinion of Ivanov, phylogeny is indicated by investigation of the substance of chemism more precisely than by observation of morphological characteristics because the chemical characteristics are functional ones and thus of a more conservative nature than the morphological ones. We are of the opinion that this statement can only be accepted in the case of certain morphological characteristics though, in general, functional changes are the primary ones. Doroganevskaya

(1953) stated that the difference in subspecific taxa "is not limited to the external criteria of morphological, anatomic structure but is based on deeper foundations" — on metabolism. Soó (1953), on stating the primary nature of the type of metabolism, declares that the form does not always correspond to the contents since the function may develop while the form is retained at certain, earlier attained stages of evolution. Later (1964), Soó emphasized that specific proteins of the species play a fundamental role in morphogenesis. In accordance with that, Heywood (1966) claims on the basis of molecular biology that at the level of "informational molecules" i.e. proteins and nucleic acids, there is some justification for considering chemical information to be more fundamental.

Turowska and Skwara (1959), in turn, investigated whether the anthocyanins bearing taxa, i.e. which have morphologically different individua, contain higher percentages of essential oils than the anthocyan-free individua, taxa of the same species. However, their experimental data did not state any correlations between morphological characteristics and chemical contents. Thus, the hypothesis of "anthocyanic filter", according to which the plants of this type have slower rates of metabolism and they accumulate the secondary metabolites to an increased extent has not been confirmed.

This is quite in accordance with the fact that conspicuous morphological differences have no consequences as regards deviations in the content of active substances. According to Dillemann (1959), the plants *Drosera rotundifolia* L., *D. longifolia* L. and *D. intermedia* Heyne contain the same active substances though their external specific characteristics are different. Similarly, it was found by Hoffmann (1961) that the same flavonoid components are present in the leaves of the plants *Crataegus monogyna* Jacq. and *C. oxyacantha* L. em. Jacq. These examples indicate that chemical differentiation does not always coincide with the botanical classification of the species, and that certain chemical criteria may be of a superspecific nature. Consequently, we accept the view of Mirov (1963) and Luten (1964) of the necessity for cooperation between chemical and botanical experts in this field.

However, the occurrence of the same secondary substances does not mean in itself a close biochemical relation as pointed out by De Wildemann already in 1941, since e.g. the alkaloid of frogs, bufotenine, occurs also in the flowering plant *Piptadenia falcata* Benth. (Alston et al., 1963), and tropolones are present both in the species of *Penicillia* (stipitic acid) and of *Coniferae* (nootkatin).

In addition to these, one must take into account too that the biosynthetic or eventually enzymatic routes leading to the same substances may be quite different as proved by Mothes (1962) in the case of anabasine, using isotope techniques. Namely, this alkaloid can be detected both in the plant *Anabasis aphylla* L. (*Chenopodiaceae*) and in the extract obtained from germinating pea seedlings, though the biogenesis of the compound deviates (Hegnauer, 1963). Hillis and Hasegawa (1966) examining *Eucalyptus sideroxylon* (Benth.) Cunn. have shown that the synthesis of lignin originates in the leaves of a physiological variant containing L-tyrosine-ammonia-lyase not from acetate but from phenylalanine. Zenk (1967) demonstrates the two ways of antrachinone-synthesis as is indicated in Fig. 6, on a fungus and on a more developed plant. Thus, Heywood (1966) is quite correct in concluding: "It is widely stated that it is the pathways that are more significant taxonomically than the distribution of the compounds concerned."

In connection with the taxonomic importance of the biosynthetical routes let us mention here the example of lysine which can be built up either from diamino-pimelic acid (flowering plants, green algae or bacteria) or from α-aminoadipic

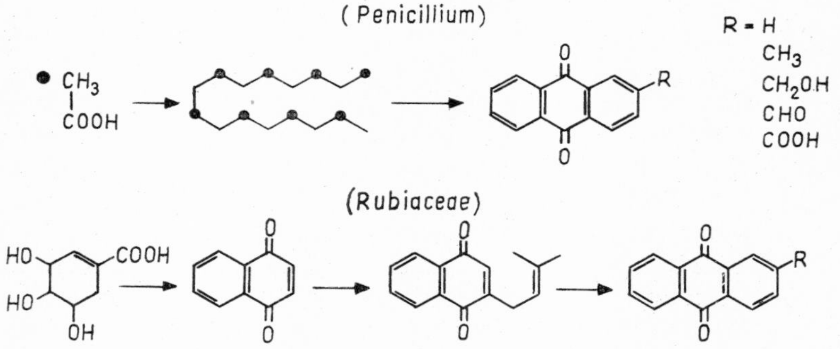

Fig. 6. Two fundamentally different ways of anthrachinone-biosynthesis (Zenk, 1967)

acid *(Euglena, Ascomycetes, Basidiomycetes, Mucorales, Blastocladiales)* while in *Phycomycetes*, though in various genera, both types of biogenesis simultaneously occur.

An interesting aspect of the investigation of the biosynthetic route is connected with the pathologic state known as lathyrism. It was proved that this is caused by two so-called "Lathyrus factors" which simultaneously occur in the same species. One of these factors, β-aminopropionitrile causes disturbances in the skeletal system while the other, L–α–γ–diaminobutyric acid is responsible for disturbances of the nervous type. The common precursor of both factors, β–cyano–L–alanine has been found in two species of the genus *Vicia* (Alston and Turner, 1963).

Let us now examine the problem whether the differences in the special metabolism and in the contents of active substances manifest themselves morphologically too.

Guillaumin (1930) was the first to deal with the correlation of chemism with morphological characteristics. He concluded by stating that "within a botanically well characterized species the existence of elementary species must be presumed which differ only in chemical respects from each other". According to the investigations of Gurvich (1938, 1938), no correlations could be established between 29 morphological criteria and 3 types of essential oil composition in 125 individua of the species *Thymus transcaucasicus* Ronn. According to Mansfeld (1953), the physiological characteristics are not always reflected morphologically as well. Later, he extended his view (1954) by pointing out that in the case of important physiological deviations, e.g. of resistance, there are often no systematically applicable morphological differences.

On referring to the experiments of Gartner, Os (1957) cites that morphological differences are perceivable in those varieties of *Fagopyrum tataricum* (L.) Gaertn. the rutin content of which deviates from each other. Referring however to his own observations, Os declares that, with the exception of a sole case, the selection of plant individua of *Digitalis purpurea* L. on the basis of morphological characteristics is useless because no connection exists between the contents of active substance and the habitus of plants. Hegnauer (1957) is of the opinion (which he attempts to confirm by citing the example of *Acorus calamus* L. otherwise refuted later) that physiological and morphological (in ploidity) alterations accompany each other. In contrast with this, even Hegnauer declares that within the same species such significant chemical differentiations may exist which are not followed by any detected or perceivable morphological deviations. In a later paper (1959), Hegnauer states that it is likely that several variations of the connection of ecological-morphological changes with genetical alterations exist. This is indicated by observations by Forde and Blight (1964) as regards the species *Pinus muricata* Don. and by Brehm and Alston (1964) in respect to the species *Baptisia leucophaea* Nutt. leading to the conclusion that the geographical distribution of chemical and morphological characteristics do not coincide. According to Merxmüller (1967) the chemical and morphological characters do not coincide because the hybridization-barrier (always present in cytological differences) was absent.

Mothes (1957) contradicts the view according to which the inherited chemical differences are always combined with morphological ones. Consequently he believes that their occurrence in nature is rather limited because in nature generally just the morphological formal deviations offer possibilities for the genetic fixation of the occurring individual difference, i.e. for the formation of the taxon proper. Steinegger (1957), in turn, progresses by still another step in declaring that on elucidating the concept of "chemical races" it is an extreme view to qualify only the morphologically absolutely identical but chemically differing groups as "chemical races". Namely, there is no absolute identity in nature and form, morphology depends in some way on chemism. According to Dillemann (1960), the case when no morphological but only chemical differences exist is an "ideal case" which obviously occurs only rarely.

In respect to the essence of taxon, the biochemical-physiological characteristics are more significant than if only the morphological and ecological characteristics are considered. Taking into account the interrelations of form and function, and the determining nature of the latter, we find that in the case of taxonomical units producing different (or sometimes identical) substances e.g. the afore-mentioned anabasine, the types of metabolism of these units differ, and this type of metabolism is primary in respect to morphological characteristics. Thus, Hegnauer (1957) is on the whole right in stating that no strict borders exist between chemical and morphological varieties. This is also indicated by the fact that visible, i.e. also directly observable chemical characteristics are often classified as separate categories.

Thus, Davis and Heywood (1963) make a strict distinction between the chemical investigation of plants and serology on the one hand, and the examination of visible chemical differences (starch grains, raphides–crystal bundles, colouring matters). Gibbs (1963) classifies among the visible chemical characteristics the raphide, the non-raphide calcium oxalate crystals, lapachol, forms of silica, gypsum, other crystals, starch, cyanogenetic and other glycosides. Though this latter visible chemical characteristic may already be considered as one belonging to morphological characteristics, Jámbor (1964) suggested just the opposite, that in the sense of the chemisation of systematics, the colouring matters should be omitted from the morphology of plants.

In our opinion both views are one-sided since the deviations in the differences of colour and in other visible chemical characteristics directly appearing on observation represent a primary characteristic which cannot be omitted from morphology. The established, detected basis of these external characteristics, the difference in the compounds indicates already an intrinsic characteristic, the deviation in chemism. Distinction between observation and recognition is quite right, let us consider just the connection between the pharmacological or organoleptic characteristics and their recognized, detected chemical grounds.

On the basis of the data of literature and of our own experimental results we are of the opinion that infraspecific morphological differentiation and chemical differences do not always coincide. In respect to the more dynamical changes in chemical composition, the morphological criteria may be better preserved, their differentiation is not absolute, they are relatively segregated. The concept of chemical taxon means, (and this is a new concept supported by the data of molecular biology too, against the earlier concept of taxa) that chemism, or metabolism is the primary while the morphological characteristics only the secondary criteria. Though the primary chemical change may be accompanied by a morphological consequence, this is not an absolute necessity. Owing to the relative independence, scientists became interested in "chemical races" first just in plants where physiological differentiation was not followed by a morphological one, and this is the "ideal case". From this extreme case on, however, corresponding to the dialectic connection of the two groups of characteristics, a great number of transitions, to the coinciding differentiation of the chemical and morphological characteristics are possible. If, in turn, only a morphological differentiation manifests itself and no chemical-physiological differences appear, we are facing an extreme case of morphological taxa. It can be accepted in general that chemical taxa are systematical units between which essential chemical differences exist without any macroscopic morphological deviations, and, respectively, without being connected to infraspecific morphological differentiation. An exceptional case is when the chemical deviation itself serves as a direct basis of the macroscopic morphological difference (e.g. differences in pigments of flowers).

As a final conclusion, in respect to active substances essential inheritable differences may exist and actually exist within the same species even if completely morphological identity is present. Just for this reason the essential criteria of the distinction of infraspecific chemical taxa are of chemical character instead of being morphological ones. In the case of taxa with proved chemical differences, it is sometimes possible to detect certain deviations in morphological criteria which were earlier not taken into account at all, and so the correlation of both factors can be established.

Thus practically speaking, it is advisable to begin classification of the species of medicinal plants always with the investigation of chemical characteristics which are coupled with metabolism in the closest way, and then on the basis of the obtained data to take into account, also the morphological characteristics of the taxa. This however, is already a transition to the theme of the next chapter.

2. CLASSIFICATION OF INFRASPECIFIC CHEMICAL TAXA

2.1. REFLECTION OF INFRASPECIFIC DIFFERENCES IN CLASSIFICATION

The infraspecific differences of wild species and cultivated ones are reflected in the descriptions and classifications of subspecific categories (taxa). This represents, even if it is carried out in the most objective way, a human necessity, a classification of great importance to man. This scope is not revealed by some authors who e. g. Jurjev (1952) starting from the polymorphism of the species, emphasize the necessity of classification into smaller units. However, the majority of scientists as Mansfeld (1953) point to the anthropomorphic requirement: i.e. to make possible a survey of the infraspecific multitude. In fact, for man introducing, cultivating and breeding plants, the classification of infraspecific taxa is of great importance. Still, it must be mentioned that some authors (Prohanov, 1949) refuse to accept any type of infraspecific classification. This view however, is lacking any acceptable foundation. Moreover it is opposed to reality, to really existing infraspecific taxa as well, and thus it impedes the further development of both human recognition and human utilization.

An objective possibility for arrangement in groups and classification is offered by the fact that certain characters were highly affected by phylogeny while others only to a slight extent. Owing to this circumstance, inheritance is discrete in respect of certain characters (Fejginson, 1958). This discrete nature presumes that some of the characters of differentiated taxa are specific ones, in that they do not appear in every group or they do not manifest themselves to the same extent. Owing to variability, the characters appear in certain variation breadth or may be absent too. Other characteristics, in turn, may remain almost constant and they represent a kind of important identity in groups otherwise differentiated. In this way it is possible to establish the relationships between groups and to evolve a natural system corresponding to the degree of relationship, to reality.

According to Mansfeld, two possibilities are actually available: classification on the basis of similitude and that based on deviations. The first alternative is a natural one because it is possible to take into account all the characteristics, their homology and in this way also the descent. If only some selected characters serve as bases of classification as e.g. in the work of Linné, an artificial system founded on deviation is obtained. According to Heywood (1966), the border between the two types is not distinct, one must begin with an empirical classification based on external similitude. This is later modified, corresponding to the factual or very likely evolutionary evidence, after detecting the correlation of characteristics to each other.

However, it is a cumbersome and almost frustrating task to consider all the characteristics. As an example, those authors may be mentioned here who attempted to build up such systematization on a combination of characteristics. Thus, in the opinion of Clausen (1921), on taking into account 19 characteristics of *Viola tricolor* L., the existence of more than 5 million combinations and infraspecific taxa are likely. "Division into groups" of that type are however, instead of serving as a survey, rather a kind of maze which can hardly be solved by even numerical methods of taxonomy.

Therefore, the majority of scientists attempt to obtain artificial information on the basis of one or a few correlated characters. This can be carried out *a priori* or *a posteriori* (Heywood, 1966). For the former mode an example is given by cytosystematics attempting to derive all other characteristics from the number of chromosomes. Still, the majority of scientists carry out classification *a posteriori*, taking into account also the cytological data. Some authors start from a Darwinian point of view and desire to follow the principle of descent also in infraspecific systematization (Juzepchuk, 1948; Pangalo, 1948). This is however facing certain difficulties even when wild and cultivated varieties within the same species are to be classified (Rothmaler, 1964), since in that case classification in a parallel way must be conducted (Luks, 1958), and the genealogical sequence is instantaneously disturbed by that. Anyway, Juzepchuk also confesses that establishing the infraspecific line of descent has little practical usefulness, and that it hardly meets the requirement of anthropomorphy of systematization. For this reason, infraspecific phylogenetical classification is entirely discarded by Jirásek (1958).

Another group of scientists attempt to carry out infraspecific systematization on a floristical (Komarov, 1940), on an ecological-biosystematical (Sinskaja, 1948; Grossheim, 1949; Valentin and Lőve, 1958; Daubenmire, 1959) or on an areal-geographical basis (Rothmaler). In this way, the error committed by neglecting to consider the mode of life of the plant forms and obtaining an abstract system can doubtlessly be eliminated (Jurjev). An indisputable advantage of this type of classification is that it considers just the intrinsic, essential aspects of taxa.

With an interesting method, Lamprecht (1959) combines ecological systematization with chromosomatic elements of multiplication. However, this multiprincipality renders his system heterogeneous. Instead of a hierarchical-vertical structure, the system rather extends horizontally, and this is correct only in the case of species hybrids. Another drawback of the system is that when systematizing on the basis of various principles, the same taxa may be classified into various categories, and this may occur at the expense of the determination itself.

However, the majority of scientists perform infraspecific classification rather according to the descriptive technique of biology, on the basis of external, morphological, but rarely anatomical criteria. Though this is in itself an easy, objective method, it may become difficult if a multitude of insignificant, variable characters are to be taken into account. Another drawback connected with the method is that it is entirely unsuitable for distinguishing plant groups differing from each other in their physiology, that is, in their chemism.

The infraspecific systematization of cultivated plants does not differ in essence from what has been said above of the systematization of species mainly living wild. Still, in the systematization of cultivated plants considerations in respect to human practice and utilization predominate to a greater extent. However, the suggestion of Grebensčikov (1949) to establish the borders of the single taxa in the systematization of maize on the basis of endospermia by taking into account the demands of breeders (according to Jirásek quite arbitrarily) is unacceptable. It is not subjectivism but rather the correct recognition of the principle of anthropomorphism that the infraspecific system of cultivated plants is defined by the degree and quality of requirements, the economically valuable characteristics. Consequently, Zhukovski (1957) was quite right in declaring that variety as the most important cultivated taxon is rather an economical than a systematical unit. In accordance with that, variety is considered according by Lysenko (1950) to be a means of agricultural production.

However, the cultivated species or cultivated variety is a relative category. Technological advances, fashions etc. demand or discard gradually new and new species and varieties from crop production. *Phaseolus* is consumed in place of *Vicia*, paint plants are hardly used at all, the introduction in culture of several species of medicinal plants is indispensable (e.g. of *Matricaria chamomilla* L.) while the cultivation of other medicinal plants (such as *Ephedra distachya* L.; *Lobelia inflata* L.) is suppressed, due to the development of the production of synthetic drugs. Consumption depends to a steadily increasing extent on chemical characters: e.g. a protein rich maize variety has been produced in the German Democratic Republic; it was proved later that enrichment in essential amino acids did not take place and thus the variety did not offer any advantages in feeding, therefore the aim of breeders was set on increasing the contents of essential amino acids (Mothes, 1957).

The infraspecific classification of the cultivated species must run parallel with that of species occurring in nature. Still, it is often very difficult to apply this principle to species growing wild because the cultivated taxa may be at the same time of hybrid origin, of an anomalous build-up or of a different tint (Kárpáti, 1961). Cultivated taxa which do not spontaneously occur have no area (Juzepchuk; Venema, 1947). Thus, we may accept the opinion of Rothmaler that in the classification of these species, instead of geographical origin, the morphological-biological characters are decisive. Wild taxa and those cultivated taxa which are related to them sometimes form a unit, and these are not classified separately by systematizers: *Lycopersicum esculentum* Mill. (Lehmann, 1955), *Papaver somniferum* L. (Danert, 1958), *Arachis hypogaea* L. (Tétényi, 1960a). Otherwise, cultivated species can be treated as independent species even in the case when their hybrid origin is likely or proved.

Classification of cultivated plants by stressing the important economic characters began in the twenties of this century on the initiation of Soviet scientists. According to the report of Pangalo, (1948) more than 300,000 foreign and domestic taxa had been processed in the stations of ВИР (Institute for Plant Production of the U.S.S.R.). Recently, quite a number of papers and publications indicate a similar activity of the German Democratic Republic (Kulturpflanze I—XIII,

1953–1966; Beiheft 2, Mansfeld, 1959). The publication on cultivated flora has been begun also in Hungary (e.g. ergot Békésy and Garay, 1960; *Solanum laciniatum* Ait. Máthé and Földesi, 1965, etc.).

2.2. CHEMICAL CLASSIFICATION*

The idea that the relationship of plants manifests itself not only in their external forms but also in their chemism, in the similarity of their contents (of active substances) is long widespread among botanists. In ancient times (cf. Table I), corresponding to the level of science of that age, the identical physiological effects were attributed, instead of the chemical relationship of the substances, obviously rather to an identical "force" hidden in plants. The experimental investigation of the connection between form and therapeutic effect was began by De Candolle already in 1804. The development of chemical methods made it possible for Rochleder to be the first to declare as early as 1854, on the basis of objective evidence obtained in investigating the plant family *Rubiaceae* that ". . . a definite connection exists between the systematical place of the plant and the chemical substances present in it".

After the survey work carried out in the last century from several chemical aspects, the concentration of research was indicated by the Javanese school under the leadership of Greshoff. Later, the research became differentiated in that either the widespread appearance of a defined "secondary" kind of substances (e.g. of alkaloids as shown in Fig. 7; see also the bibliography of "Phytochemical Surveys" in Hegnauer's paper, 1962–1964) or the occurrence of a certain substance in a definite taxon, as investigated, and this enabled also the scientists to develop the theory of chemical taxonomy (cf. Table I). The start of serological research (Mez, 1924; Moritz, 1958) may be evaluated as a side-branch of investigations. For the sake of completion, we must mention here the research into the determination of the taxonomic, phylogenetical place of a given taxon on the basis of chemism. Since the earlier (1907) data of Rosenthaler in this field (dealing with several related aspects of the chemism of *Euphorbiaceae* and *Urticales*), we may mention, among others, the works of Steinegger and Steiger (1959; separation of *Oleaceae* from the order *Contortae*), Hegnauer (1960, on the close relationship of *Aristolochiaceae*, *Polycarpicae* and *Annonaceae*.

Why are just the products of "secondary metabolism" mainly suitable for promoting systematization? It was found by Hörhammer and Hänsel (1955), further by Hänsel (1956) that relationship is most reliably indicated by the order of linkage of proteins and within the proteins, that of amino acids. However, the detailed investigation of this order is still rather far, for the time being only initial results

---

* An exhaustive survey of this field is to be found in an earlier paper of mine (Tétényi, 1965).

TABLE I

HISTORICAL SURVEY OF CHEMOTAXONOMY

Primary recognition of the interrelations between habit and chemism ("virtus", "facultates")

1583	CESALPINO
1673	GREW
1699	PETIVER
1699	CAMERARIUS
1751	LINNAEUS

Establishment of the connection between systematic position, morphological relationship and chemical substances

1804	CANDOLLE
1830	LINDLEY
1836–40	ENDLICHER
1854	ROCHLEDER
1879	DRAGENDORFF
1893	GRESHOFF

Proving the phylogenetically determined character of chemism

1886	ABBOTT	
1913	HALLIER	
1915	IVANOV	(Biochemical principal law of evolution of organic matter)
1934	NILOV	(Chemical homologue series of species rule)
1935	McNAIR	(Mean of chemical family properties rule)
1943	WEEVERS	(Criticism of the rule)
1963	WILLAMAN–LI	(Development of rule: Dimension of alkaloid motion)
1950	BLAGOVESHCHENSKI	(Theory of phylogenetical changes in the level of energy; primary character of specialized metabolism principle)
1951	RUBIN	(Criticism of the theory)
1952	SOKOLOV	(Criticism of the principle)
1956	HÄNSEL	(Percentage of frequency rule)

Codification of chemotaxonomy

1933	MOLISH	(Monograph)
1962–66	HEGNAUER	(Encyclopaedia in 4 volumes)
1963	ALSTON and TURNER	(Monograph)
1963, 66	SWAIN	(Publication of the Symposia proceedings, held in Paris, 1962, and in Cambridge, 1965)
1968	HAWKES	(Symposia proceedings held in Birmingham 1967)

of serology and enzyme chemistry are available (e.g. Sgarbieri et al. 1964, detection of deviations in the proteolytic enzyme of the latex of *Ficus*; and the comparative study of the primary structure of similar and possibly analogous enzymes mentioned by Alston et al. 1966). According to Alston and Irvin (1961), free amino acids differ slightly and mainly from a quantitative aspect while greater taxonomical possibilities are hidden in 25 types of "secondary" substances. Similarly, it was proved by Bell and Fowden (1962) at the Kansas conference on taxonomy that only two of the 29 amino acids examined could be evaluated taxonomically, and both were non-proteinic. In the opinion of these authors, systematization should be carried out rather on taking into account all the ninhydrin-positive substances than on the basis of a few amino acids. Also Brehm and Alston (1962) proved in the case of the genus *Baptisia* that, owing to their slight variability, the free amino

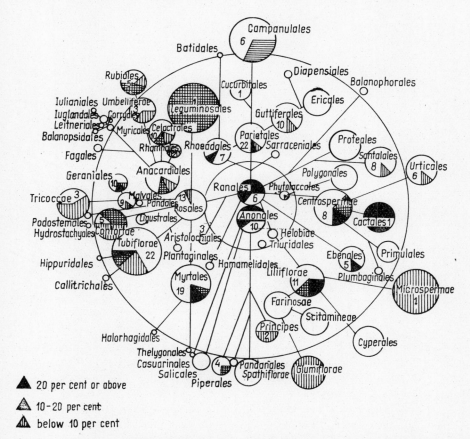

▲ 20 per cent or above

◭ 10–20 per cent

◭ below 10 per cent

Fig. 7. Distribution of alkaloid families according to Grossheim's system (Sokolov, 1952). Number of families indicated below the names of orders; percentages show the ratio of alkaloid-containing genera within the families

acids are much less suitable for taxonomical evaluation than the quinolizidine alkaloids. In this way, these secondary metabolistic characters may furnish the systematizer with valuable information. In accordance with Davis and Heywood (1963), we may state that "it is unreal to consider protein chemistry as a universal drug of all the taxonomical diseases". On the other hand DNA "hybridization" and the affinity of derived single strands of the helical DNA are the latest and most rewarding techniques applicable to chemotaxonomy (Alston et al. 1966). Brehm and Alston (1964) point to the relic-like, primary basic chemical character of secondary metabolites, and they attribute only a slight distinguishing value to them.

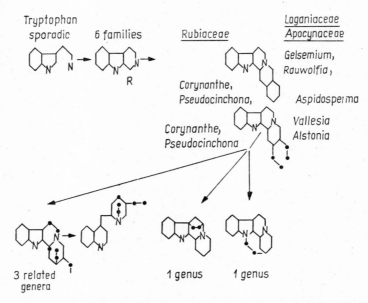

Fig. 8. **Tryptophan derivative alkaloids suitable for detecting the relationship between** *Rubiaceae* and *Loganiaceae* (Hänsel, 1956)

In contrast to that, Weevers calls attention to the fact that the chemical characters of taxa must be taken into account in their totality, and that the complex organic compounds are of an importance exceeding that of compounds of simpler structure. Namely, simpler compounds may be formed readily and may occur ubiquitously, being thus less suitable for purposes of systematization (e.g. berberine, nicotine). Organic compounds of a more complex structure, such as the phenylisoquinoline alkaloids are more valuable. On this basis, Bate-Smith (1959) succeeded in proving that *Rutaceae* are closely related to the orders *Ranales-Rhoedales*.

According to Hänsel, the systematical value of the occurrence of the various substances depends on the "rule of frequency percentage". The more complicated is the structure of a substance, the rarer is its occurrence, and the more suitable it is for use as taxonomical criterion (Fig. 8). Alston et al. (1963), though in general accepting this criterion, however also give an example of an opposite nature: benzoquinones are less widespread than naphthaquinones though the latter are bicyclical compounds. A connection is also presumed by Erdtman (1963) between the "biosynthetic complexity" and taxonomic significance of these substances which are, according to Linstedt (1951) taxonomic tracer substances. However, one must take into account that intraindividual deviations are likely, and thus only substances originating from identical and healthy organs are comparable. Fujita (1962) calls attention to the opposite extremity: compounds of exceedingly great molecular size and complicated structure have smaller taxonomical value. McKern (1965) says nevertheless, "the selection of an unusual compound as a taxonomic tracer is scientifically unsound".

Therefore on estimating the systematical value of the occurrence of substances it is more correct to take into account, in addition to the frequency of occurrence, in all actual cases the principle of homology and analogy, the possibility of parallel or eventually convergent evolution. Namely, the appearance of anabasine formed by various routes of biogenesis, according to Erdtman's terms, by "ontogenetical" deviations, is analogous, while e.g. in several species of *Solanaceae* (*Duboisia, Withania* etc.) the combined occurrence of nicotine and of the alkaloids with tropane skeleton is a homologous case. Mainly this latter is of a phylogenetical, systematical value. Otherwise, it is not so much the synthesis but the accumulation of substances that represents a chemical character of taxonomic value (Rimpler, 1965). That is, the phylogenetically evolved mechanisms of active secretion from the plasm are different: in the case of lipophilic compounds (terpenes, phenylpropane substances) they are glandulotropes or epidermal ones while the hydrophilic substances are chymotropes (they accumulate in the vacuoles). In the case of an identical mode of accumulation or secretion structure, deviations of compounds or types of compounds possess a significant taxonomic value, particularly in respect to chymotropic substances. Lastly, one must not consider schematically only the single substances but rather the fundamental tendencies of metabolism e.g. in the case of plants containing essential oils, one must consider, in addition to the components of essential oils, also the occurrence of flavonoids bearing lipophilic groups.

Florkin (1949), on evaluating chemical systematization stated, mainly on the basis of zoological research, that the external form is the result of a variety of biochemical processes linked to each other. Thus, if instead of morphology, chemism would be investigated by the systematists, the identical features of chemism would have certainly been recognized by them, and they would have resulted in a biochemical taxonomy in place of the present morphological one. The chemical method of systematical research is accepted and deemed as a significant one by Kozo-Poljansky (1950) on the basis that biochemistry is considered as the anatomy of minute components (cell organelles). In his opinion, no sharp borders exist between cell organelles and cell products. According to Reznik (1955), chemical characters can be characteristic at the level of "races", species, genera, families or orders in the same way as morphological characters. Therefore, their use is justified. Mansfeld (1958) states that up to the present the physiological characters played a subordinate role in that systematics was based on external and intrinsic morphology. In contrast to that, there are some examples of recognising the physiological-biochemical characters: the pigments of lichens, the physiological behaviour of bacteria etc. In the opinion of Mansfeld, physiological characters come more and more into prominence because they may be of importance from various aspects. Physiological differences occur mostly within groups which cannot be classified morphologically into subgroups, and are characterized by constant deviations. As regards the detection of relationship, it is very important in the view of Erdtman (1963) that certain routes of synthesis may be blocked, and thus the corresponding chemical character may remain "hidden" for a prolonged period; it is retained in a primeval, not specialized nature, let us say, in a discrete

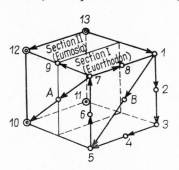

Fig. 9. Cubic model of *Orthodon (Labiatae)* genus showing identity or deviations of chemical properties (Fujita, 1957)

1. *O. chinense* Kudo
2. *O. hadai* Kudo
3. *O. leucanthum* Kudo
4. *O. perforatum* Ohwi
5. *O. hirtum* Hara
6. *O. tenuicaule* Koidz
7. *O. grosseserratum* Kudo
8. *O. formosanum* Kudo

9. *O. elemiciniferum* F.
10. *O. asaroniferum* F.
11. *O. lanceolatum* Kudo
12. *O. punctulatum* Kudo
13. *O. linaloöliferum* F.
A. *O. methylisoeugenoliferum* F.
B. *O. pseudo-hirtum* F.

way. On the basis of similar considerations, it is likely according to Erdtman that the morphological convergence is followed by a chemical one. Similar conclusions are drawn by Kozma (1964), who states that certain atavistic criteria had completely disrupted themselves from metabolism, while changes in metabolism result in essential morphological alterations only in the case when they previously alter the structure as well. Fujita is of the opinion (his interesting way of presentation is shown in Fig. 9) that the comparison of morphological characters with the physiological ones is in practice the most useful and most logical procedure. He considers the research of chemism as the most efficient method of discovering the taxa because the end products of metabolistic processes taking place in the living organism are primarily suitable for purposes of classification and distinction, since they become characters of the taxon.

Soó (1953, 1967) agrees with the utilization of biochemical data in systematical work, and is of the opinion that classification based on biochemical foundations leads to an *exact* system. The chemical method is mentioned by Grant (1960) as an important auxiliary science of taxonomy. Turner and Alston (1959), in turn, describe definitely the "chemical profile" of taxonomy and its usefulness, and later (in 1963) the "biochemical period" of taxonomy (1950 is mentioned as the starting date of this period). In the book titled *The Fundamental Principles of Angiosperm Taxonomy* by Davis and Heywood, these authors devote a separate chapter to phytochemical evidence.

The greatest obstacle to the development of this field of sciences is, according to Hegnauer and Sokolov that up to the present hardly more than 7 per cent of all the plant species on earth, by the estimation of Steinegger and Hänsel (1963) even less than 2 per cent of the seed-plants, have been investigated from biochemical aspects. Willamann and Schubert (1955) quote that hardly 2 per cent of 191,000 plant species had been examined thus far in respect to alkaloid contents. In addition to that, this chemical investigation is still far from being completed, and, on the other hand, substances present in plants cannot be classified by a generally accepted system. Different modes of grouping are applied by every author. Thus, only the work of Karrer (1958) and Moritz (1962), respectively, and the corresponding volumes of *Handbuch der Pflanzenphysiologie* (1956–1959) are suggested for purposes of comparison.

For the time being, several teams deal with systematic research into chemical classification. A series of papers was published by Korte (1963) under the title *Zur chemischen Klassifizierung von Pflanzen* while the results of Weisbach et al. (1963) appeared in the volume titled *Problems in Chemotaxonomy*. A series of papers by Steinegger and Bernasconi published recently (1963–1965) reports on research into the alkaloids of *Fabaceae:* "Chemotaxonomisch-phylogenetische Gliederung des Genus *Genista* s. 1.; *Cytisus.*"

The works of Hegnauer (1948, 1952, 1955, 1956, 1958, 1962) in the elucidation of the connections between phytochemistry and classification deserves to be mentioned separately. He believes that the main scope is to present, on the one hand, a survey of the occurrence of the chemical substances in plants, and to clear up, on the other hand, the way of evolution, the defined trends of these substances. This aim is served by the recently published (1962–1966) four volumes of his great comprehensive work *Chemotaxonomie der Pflanzen*, planned up to six volumes. This work discusses all the chemical data published so far up to the species level inclusively but mainly on family level, and evaluates them from systematization aspects.

On taking into account this brief historical survey and the present opinions of authors we can state that at the classification of taxa, chemical characters may be equivalent to other characters (Fujita, 1962) or their significance may even exceed that of others. Obviously, during phylogeny, not only the biochemical characters but also all other criteria connected with them change; no autonomous biochemical evolution exists (Goldovsky, 1947).

Our present knowledge prescribes by necessity the eventually exclusive consideration of morphological, anatomical etc. data when deciding certain problems. However, in the future, the chemical results of investigations will be more and more indispensable. This view is supported, in addition to the development of chemical taxonomy, also by the recently evolved methods of research into infraspecific chemical taxa. We cannot accept the view of Tyler and Abou-Chaar (1960) who recognize only three types of chemotaxonomical trends (occurrence of secondary substances, substances of supraspecific systematical units, systematical generalization), quite neglecting the use of biochemistry in paleontological research (Abelson, 1959) in the research on the rise of continents (Fujita, 1961) discarding all possibilities of utilizing infraspecific chemical classification which emerged in the last half century. In addition Dass and Nybom (1967) linked numerical taxonomy (Sokal and Sneath, 1963) and chemotaxonomy by their new method, the *numerical chemotaxonomy.*

On summarizing what has been said above we can state that chemical classification is in fact a more exact trend of systematics which includes also the rules of the lower form of motion. It has actually been proved by historical evidence, that with the advance of our knowledge of phytochemistry, the chemical trend plays an increasing role in the development of the correct phylogenetic system. We may expect that our present morphological system will be converted into another of biochemical character by the future development of our chemical knowledge of taxa. This is however no mechanical "reduction" but rather the real expression of the chemical connections of the living. One-sided presumptions are reliably refuted by the history of chemical systematics up to the present, by the great number of collected data and established theoretical theses which demonstrate not only that chemical classification is actually in its period of development and flowering but also that its utilization may facilitate obtaining a more correct recognition of phylogeny, a more complete knowledge of the truth.

2.3. INFRASPECIFIC CHEMICAL CLASSIFICATION

The chemical classification of the species and of taxa of a level higher than species is a branch of research already several centuries old. The necessity of infraspecific chemical classification emerged however only later. Morphological and geographical-ecological classification appeared to be sufficient until the scientists did not face the "chemical races", i.e. the phenomenon that although no morphologically acceptable differences exist, still significant deviations occur in the chemism of plants. Phylogenetically, Stapf was the first (in 1906 already) to deal in principle with the phenomena of "physiological races" and with the problem of the position of morphologically indistinguishable units in the system. The first practical method is even older in that two chemical varieties of *Cinchona ledgeriana*, a quinidine-bearing and a cinchonidine-bearing variety had been segregated by Moens as early as 1882. Some recent examples of the biochemical-physiological classification of infraspecific plant groups are also available: Koroljeva, 1948; Penfold et al. 1950, 1951, 1953; Hirota, 1951, 1953. However, the method is applied rarely and has not found general use so far.

Chemical classification within the species is just as arbitrary as the recognition of any other characters would be for bases of evaluation. Even for that reason one must not overestimate the systematical value of chemical characters. The opinion of Asahina (1937) according to which the taxa of the same structure but differing from each other in respect to their chemism represent *ab ovo* a species level, cannot be proved by any evidence. Though the view of Asahina has been accepted by Briggs (1946), Culberson and Culberson (1956) and Culberson (1961), it is extremely metaphysical. Namely, the species as a biological unit cannot be characterized by only one criterion. Any systems based only on morphological or chemical characters are arbitrary and one-sided. The chemical character of a taxon may represent the attainment of the level of a biological species only when the chemical character is combined with morphological, genetical, reproduction-biological etc. characters as well. We must agree however with Harrison's remark (1964): "One should not count the DNA code, then the RNA code, then the enzyme that this produces, then the products and so on the observable phenotype effect."

That type of classification, in turn, which takes into account, over the morphological describing trend, also characters relating in a more direct way to the type of metabolism, i.e. the chemical-physiological characters, represents an advanced step to the more significant criteria, even if the classification is artificial. The fact that systematics are limited to the statical aspect of chemical characters may be considered as a transitionary feature (Wagner and Mitchell, 1958) and one may expect that differences in the enzyme system of the varieties and other differences will be cleared up in the future, too. Then it will be possible to elucidate the differences in the types of metabolism as well, which will show the way to the infraspecific development of the natural system.

However, the a priori negative view, on principle, of the necessity of the classification of infraspecific chemical taxa cannot be accepted. According to the negative opinion of this type, stated by Vent (1960), "one is dealing with plants also in the case of these (e.g. chemical) taxa, the difference is due *exclusively* to the application of the *deviating method*". Further, though sciences are enriched by an increasing amount of knowledge, due to the greater utilization of quantitative and qualitative methods, "on our plants however, we cannot determine anything else but morphological marks in their widest sense". Deviations in morphological criteria can be detected by various ways, and tools, "thus not the method alone but rather the *tool* means the difference". Taking into consideration the practical aim of systematics in his later publication even Vent (1962) separates the chemical characters from the morphological ones, although he remains of the opinion that the difference is due to the different methods of determination. Pirie (1962) discusses in a similar sense that instead of speaking of biochemical taxonomy one should refer to it as an analytical one.

Is the difference between taxa in fact due only to the use of different methods and techniques of research? Certainly not. These differences exist actually, quite independent of the employed methods and technique, and independent also of the fact whether these differences have already been observed or whether they will only be detected in the future. It is certainly an advanced step that we are already able to detect not only morphological-anatomical but also chemical differences with the aid of the present techniques and methods. We may expect that at some time in the future, owing to modern technical development, the recognition of such biophysical differences between taxa will be possible which are e.g. indicated by the results of research into the energy levels carried out by Blagoveshchensky. These differences are of biochemical and biophysical nature, i.e. they indicate connections of the living and they are not mechanically "reduced". All these arguments prove that differences between the infraspecific chemical taxa of plant species are objective facts entirely independent of our methods and technique, though they are becoming ever more recognized.

In respect to the nature of this difference one cannot accept the view that only one type, i.e. the morphological type of differences exists. Namely, differences may exist in the structure of the plant organism or in the life processes of the organism as well. Morphological and physiological differences may occur at the same time, though this is not necessarily and not always the case. Frequently, genetical divisions of morphologically homogeneous taxa are indicated by differences in the date of flowering, by deviations in the resistance to diseases and by special processes of metabolism. This means in principle that the taxa deviate from each other not always and not primarily in respect to their form but rather in their intrinsic qualitative characters; the existing differences are thus functional (Tétényi, 1960).

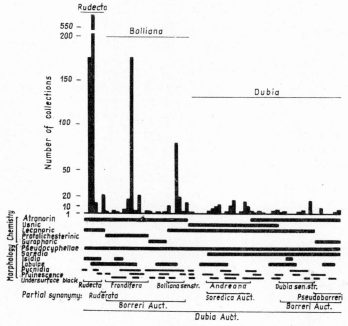

Fig. 10. Fluctuations of chemical and morphological properties in *Parmelia dubia* complex (Culberson and Culberson, 1956)

On classifying infraspecific chemical groups the problem emerges what are in fact the criteria for qualifying a character as a chemical taxon. In the opinion of Garber and Strømnaes (1964), it is hardly possible to evaluate active substances taxonomically! In contrast with this the basis for qualification is present if the chemical character specific to the taxon is inheritable (this includes irreversibility as the prerequisite claimed by Fujita), and if the condition set by Hegnauer (1957): the interruption of the chemical character, the *hiatus* occurs.

Chemical characters just as the morphological ones, show quantitative fluctuations, they are variable (Doroganevskaya, 1953). This is shown also by Fig. 10. According to Hegnauer (1957) and Steinegger (1957), chemical taxa may be accept-

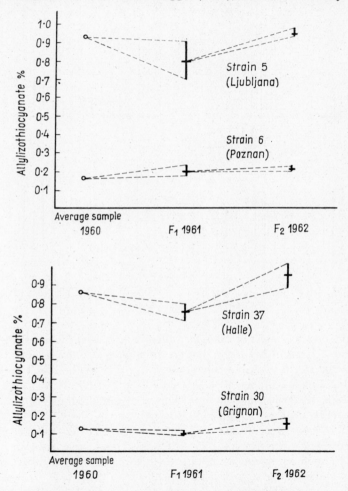

Fig. 11. Glycoside content differences among *Brassica nigra* (L.) Koch strains obtained by family breeding

53

ed on the basis of quantitative differences only when the differences exceed the usual fluctuations, and when they are statistically proved. However, this statement has not been accepted by Schratz in Copenhagen (1960) and in Zürich (1963), either. The occurrence of a significant quantitative discontinuity serves generally as doubtless evidence proving that the differences are of a genetical nature and they do not originate from deviations of individua or ontogeny. However, that must be proved by investigations, as shown in Fig. 11, because segregation on a quantitative basis, quite in accordance with the opinion of Schratz in this respect,

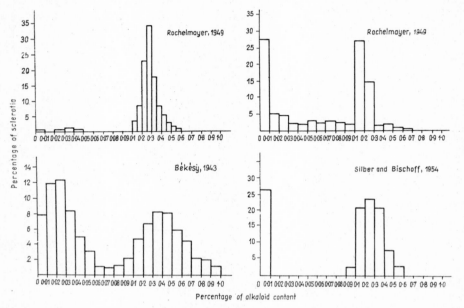

Fig. 12. Distribution histograms of *Claviceps purpurea* (Fr.) Tul. strains according to various authors

may be hidden by the stage of ontogeny affecting the level of active substances, by environmental effects or by intraindividual differences in plant organs. If the differences between the taxa are smaller than those due to the affecting conditions, the deviations remain hidden. It is proved e.g. by Arasimovich (1951) that differences between the sweet and the pungent varieties of onions are reduced by climatic and cultivation (irrigation) conditions.

Qualitative deviations in chemical characters are always reliable and specific criteria necessary. The presence or absence of an active substance points to deviations of such an extent in the type of metabolism that the distinction of the two taxa is undisputable and may be considered as genetically proved. Those infraspecific units at which changes occur in the ratio to each other of the components of active substance are classified by Hegnauer as transitionary stages between chemical taxa distinguished on quantitative and qualitative bases. In his opinion, qualitative changes are in fact caused by the complete absence of one of the components, and thus they represent extreme cases. But we cannot accept McKern's (1965) views that the theory of qualitative variation must be abandoned because some substances were thought to be absent until now. Hegnauer is right: these facts are and will remain limit cases between qualitative and quantitative chemical differentiation. Thus, chemical taxa may ultimately be distinguished both on a quantitative and on a qualitative basis. This has been confirmed also by

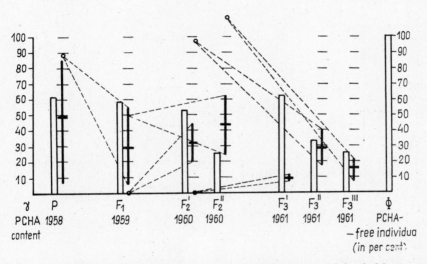

Fig. 13. Qualitative distribution and quantitative dispersion of inbred *Matricaria chamomilla* L. strains

us, both by processing the data of literature in respect to ergot (Fig. 12) and by taking into account the results obtained in our own experiments with chamomille (Fig. 13) (Tétényi, 1961).

We must mention here two disputable opinions. According to Hänsel (1956) and Steinegger (1957), only the plant individual is a real entity, all the categories above the individual are considered only as the results of the "classifying spirit" of man. On discussing chemical taxa they declare that the data of genetics, paleobotanics, phytochemistry and serology support the nature of "such a system". However, this opinion originating from Hochreutiner (1937), namely that only the individual plant really exists, everything else are only subjective ideas, is quite unacceptable. In fact, the infraspecific taxa, just as the individua constituting them, really exist.

BREEDED* VARIETIES OF MEDICINAL PLANTS;

Name of the species	Total amounts of agents
Achillea millefolium L.	−
Althaea officinalis L.	185 (Oswald N°) of mucilage
Angelica archangelica L.	a lot of essential oil
Artemisia cina (Berg.) Willk.	3·5 % santonine
Atropa bella-donna L.	1 % total alkaloid
Brassica juncea (L.) Czern. & Coss.	1 % mustard oil
Cannabis sativa L.	1·9 % resin
Capsicum annum L.	0·8 % or less than 0·02 % capsaicine
Carum carvi L.	7·7 % essential oil
Chrysanthemum cinerariaefolium (Trev.) Vis.	2 % pyrethrin
Cistus villosus L.	7·1 % resin
Coriandrum sativum L.	1·4 % essential oil
Cymbopogon species	double essential oil
Datura innoxia Mill.	1 % total alkaloid
Datura stramonium L.	0·4 % total alkaloid
Digitalis lanata Ehrh.	0·36 % total glycoside
Digitalis purpurea L.	0·39 % total glycoside
Ephedra sinica Stapf	1·3 % ephedrine
Erysimum canescens Roth	2·2 % total glycoside
Humulus lupulus L.	more resin
Lavandula angustifolia Mill.	2·1 % essential oil
Libanotis transcaucasica Schichk.	2·4 % essential oil
Lilium candidum L.	0·15 % concrete
Matricaria chamomilla L.	1·1 % essential oil
Mentha arvensis var. *piperascens* Holmes	
Mentha piperita L.	3·3 % essential oil
Mentha sachalinensis (Briq.) Kudo	4·6 % essential oil
Mentha spicata L.	−
Nepeta transcaucasica A. Grossh.	0·9 % essential oil
Ocimum basilicum L.	−
Ocimum gratissimum L.	0·5 % essential oil
Papaver somniferum L.	1·3 % morphine
Pelargonium graveolens L'Hér.	0·3 % essential oil
Polemonium coeruleum L.	30 % saponin
Rosa damascena Mill.	0·23 % essential oil
Salvia officinalis L.	1 % essential oil
	4·1 % oleoresin
Salvia sclarea L.	0·8 % essential oil
Thymus vulgaris L.	2·6 % essential oil
Valeriana officinalis L.	1·4 % essential oil
Vetiveria zizanoides (L.) Nash.	5 % essential oil

* Except the results of interspecific hybridization and mutation

The other disputable point originates from the views of Nilov who, though evolving to the analogy of the theory of Vavilov (1920) the principle of a chemical homologue series in the case of plant species bearing essential oils, limits the possibility of occurrence, to taxa at species level or higher; and within the species he accepts solely the quantitative differences in composition. In contrast with this,

TABLE II

LEVEL AND COMPOSITION OF THE ACTIVE AGENTS

Principal constituent	Authors
379 mg-% azulene	MICHALUK–OSZWIECIMSKA, 1959
	CHLÁDEK, 1963
	ANONYMOUS, 1960
	MATVEJEV, 1959
	MATVEJEV, 1959
	VOSKRESENSKAJA–SHPOTA, 1962
	SABALITSCHKA, 1925
	OHTA, 1960; BENEDEK, 1960
	BRÜCKNER, 1965
	ANONYMOUS, 1962
	NEVSTRUIEVA, 1959
	SHILIKALNOVA, 1958
more citral	ANONYMOUS, 1964
70 % hyoscine	MATVEJEV, 1959; HEGGLIN, 1957
a lot of hyoscine	CARLSSON, 1959
prevalence of lanatoside A or C	FAUCONNET, 1960; STARY, 1965
74 % digitoxin	CZABAJSKA, 1963
	SIEVERS, 1938
	MATVEJEV, 1959
	ZHIDKO, 1959
72 % ester	NEVSTRUJEVA, 1959
	HOTIN, 1958
	HOTIN, 1958
67 % chamazulene	CZABAJSKA, 1963; BRÜCKNER, 1962
75 % menthol	GUENTHER, 1956
60 % menthol	MATVEJEV, 1959; CZABAJSKA, 1963
64 % carvone or 55% linalool	SACCO, 1953 1959
85 % menthol	NIKOLAIEV, 1960
	HOTIN, 1968
74 % fraction of terpenes	VIAZOV, 1956
75 % eugenol	GUENTHER, 1956
	MOLDENHAWER, 1963
81 % citronellol	KRATSHKOVSKAJA, 1958
	MATVEJEV, 1959
	MAICHENKO–SHALIMOV, 1962
	MATVEJEV, 1959
	STAJCOV, 1965
83 % ester	ILIEVA, 1963; MAICHENKO–SHALIMOV, 1962
70 % phenols	ROSENTHAL, 1943; CHLÁDEK–KOSOVA, 1957
	BRÜCKNER, 1960
laevorotatory	KRACHKOVSKAIA, 1958

Gurvich (1936, 1940) proved the existence of homologous series within the species belonging to the same genus which follow from the qualitative differences in the composition of essential oils.

In respect to infraspecific groups, chemotaxonomy is of general validity and applicability. Chemical characters had been primarily taken into account by Rubin and Trupp (1936) in the systematization of sweet and pungent varieties of onions. The special nature of the "Vengerka" plum (or Hungarian "Beszterce" plum) has been proved by Grebinsky (1940) by detecting that the fruits of this plum

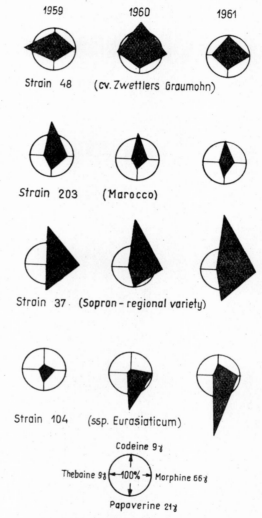

Fig. 14. Relative stable composition of alkaloids in various inbred *Papaver somniferum* L. strains during the years 1959 to 1961

variety, quite in contrast with other varieties, contain always more invert sugar than sucrose. Ulmann (1951) in his review of the plants yielding coutchouc describes some cases of infraspecific variation of chemical composition. Further, Van

Os (1957) mentions the occurrence of "chemical races" in respect to several species of ornamental plants and fruits. In 1968 he refers to the fact that the breeding of potatoes in the Netherlands is now based on chemical characters. Experimental applications in this direction in Hungary are described by Sági et al. (1960) in connection with some plant species of berry fruits, and by Koch (1960) in respect to studies with tomatoes. Also certain taxa of fodder may be also mentioned here, such as the alkaloid-free varieties of lupin, sorghum free of cyanogenetic glycosides (Jermakov, 1960), the raps poor in mustard oil of Troll (1961), the coumarin-free melilote and, respectively, the nicotine-free tobacco varieties of Sengbusch (1932) and Latuszinsky (1960), the spinach of Bredemann et al. (1956) poor in saponine but containing oxalate etc.

The present work deals only with medicinal plants, with their infraspecific chemical taxa, e.g. the diagram of inheritance of the taxa of poppy in Fig. 14, with the special part of the general phenomenon. However, the grouping of chemical taxa on principle is a task preceding actual classification and *a priori* setting the aims since just the detection of infraspecific polychemism brought with itself the classification of the species, e.g. of *Cinnamomum camphora* Sieb. (Hirota, 1951–1953).

According to the arrangement of Steinegger (1957), chemical taxa may be distinguished from each other on the basis of their natural or cultivated character. The "chemical races" of cultivated species may attain the level of the pure breed, i.e. they may be converted into homogeneous ones while the natural "chemical races" may hardly be considered as genetically absolutely homogeneous taxa, and in the case of allogamic species they are in fact always populations.

At the Wageningen discussion in 1957, Schratz contradicted the opinion of Steinegger. Namely, Schratz refuted that any distinctions should be necessary between wild chemical taxa and those living in cultures. Though the genetical determination suggested by Steinegger appears to be acceptable, the truth is better approached by Schratz in that the chemical taxa were formed within the group of cultivated species even thus far spontaneously, at least by an unconscious selection. An example serving as evidence is that of Dillemann (1963) who found plant individua containing cyanogenetic glycoside and free of cyanogenetic glycoside within the same clone of *Trifolium repens* L., subsequent to 7 years of French breeding preceded by another 5 years of Dutch breeding. Thus, a cultivated variety even if it is an entirely "pure line", may be a population from the biochemical aspect, and its decomposition to strains, its further breeding may bring positive results.

In contrast with that, in the case of artificially produced chemical taxa, the aim set by the breeder is *a priori* the conversion of the biochemical characters, their alteration from quantitative and qualitative aspects. The borders are here in fact real, a distinction is made between the "gift" of nature and the product of human activity, though even these borders are far from being absolute. The varieties produced so far by the breeders of medicinal plants with maximum positive or negative deviations which may be considered as infraspecific taxa are listed in Table II.

Along with the arrangement of chemical taxa, two other types of grouping are mentioned. One of them has been suggested by Jaminet (1960) who classified the chemically differentiated infraspecific taxa according to the mode of their origin and reproduction, respectively, into *autogamous, apogamous, long-life allogamous,* and *geographically isolated allogamous groups.*

According to another mode of arrangement, Gurvich (1960) distinguishes taxa bearing essential oils determinable directly (on the basis of their aroma) and those detectable only indirectly (by chemical analysis). Consequently, taxa with different chemisms may be hidden or concealed ones.

Thus, on taking into account their origin, their mode of reproduction or their degree of manifesting their chemism, infraspecific chemical taxa may be arranged in different ways. Still, their classification and grouping is necessary. For that purpose, chemical characters together with other characters may serve as bases. The actual principles of classification and diagnosis based on the idea of taxonomy are summarized in the rules of nomenclature. They will be discussed in detail in the next chapter.

3. NOMENCLATURE OF INFRASPECIFIC CHEMICAL TAXA

3.1. THE CONCEPT OF TAXON; INFRASPECIFIC CATEGORIES AND CATEGORIZATION

The existence and systematization of infraspecific units compels the preparation of a hierarchy, the categorization and the determination of taxa by separate names. This nomenclature must be based on an international agreement and convention in order to attain unequivocal determinations. The formulation according to the international agreement is formed along with the discussions of a congress or symposium, then the text is included in a guiding principle or eventually the earlier principle is modified. The nomenclatures accepted actually specify in a comprehensive way the principles of categorization and the possibilities and ways of naming. Therefore this taxonomical regulation is in principle timeless, according to Mason (1950) and to Merxmüller (1967) when compared with the changed ideas of systematics. In spite of this way of regulation, there are rather many disputes in this field which possibly will remain in the future. McAtee (1952) is quite right in stating that this is due not only to the discovery of new plants but also to alterations in the opinions of authors. A stable nomenclature would point to a static phase in biology. Indeed, taxonomy is only relatively timeless, it changes with the improvement of techniques and advance of knowledge.

Even the basic category, the concept of *taxon* itself is a disputed item. Although its introduction has been accepted already at the Stockholm congress in 1950, its interpretation was in 1958 still far from being uniform. According to the review of Rothmaler (1954), taxon is every systematical unit specified by common and uniform descent and defined morphological and physiological characters. In the case of cultivated plants the common descent is no indispensable criterion. Article 1 of the International Code of Botanical Nomenclature (denoted always as ICBN; 1956) accepted the interpretation of Rothmaler and specifies the systematical units as taxon (plural: *taxa*).

Subsequently, a discussion was begun on the problem whether the name taxon is only a summary of the terms of the rank categories (form, species, genus etc.) or indicates at the same time also the plants belonging to these categories. Though several authors considered taxa as a summary of terms, the view of Rickett (1958) was quite correct in that the name taxon refers both to the category of nomenclature determined and to the plants of specified characters forming this category. However, the further declarations of Rickett (according to which taxon is no abstraction and does not include the categories of thought) is unacceptable. Namely, though all concepts are based on a mass of phenomena, they are also the results of a generalization, preclusion and abstraction at the same time. All sciences, and

61

systematics as well, operate with the concepts obtained in that way. Consequently, Soó (1953), Leroy (1958) and Ross (1958) are quite right in stating that the taxon is a concrete group of plants but at the same time also an abstract category. The suggestion of Lam (1959) to use the term *nomtaxon* in the sense of a category while preserving the term *nattaxon* for groups of concrete plants may be considered as a compromise, and can hardly be accepted. Jirásek (1958), in turn, accepts the double meaning of the concept of taxon and suggests the term *taxoid* for distinguishing the cultivated plants.

The nomenclature of biosystematics takes into account circumstances and ecological conditions not specified in the Codex. Their general term is *cline* in the case of a continuous variation (Huxley, 1938) and the suffix -*deme* in the case of an interrupted one. This latter is employed for denoting taxa not yet classified into the system though specialized from some aspect (Gilmour, 1960). Thus, a taxon with a deviating inheritance is denoted as "genodeme", the ecologically, morphologically differing one as "ecodeme" or "phenodeme" etc. (Valentin and Lőve, 1958; Heslop-Harrison, 1960). Though the biosystematists are ataxonic and they do not desire to create any systematic terminology, Heslop-Harrison still applies the terms *gamodeme, cline* as distinctions, depending on the degree of differentiation of the population.

As regards the naming and ranking of infraspecific categories, the ecological trend of naming introduced by Turesson (1922) and applied by Sinskaya in the Soviet nomenclature and discussed in 1948 still has followers. Though Turesson handled his categories exclusively as ecological concepts, his followers attributed a systematical interpretation to them. The species has been built up by Sinskaja by regional and local ecotypes which, in turn, can be grouped into series or cycles. Seven ecotypes have been distinguished by Sinskaja. Of these the *agrotype* is the direct creator of the cultivated species proper. The expression *ecorace* and, in the case of smaller differences, respectively, *ecoform* has been suggested by Grossheim (1949), while Timofejev (1960) coined the term *isoreagent*. The terms *ecospecies* and *coenospecies* of Valentin and Lőve (1958), and *semispecies* by Zavadski (1961) referred to the species or to taxonomical levels higher than species. Thus, a system of several grades has been evolved for the ecosystematic denominations.

The views of Sinskaya and Grossheim were not accepted by the majority of systematists. Juzepchuk (1948), Rothmaler (1954), Soó (1956) and Vasilchenko (1958) pointed out that the ecotype does not mean any categories of systematical value. Systematists operate with special terms. Though these may possess ecological criteria, they cannot be based on other facts than on the interrelation of descent. The reference to ecological aspects in the naming of categories makes the situation even more complicated. Besides, the term ecotype does not mean any precise ranking since it refers sometimes to a species while in other cases to a subspecies or varieties.

Deviating from the systematical principle of descent, a mode of denomination is suggested by Lam, following the hints of Danser (1929): for units

62

lower than species the names *comparium, commiscuum, convivium* are proposed.*

The majority of botanists, accept the categories of ICBN, instead of the ecological nomenclature or other nomenclatures based on different principles. As regards the infraspecific systematical categories and their ranking, the problem is so far unsettled. The oldest mode of classification distinguished only a single level within the species: this has been denoted by Persoon (1805) by an asterisk, while the names *race* (Roth, 1810) and *forme* (Gaudin, 1828) had been coined for it as well. Later, the term *subspecies* became widespread the scientific determination of which has been presented by Korzhinsky (1892) and Wettstein (1898), respectively.

In the comprehensive works on flora, however, generally not only a single subspecific category is given. Instead, one operates with a multilevel ranking. Rouy and Foucaud (1893) use, in addition to *subspecies,* the categories *forma, varietas, subvarietas,* i.e. four different levels are distinguished. Engler and Prantl (1897), in turn, operate with five categories. The Engler school is responsible also for the exaggeration in the number of levels. Ascherson and Graebner (1896–1935) in their work on flora distinguish similarly five different levels. However, they deviate from the binomial nomenclature and, on denominating a *subforma,* they mention, in addition to the species, also the names of all intermediate categories. Consequently, rather long phrases are given as names (e.g. *Saxifraga aizoon,* subspecies *euaizoon,* varietas *typica,* subvar. *brevifolia,* forma *multicaulis,* subf. *surculosa*). The majority of botanists disapprove of this method. Rothmaler (1950) speaks of a disintegration of the concept of the species, while Juzepchuk (1958) outrightly condemns the "pulverization" of the species by this "aschersonism". In contrast to these, the new edition of the great work on Central European flora (Hegi, since 1958) employs only the level ssp. var., and f., while in *Flora Europaea* only the category subspecies is used. A similar procedure is followed by the Dutch author van Steenis (1957) on describing the Malayan flora, though the correctness of his views is criticized by Bremekamp (1959). Soó, in his taxonomical-phytocenology handbook on Hungarian flora and vegetation (1964–1966) accepts the levels ssp. and var. while in connection with the deviations observed with the evaluation of forms he declares that they do not mean always a taxonomically acceptable constant shape.

Most botanists, in order to avoid the use of a too small or a too high number of levels, are of an intermediate opinion. In the ICBN (1956), five subspecific levels are distinguished and accepted: *subspecies, varietas, subvarietas, forma, subforma*; and, in order to avoid "pulverization", a trinomial denomination is prescribed. Thus, after the name of the species, omitting the intermediate levels, the category

---

* In the following, the discussion of several such terms will be omitted which so far had not been generally accepted and which do not fit our present system such as *mutaspecies* (Cortes–Latorre, 1952); *morph* (Edwards, 1954); or the 14 infraspecific categories of Lam (1959) e.g. *apogameon, stropha;* and, respectively, the term *syngameon* suggested by Grant (1960) etc.

and the name of taxon can be given directly. (The above-mentioned example reads thus: *Saxifraga aizoon* subf. *surculosa*.) Besides the approving paper of Takhtadzhyan (1955) it must be noted that the principle of the five levels accepted at the Paris convention has been maintained in an unchanged form by two international botanical congresses held since then (1959, Montreal; 1964, Edinburgh), and also by the recently published new codes of nomenclature.

In the infraspecific classification of cultivated plants* *five* levels had been distinguished already in the Moscow discussions in 1948 (Pangalo; Juzepchuk). This system of levels has been accepted by the German scientists (Mansfeld, 1949; Grebensčikov, 1953), and thus the subspecific taxonomy for cultivated plants is parallel to the system of plants living wild. Though several proposals and modifications have been suggested for the names of the single levels, the taxonomical works for cultivated plants accepted the above-mentioned five-level system (Helm, 1957; *Kulturnaja Flora USSR*, Tom. 20, 1958; Danert, 1958, 1959; Grillot, 1959; Mansfeld, 1959; Soó, 1964–1966). The number of levels of infraspecific taxa is the highest in the paper of Jirásek (1959) in that, on taking into account all the categories, ranking into as many as eleven levels is possible. However, this type of classification enters into too many details and thus misses the point: easy surveyability. In contrast with that, only a single level, that of the *cultivar* (variety) has been made compulsory by the International Code of Nomenclature for Cultivated Plants (in the following: ICNCP 1958, 1961).

If several levels are necessary, then the complexity of varieties similar to each other in certain aspects is denoted by the name group. In the case of complex species, the necessity of a more detailed hierarchical ranking into several categories may emerge. The suggested terms may be found in the list of Jirásek (1961) prepared according to ICNCP.

3.2. LEVEL OF CHEMICAL TAXA
AND EXPRESSION OF THEIR SPECIFIC NATURE

After the recognition of chemical taxa, the development of their correct nomenclature was urgently necessary since the phenomenon described so far in very diverse ways was to be arranged in a uniform mode. Though according to Heslop-Harrison (1960), from the aspect of botanists the naming of infraspecific units is completely irrelevant because it has no biological significance, and the necessity of distinguishing chemical taxa by names has been denied by Vent (1960), it still appeared to be indispensable to establish a nomenclature.

According to the objections by Vent, in the case of introducing a new research tool "it may be quite right to require that also the taxa characterized by this tool must also be designed by separate names which in turn would result in a further

---

* The history of the nomenclature of cultivated plants has been summed up by Stearn (1952) and Kárpáti (1961).

complexity of our nomenclature". We may agree with the view that one must avoid the complexity of the nomenclature though it is hardly possible not to meet the requirement of expressing the chemical differentiation also in the names of taxa. We cannot dispense with the further development of the nomenclature. Just on the contrary, it is more correct to convert the morphological nomenclature into a form suitable for the denomination of taxa separated on another qualitative basis as well. Thus, in the case of chemical taxa we may refer to the fact that genetical differences are not only or not at all of a morphological but of a physiological nature.

In Ehrendorfer's works (1963, 1965) we repeatedly meet the term "biochemical polymorphism" as a result of similar adherence to the usual. This term is a contradiction in itself; but in addition to this, the chemical differentiation is characterized by the fact that often it takes place in morphologically homogeneous, and by no means polymorphic, taxa. In chemical taxa, only the processes of metabolism are different, while the forms are not. Consequently, if we wish to be precise we can only use the term: polychemism.

It is quite out of question to suspend or to suggest to suspend the validity of the present principles of nomenclature. Instead, the limits of this nomenclature should be extended by including a new phenomenon. However, the evolution of all the branches of science proved that subsequent to that extension of validity, in the light of the new case, the earlier one becomes the extreme case. It is likely that the nomenclature will be more complex by this modification but the difficulties can be overcome. However, one cannot overlook reality, and since the existence of chemical taxa is a fact, one must find also the mode of their naming (Tétényi, 1960). Namely, the capability of denomination, of abstraction and of developing concepts is in fact, of the same age as man.

In the opinion of Flück (1960), precise nomenclature is necessary because it makes designation possible in pharmacopeias. Even from the aspect of pharmacology it is not irrelevant whether a "chemical race" of citral content or of carvacrol content of *Thymus pulegioides* L. is present.

According to the earliest categorization (Moens, 1882) systematical units bearing different active agents are of *varietas* level. A more up-to-date view of Tschirch (1930–1932) employs in the case of chemical deviation the term "physiologische Varietät" (physiological variety). Though this type of naming is accepted also by Stahl (1957) and Steinegger (1957), the solution is not satisfactory. On the one hand, the problem emerges whether really only a varietas level is represented by chemical taxa. If not, the "physiological" term must be extended to all the infraspecific levels. On the other hand, this procedure, and already the original name as well, is cumbersome because the "technical term" of the concept is given in two separate words. The categorization of Tschirch is accepted by the Australian scientist Penfold (1922–1950) when he mentions "physiological forms". According to Ligeti (1958, 1959) quite similarly: "the strains of *Digitalis lanata* described by us must be considered as *physiological varietas* (chemical *varietas*) produced by breeding." However, strains cannot be considered as *varietas* since the strain material represents a mode of plants the inheritance of which is still unsettled and which does not approach the rank of varietas (Luks, 1958). The strain is the precursor of a variety with constant inheritance or of a variety maintained as constant. Even the variety does not correspond to cultivated taxa of *varietas* level, either. Within the morphologically well distinguishable taxa of lichens representing species level, the morphologically inseparable "chemical strains" are defined by Asahina (1937). However, he considers that only as the first approach of nomenclature because in his opinion taxa must be handled later as "chemical species".

Taxa of deviating chemism are classified by Koroljova (1948) at *subspecies* level. According to Lanjouw, "chemical race" which deviates in respect of only one single character is of a *form* level, that deviating in respect to several characters, in turn, of a *varietas* or *subspecies* level. Steinegger qualifies the spontaneously occurring units, with respect to their population nature, as those belonging to the category of *varietas* or *form*. Chemical units are denoted by Hegnauer, in turn, by the name "*forma biochemica*", i.e. they are evaluated as a lower systematical unit. Though this denomination corresponds with up-to-date botanical nomenclature, because it acknowledges in the case of fungi the separation according to the host plant, i.e. on a physiological basis, as "*forma specialis*", the double name is still unfavourable.

Against the use of these ways of denomination, until the conference held in Wageningen, the term "chemical race" had been accepted by the majority of scientists as the category of infraspecific plant groups differing chemically from each other. Historically, Klein (1921) was the first to employ this term, though the term "physiological races" has already been applied in that sense by Stapf (1906) and introduced into general use by Flück (1954).

The term "race" has not been included in the recent editions of ICBN. Some botanists considered race as a synonym of subspecies (Komarov, 1940). Others classified the subspecies as a group of races against which the race alone was held to be of a lower taxonomical level. Thus, the race has been subordinated by Rothmaler (1954) and by Mansfeld (1953) directly below the subspecies, and considered as a term corresponding to "proles". According to Bobrov (1959), in the case of very variable species of large area, race is a term corresponding to species, and the group of races forms a series of species. Zhukovsky (1949) accepting the Vavilovian geographic isolation as the main criterion of race declared that just for that reason, race is not identical with form or varietas, either, but of a level higher than these. In contrast with that, at the designation of cultivated plants, article 10 of ICNCP (1958) accepted the Italian term "razza" and the Dutch term "rass" at variety, i.e. *cultivar* level. Also Dillemann (1961) considers race as being of variety level, and believes that its applicability is limited because, in his opinion, it can be employed only in the case of a "line", excluding its use in the case of hybrid origin.

It follows from what has been said above that the term race has a versatile meaning and a manifold use. Namely, chemical race is varietas according to Stahl while only form according to Hegnauer. Later, Hegnauer (1958) already mentions it as a "Sippe", and recently (1965) as a "type". The uncertainty of the term race is connected with the originally undetermined nature of this term, with its too general character (Tétényi, 1958, 1963). Thus, race means not only different systematical units in the opinion of various scientists but in addition to that, it does not indicate in a general sense and does not include all the taxa below species level. Dillemann (1960) is quite right in stating that the way out of this maze can only be found by avoiding the use of the term "race" at all.

On evolving the common concept of chemically differentiated systematical units, the nature of the phenomenon, the differences in the inheritable biochemical-physiological characters must be taken into account. This infraspecific chemical differentiation can be observed both in spontaneously occurring and in cultivated plant species, and at all subspecific systematical levels. In respect to the principles of nomenclature, only the term infraspecific chemical taxon (Tétényi, 1963) may serve as a general name, instead of the usual term "chemical race" which is not unequivocal and thus rather indefinite. The term infraspecific chemical taxon indicates the infraspecific nature, the existence of the units of chemically differentiated plants in the same manner as the term taxon points to the inheritable character and to the occurrence in all the infraspecific categories. This term is related not only to the group of chemically characterized plants but also to the category itself. How is this general term applicable at the various taxonomical levels and in the various categories by using only one single word?

According to Mansfeld (1958) the physiological taxon is to be denoted by a single word and this term must also express that no morphological differences are actually involved. Mansfeld discards indication by separate words and arrives at the conclusion that physiological-chemical differences must be indicated by a prefix (Vorsilbe in German) because this offers possibilities of introducing the term into the present nomenclature and by this into the system. In the opinion of Mansfeld, the German term *Gleichform* or *Beiform*, *Nebenform*, respectively the corresponding Latin terms "*aequiforma*", "*adforma*" or Greek terms "*isomorpha*", "*homomorpha*" would be suitable for that purpose. Since however the present nomenclature is based on Latin words, he discards the Greek terms, and suggests the prefix "*aequi-*" for infraspecific taxa. He is against the use of the prefix "con-" suggested by other scientists because it is already reserved for other taxonomic terms. Mansfeld is of the opinion that a uniform denomination of external and intrinsic differences is necessary, i.e. one single and identical term must be coined for the indication of all the chemical, metabolistic and other physiological differences. This should be based on the fact that at the indication of morphological differences the nomenclature does not make any distinctions between external and intrinsic characters. A similar view is reflected in the opinion of Fujita (1962) who classifies among the morphological characters also the external, the anatomical-histological characters and those which manifest themselves in the pigments, while the ecological, the reproduction-biological (reproductive isolation) and the "incorporated" chemical characters are considered by him as physiological characters.

The nomenclature of chemical taxa must mainly express the fact that a physiological chemical phenomenon is present. The term to be applied must meet the requirements of the botanists because the term must be in accordance with the accepted nomenclature. From a practical aspect it is of similar importance that the nomenclature should be easily applicable by plant producers and breeders, and that it should be also applicable in phytochemical treatises and in pharmacopeias and that it should be expressive. On taking into account all these requirements we suggested the taxonomical use of the prefix "*chemo-*" (Tétényi, 1958). Namely, this prefix corresponds to the phenomenon actually described by it in that it expresses reliably the character of the plant which has been formed as a result of complex chemical processes. This term is more expressive than the prefix "*aequi*"-suggested by Mansfeld. Namely, in the case of chemical taxa, instead of considering physiological characters to be equivalent to the morphological ones, the essential criterion is to emphasize, at the cost of the morphological aspects, just the physiological-chemical ones, using them as the basis of the determination. In addition to that, the term "*chemo-*"clearly expresses that the correlation of biological and chemical phenomena have been taken into account in this case. The suggested way of indication can readily be applied since, simply by coupling the prefix to the term, it can be converted into a unique expression, combined with the categories accepted so far. In the case of the various infraspecific chemical taxa, on applying the prefix "*chemo-*", the following procedure is to be employed in order to take into account the level of the taxon and the nature of the plant (cultivated plant or plant living wild): *chemosubspecies* (abbreviated: chssp.), *chemovarietas* (chvar.), *chemoforma* (chf.) in the case of taxa occurring wild, and *chemoconvarietas* (chconv.) *chemocultivar* (chcv.) in that of cultivated taxa, respectively.

Also the nomenclature problem of polyploids emerges here because in the case of these taxa the active agent alters to a greater or smaller extent. The artificially produced polyploids differ from each other mainly in the percentage of active agent. Consequently, they may be considered and denominated as *chemocultivars*. If however, in addition to quantitative differences, some qualitative deviations occur, the level *chemoconvar.* can be applied.

In the case of spontaneously occurring plant species, ploidism is always combined with a genetical separation. Taxa of this type are generally treated by botanists as new species or at least as special *varietas*, and it occurs only rarely, as e.g. in the work of Grubev (1955, 1958) at the discussion of *Valeriana nitida* Kreyer, that chromosomal and corresponding metabolistic differences are not taken into account at all.

Alston and Turner (1963) raise an objection, to the nomenclature of chemical taxa but, their objection is not one of principle but rather one of practicality. Referring to the biochemical individuality of man as an example, they state that with this concept "there would be as many formal 'varieties' as there are people". If we were looking only for a practical denial, we could say that morphological individuality also does exist but still there are not as many varieties as individua. However, it is theoretically evident as well that all features have a certain hierarchy, depending on their own importance, consequently it becomes possible to carry out classification at different levels. One must not fear that "inherently difficult complications" may take place since there is a possibility for comparison. Thus, e.g. it has been stated by Mansfeld (1958) that there are two possibilities for denomination. On the one hand, to separate the chemical *aequivarietas* at the level of morphological *varietas* (co-ordination), and, on the other hand, to distinguish certain *aequivarietas* within the existing morphological *varietas* (subordination). In Mansfeld's opinion the latter method would be the best one to meet the requirements of an up-to-date nomenclature.

We are of the opinion that those methods can be accepted with the use of which, within the range of certain geographically-morphologically homogeneous taxa, it is possible to distinguish chemical taxa of the same rank. These are however at a lower level than the comprehensive taxa separated from the others on the basis of morphological or other characteristics; e.g. the *Matricaria chamomilla* ssp. *bayeri* (Kanitz) Hay. which is a variety with small flowers, consists of a taxon (see Fig. 13 on p. 55), called *chemovar*, containing prochamazulene and of another one in which prochamazulene is absent (Tétényi, 1961). Accordingly, the only suitable mode of nomenclature would be subordination (instead of co-ordination), as a consequence of the recent trend of taxonomy.

Obviously, it may happen that we must subordinate one of two chemical features to the other. By doing so, on examining our *Papaver somniferum* L. assortment, (Fig. 4 on p. 29) we have found (Vágujfalvi et al., 1966) that the appearance of different alkaloid types (morphinane, benzylisoquinoline) as well as their relation to each other is, at the level of a *chemoconvarietas*, of a greater importance and permanence than the absolute or relative value of certain alkaloid compounds (such as morphine, codeine, papaverine etc.) which is therefore only of the level of a *chemoprovarietas* or *chemocultivar*. Finally, it may happen that we must subordinate the morphological characteristics to the chemical ones: the three morphological varieties of *Datura metel* L., [the var. *metel*, var. *muricata* Danert, var. *obscura* (Bernh.) Dan.] are characterized by the presence of hyoscyamine, the var. *fastuosa* (Bernh.) Dan. and the var. *rubra* (Bernh.) Dan. by hyoscine and by hyoscyamine plus hyoscine, respectively (Verzárné-Petri and Sárkány 1964). Consequently, in this case, chemical differentiation should be considered as a primary one, taxonomically and we can consider the taxa containing hyoscyamine, as a *chemosubspecies* which consists of three subordinated morphological varieties.

However, chemical differentiation should not be overestimated and ranked as a species, according to the method of Asahina (1937) or of Fujita (1965). It is improper for instance to pick out the myristicine-bearing taxa as *Mosla myristicinifera* Fuj. from the *Mosla grosseserata* Maxim., for the only reason that a different constituent exists in its essential oil, without reference to its morphological identity and compatibility. This difference is namely of a *chemovarietas* level only.

Owing to the practical demand of a compulsory nomenclature, as mentioned already in the foregoing, we cannot accept Ehrendorfer's proposals (1963) according to which he takes into account only the morphological differentiation, entirely neglecting the chemical ones. It is a half admission that in spite of that Ehrendorfer himself uses a certain arrangement where the chemically differentiated taxa are actually at the level of a variety proper. This solution is however unsatisfactory because chemical differentiations are spontaneously (and not deliberately) included with it, even in the case of cultivated species (disregarding the varieties bred to contain certain active compounds), consequently the nomenclature of cultivated plants and its Article 5 cannot concern them. In accordance with this, chemical taxa, depending on their origin, should be classified variously to different levels according to their differentiation, just as proposed by us in 1957 in Wageningen (Tétényi, 1958). The unity of nomenclature, a prerequisite of prominent importance, could be preserved only in the mentioned way. Therefore, the statement that there is "little merit in formal system" (Alston and Turner) cannot be accepted.

Consequently, infraspecific taxa should be classified into the system according to the procedure prescribed by the rules of nomenclature, and this is "nomenklatorisch verbindlich" (compulsory from the aspect of nomenclature) in every case, in spite of Ehrendorfer's proposal (1965). The "formalized nomenclature" has been formed, much as Alston and Turner protested against it. Besides, chemical taxa have achieved the "formal recognition" of which Brehm and Alston (1963) were afraid. This is however by no means the formal but the real recognition of chemical taxa. Chemical taxa, as we have referred to it previously when disputing the point of view of Vent (Tétényi, 1960), exist in fact, quite independently of whether we recognize their existence, determine their level or not. Consequently, the charges brought against us by Ehrendorfer according to which we desired to create ("kreieren") chemovarieties are unfounded since these chemovarieties in fact exist, independently of whether they were already recognized or not.

It is a kind of revocation or restriction that Ehrendorfer disputes the necessity of a special marking of the category. In his opinion, on using the procedure suggested by us, there is a possibility of a double denomination which may cause some uncertainty and some hazards in building up the system. However, one must not take into account this hazard because, as it has already been demonstrated above, subordination is in fact the only method suitable for the systematization of chemical taxa. Just for that reason, we have the same possibilities as those involved in the case of taxa with other characteristic features. In the case of a proper classification, subordination is enforced and the different chemical features, depending on their own importance can serve as characteristic signs of infraspecific chemical taxa of gradually higher levels. In that case, the "deluge of names" predicted by Alston and Turner cannot take place, either.

The prefix "chemo-" is employed in botany in connection with physiology. Expressions such as *chemotaxia, chemotropism, chemosynthesis* and others are well known. Consequently, this term indicates the reactions of an organism, qualified by a determined direction of functioning, and it is actually initiated on the chemical influence of the environment proper. However, also in the internal determination of vital functions there exists a certain chemical relation that we call chemism and this is just the chemical nature of organic life.

Because of the hidden and functional character of chemism, it has only recently come to be considered in systematics, in contrast to the formal and morphological characters which earlier have been the only basis for systematization. In the past few years, the consideration of the physiological characters has become increasingly important in systematics, and the use of the term "chemical race" has been introduced among taxonomists in the evaluation of informational character. My proposals suggested in Wageningen (1957) with reference to chemical taxa and nomenclature made possible the inclusion of several taxa with the existing taxonomic hierarchy, and definition of the categorical criteria. Since then, besides my papers explaining these suggestions on nomenclature and the possibilities of their application (Tétényi, 1958, 1959, 1960, 1963), there have been many other authors who quite independently referred to the use of the prefix "chemo-" in systematization: Jirásek (1958), Schratz (1960), Kohlmünzer (1961), Daems (1963), and Soó (1964, in his reflections on my theses).

The use of the prefix "chemo-" to denote infraspecific chemical taxa became widespread to an increasing extent in the experimental treatises of Ligeti (1958), Michaluk and Oszwiecimska (1959), Czabajska et al. (1959), Duchnowska and Pavelczyk (1960), Michalszky (1960), Schreiber and Rönsch (1963), Tyihák et al. (1963) Targé-Lambinon (1965), Hawskworth (1968). Ligeti expresses the opinion that *Digitalis* strains are *chemovarietas*. This is however not correct (Tétényi, 1959) because strains are to be treated only at the level of *chemocultivar* even if they became varieties. In this question Silva (1966) accepts my view, qualifying his experimental materials of *Digitalis* as those being on the level of chemocultivar.

Heslop-Harrison, at the Copenhagen Conference in 1960, linked the gamodeme idea to chemical differentiation. On the basis of his arguments, one can give a name also to the systematically still not aligned taxa. In my opinion, the expression *chemodeme* would be suitable. Heslop-Harrison apparently drew the same conclusion since he used this term in his own lecture in 1963.

The new ICNCP based on the resolutions of the Montreal Congress on Botany recommends that attention must be paid to the article of Jirásek (1961) discussing the selection of terms of infraspecific categories. This article refers in detail to my proposals suggesting the use of several chemically oriented taxonomic and nomenclature terms. Although Jirásek stated that this system has not been widely recognized, he evidently accepted my views since he used the terms *chemotaxon* and *chemotaxoid*, with reference to cultivated plants.

There is evidence proving that the prefix "chemo-", so much used for infraspecific taxa, may be more valuable even at the supraspecific level. Hegnauer (1958) suggests the use of the terms *chemotaxonomy* and *chemosystematics* or "systematic chemistry", respectively, for the phytochemical research into the taxonomic importance of plant substances and for the systematic application of the resulting data. This usage has been extended to German publications (Sander, 1963, Ruijgrok, 1963, Herout, 1965, Hänsel et al., 1965, etc.). American-English usage started with the term "biochemical systematics" (Alston and Turner, 1963); this was later followed by "chemical plant taxonomy" (Swain, 1963), and recently by the

71

simplified prefix "chemo-" (Brehm, 1962; Alston et al., 1963; Nigam et al., 1965, and others). According to Pirie (1963), the classification "biochemical" refers to activity *in vivo*, while the prefix "chemo-" applies to composition and construction. But Alston (1966) says: one might describe the internal regulatory mechanism controlling the synthesis of a particular compound of an organism as *chemogenesis*, and in Törő's opinion (1966), the basis of cell-differentiation is the *chemodifferentiation* at molecular level.

In conclusion we may mention that as a result of the series of chemotaxonomical conferences held in the past few years (Paris, 1962; Leyden, 1963; Kyote, 1964; Edinburgh, 1964; Paris, 1965; and Stockholm, 1966), the International Association for Plant Taxonomy and the International Union of Pure and Applied Chemistry have established a common Committee on Chemotaxonomy (Alston, 1965). The principal objective of this committee at its first session in Stockholm in 1966 was, along with several other important resolutions reported in its Newsletter No. 7, 1966, to promote the activities of "practising *chemotaxonomists*".

3.3. NAME, DIAGNOSIS AND DEPOSITION OF CHEMICAL TAXA

The categorization of infraspecific chemical taxa must be followed by naming. This can be carried out only according to the principles of international nomenclature.

The earliest procedure of denomination consisted in directly indicating the characteristic feature of the taxon in its name itself (Moens, 1882), e.g. coining the name var. *chinidinifera* for the quinidine-bearing variety of cinchona tree and the name var. *cinchonidinifera* for the variety containing cinchonidine, respectively. Though the direct indication of characters referring to intrinsic marks is not usual in taxonomy (Hegnauer, 1957), with the exception of the microbiological nomenclature (Buchanan, 1960), this mode of naming can be found in the research reports of Baker and Smith (1902–1920), Fujita (1955), Hirota, Rovesti, Sacco (1959). Since this procedure is rather cumbersome, also owing to the formation of too long names (e.g. *Orthodon methyl-isoeugenoliferum* Fujita consists of 22 letters or 11 syllables, respectively), in recent times it is employed only rarely, for instance in the papers of Ligeti.

The deviating, rather original way of naming applied by Penfold is quite unusual in taxonomical practice. The plant group first detected among the infraspecific chemical taxa is considered by Penfold as a typical one, denoted as "normal type". All the other taxa discovered later are symbolized by capital letters of the alphabet. Though the research of Penfold proved to be very successful in that it is greatly his merit to reduce to only one hundred species the four hundred species of the genus *Eucalyptus* described thus far, his nomenclature procedure does not comply with all the requirements. One of the major objections is against the use of capital letters. Namely, according to article 21 the ICBN (1956), the denomination of taxa by signs, symbols or numbers is unacceptable. Similarly, it is incorrect to consider the first detected taxon as a type. Besides, the term "type" has a rather different meaning in the newest nomenclature, belonging to another field of concepts in that it refers to the item in the herbarium in connection with the description of the plant proper (Mansfeld, 1958). Lastly, Schratz (1960) is quite right in raising the question: which "chemical race" can be considered to be a typical one without following a rather arbitrary procedure?

Asahina (1937) similarly suggests a "Penfoldian" nomenclature: denoting his "chemical strains" by numbers. Since however, corresponding to his principles, he raises these strains to species level, in his opinion e. g. within the complex *Parmelia dubia* (Wulf.) Schaer the final name *Parmelia pseudoborreri* Asahina must be ascribed to the "chemical strain" which contains gyrophoric acid and atranorin.

Koroljova (1948), in turn, distinguishes taxa with different chemisms by using (non-Latin) phantasy names. Lanjouw (1958) emphasized that the general rules of taxonomy are of a compulsory character even in respect to chemical taxa, and returned to the solution suggested by Moens in that in his view the botanical denomination must be derived from the Latin name of the active substance. He added however that the name created in this way should not be too long. In the case of the infraspecific chemical taxa of cultivated species, the use of phantasy names instead of Latin denominations is proposed by Lanjouw.

According to the provisional paragraph of the ICBN, the taxa of *spontaneously occurring species* must be denoted by *the name* of a descriptive character and of Latin form. The infraspecific taxa of cultivated species, in turn, may be indicated only by *fancy names* both according to the principle of the ICBN and to those of the ICNCP. For fancy names there are inadmittibly the numerals, symbols, abbreviations, letters or expressions of a descriptive character.

I suggested already in 1957 in my proposal (Tétényi, 1958) a mode of naming which corresponds to the guiding principles of the Codes. I have taken into account the requirement that the denomination of infraspecific chemical taxa must be uniform and it must comply with the evolution of the international scientific language. Thus, it must meet the requirements in respect to Latinized expressions (nomenclature of spontaneously occurring plants) and also in respect to phantasy names (nomenclature of the taxa of cultivated plants). In the case of qualitative differences, distinctions must be made possible by indicating the internationally accepted chemical names of the active substances characterizing the taxa. In this way, it is possible to coin uniform names which are in full accordance both with the international scientific language and with the accepted nomenclature of spontaneously occurring and cultivated plants. Chemical names offer the advantage of being generally Latin terms and at the same also fancy names. Thus e.g. the seven chemical taxa of *Cinnamomum camphora* Sieb. ssp. *formosana* Hirota may be named as

chvar. '*Borneol*'; chvar. '*Cineol*'; chvar. '*Campher*'; chvar. '*Linalool*'; chvar. '*Safrol*'; chvar. '*Sesquiterpene*'; chvar. '*Sesquiterpenealcohol*';

while the two chemical taxa of the cultivated species of *Cinchona ledgeriana* Moens as chconv. *'Chinidine'* and chconv. *'Cinchonidine'*. This mode of naming is moreover simpler and still more precise than e.g. the name of Latin form *cineoliferum* or the Chinese name "Hon-sho" derived from the essential oil.

In the case of the chemical taxa in which the main component of the active substance is the same but also a characteristic by-component exists (sometimes being absent or replaced by a component of different nature) the privative suffix "de-" ("des-") can be applied, e.g. *Matricaria chamomilla* chvar. *'Prochamazulene'* and chvar. *'Deprochamazulene'*; or *Ephedra distachya* chvar. *'Ephedrine'* and chvar. *'Desephedrine'*. However, this procedure is not entirely satisfactory because either the denoted component of the active substance is replaced by another compound and in that case it appears to be more practical to denote the plant by the compounds actually present (e.g. *Matricaria chamomilla* chvar. *'Farnesol'*), or the sensitivity of the available analytical instrument is still unsufficient for the detection of the active substance present only in minute amounts. It is likely that this is actually the case with the chemical taxa denoted for the time being as free of alkaloids (e.g. within the species *Ephedra distachya* L., *Spartium junceum* L. etc.). Otherwise, this means solely that the observed deviation is only a quantitative one, instead of being of a qualitative nature. In that case, the lower threshold value (0·01 per cent) suggested by Hegnauer (1963) can be taken into account on evaluation.

As regards the chemical taxa determined by the presence of two combined active substances, they must be denoted by combined doubled phantasy names, in accordance with the compounds present. Thus, satisfactory distinctions can be made by using the names *Brassica juncea* chvar. *'Sinigrin'* and chvar. *'Sinigrinogluconapin'* or *Rauwolfia serpentina* chvar. *'Ajmalino-rauwolfinine'* and chvar. *'Ajmalino-serpentine'*. Also care must be taken to avoid the use of the same epithet for two different taxa within the same species (article 64 of the ICNB and article 19 of the ICNCP).

The mode of naming makes possible also the indication of quantitative differences, in addition to the qualitative ones. In such cases it is sufficient to denote the corresponding percentages of active substance content after the name. Thus e.g. the two taxa of *Cinnamomum camphora* Sieb, chvar. *'Linalool'* in which the contents of active substance are different as proved by data of literature, can be denoted as chforma *'86 %'* and chforma *'71 %'* respectively, as permitted in certain cases by article 21 of the ICNCP.

In the case of ploidism, chemical taxa can be named by using a combination of the terms in parentheses suggested in 1959 by Lamprecht (3 × ; 4 × ; etc.); e.g. the species *Achillea millefolium* L. possesses two chemoconculta: chonc. *'Prochamazulene 4 ×'* and chonc. *'Prochamazulene 6 ×'*.

My above-mentioned suggestions have been proposed already at the Wageningen discussion (1957) and later in Zurich (1963). Stahl, on accepting the suggested principles of nomenclature, believed that the cases when the active substance were still unknown and only the therapeutic effects were recognized are rather problematic. Thus e.g. the active agent of the chemical taxon of *Cannabis*

74

sativa var. *indica* Lam. is not cleared yet. For that case, on the basis of the narcotic effect of the herb, the name chvar. *narcotica** is suggested by Stahl. This means that, until the problem of the active agent will be solved, the indication of the physiologic therapeutic effect may bridge the difficulties. In the opinion of Flück, the problem can be solved by employing the term *pharmaceutica* until the active agent will be elucidated, and this term is suitable for taxa with no direct pharmacological effects. In our opinion both ways of denomination are acceptable and comply with the principles of nomenclature. Besides, they offer the advantage of avoiding inconsiderate systematical evaluations and preventing eventual new denominations with a re-evaluation necessary in the case when the first name would prove to be unsatisfactory.

On the other hand, Alston and Turner's proposals cannot be regarded as a solution, because they were influenced by their fear of a "deluge of names". In their opinion it is "wiser" to give names only as "informal, descriptive categories" as e.g. "cyanogenetic race, or acyanogenetic race". Leaving out of consideration that the category "race" is rather obscure and therefore inapplicable — as has been mentioned several times — it is better to use the trivial names of plant substances which are of Latin form and at the same time a descriptive fancy name for the designation of chemical features (Tétényi, 1958, 1963). Ehrendorfer (1963, 1965), however, has proposed only to give fancy names and not names of Latin forms to biotypes of a chemical character. We have always used names of Latin form to indicate different shades of colour and other morphological characteristics of the plant substances (for example *Ophiocaulon gummifer* Harv., *Viola odorata* L. and so on). It is more correct, e.g. also to name separately the fragrant *Mentha longifolia* (L.) Nath. taxa. The Central Asian, geographically differentiated taxa, the chemosubspecies '*Linalool*' and the chemovar '*Nerol*' have names of Latin form from names which we can draw conclusions as to the main components of their essential oils. Merxmüller (1967) thinks erroneously, that my proposition denies spontaneous taxa, it in fact synthesizes the nomenclatural regulation of ICBN and of ICNCP.

The name of a taxon is complete only when it contains also the diagnosis-like description. This refers to the chemical taxa as well. It has been stated already by Greshoff that also a short chemical characterization is necessary, in addition to a morphological one, when describing a genus or a new species. As an example of realization at species level we may cite here the description of *Pinus oaxacana* Mirov nov. sp. (1958): "Resina terebinthe n-hexane 21 per centum; d- et d,1-α-pinene, 51 per centum; 1- et d,1-limonene, 15–16 per centum; n-undecane, 1·3 per centum; et sesquiterpene, longifolene, 7·5 per centum componitur". On describing a variety of *Sedum acre* L. (Priszter and Tétényi, 1963) we followed a similar procedure: "Herba plantae praecipue alcaloidam 'Sedridin' continens".

---

* It is of interest to note that in the treatises on the cultivated flora of Hungary, this variety is denominated, with reference to Soviet authors, as var. *narcotica* and var. *subnarcotica*, respectively (Mándy and Bócsa, 1962).

The rules of the ICNCP prescribe also the compulsory registration of the taxa of cultivated plants at an international or internationally accepted organization where samples or seeds can be deposited as well. No recording organization of this type exists however as regards chemical taxa though the recognition of the varieties of medicinal plants has been organized in certain countries. Lanjouw (1958) was quite right in suggesting that the chemical taxa of medicinal plants should be accepted internationally, and samples of the herb and of the active agents should be deposited in an international organization. Then, on preparing pharmacopeias or botanical treatises, these deposits may serve as bases for testing and, respectively, for identification in control tests. The notice of the French Musée d'Histoire Naturelle issued in 1965 for participation in establishing a collection of natural substances, and for registering and sending samples of substances may be considered as the first step in performing an earnest task which requires international co-operation.

SUBJECT INDEX

77

REFERENCES TO THE GENERAL PART

Abbott, H. C. S. (1886) *Bot. Gaz.* **11**, 270

Abelson, P. H. (1959) *Fortschr. d. Chemie org. Naturstoffe* **17**, 379

Adanson, M. (1763) *Familles naturelles des plantes.* Paris

Albors-Yoldi, E. (1958) *Farmacognosia* Madrid **18**, 295

Alston, R. E. (1965) *Phytochemistry* **4**, 779

Alston, R. E. (1966) In: *Comparative Phytochemistry.* Ed. T. Swain. Academic Press, London and New York

Alston, R. E. and Irvin, H. S. (1961) *Am. J. Bot.* **48**, 35

Alston, R. E., Mabry, T. J. and Turner, B. L. (1963) *Science* **142**, 545

Alston, R. E., Mabry, T. J. and Turner, B. L. (1966) In: *International Encyclopedia of Chemistry.* Reinhold Publish. Corp. New York, 226

Alston, R. E. and Turner, B. L. (1963) *Biochemical Systematics.* Prentice Hall. Inc Englewood Cliffs, N.-J.

Andersen, E. (1953) *Biol. Rev.* **28**, 280

Anonymous (1956— 1959) *Handbuch der Pflanzenphysiologie* Bd. VI, VIII, X. Springer Vlg. Berlin

Anonymous (1956; 1961) *International Code of Botanical Nomenclature. Regn. Vegetabile.* vol. 16, vol. 27. Utrecht

Anonymous (1958; 1961) *International Code of Nomenclature for Cultivated Plants. Regn. Vegetabile.* vol. 10, vol. 22. Utrecht

Anonymous (1958) Культурная Флора СССР. *Сельхозгиз.* Москва—Ленинград (Cultivated Flora USSR. Tom. 20. Sel'hozgiz. Moscow—Leningrad)

Anonymous (1960) In: *Plant Breeding Abstr.* 1962, 29

Anonymous (1962) *Ann. Rep. of Pyrethrum Res. Sect. Rep. Board.* Kenya

Anonymous (1964) *Admin. Rep. Agr. Dept. Kerala for* 1962— 63, 925

(Arasimovich, V. V.) Арасимович, В. В. (1951) *Биохимия плодов и овощей* (Biochemistry of Fruits and Vegetables) 2, 53

(Arendaruk, A. O.) Арендарук, А. О. (1953) Summary of dissert. Inst. Chem. Ac. Sci. SSR. Uzbek., Tashkent

Asahina, Y. (1937) *Bot. Mag.* Tokyo **51**, 759

Ascherson, P. and Graebner, P. (1896— 1935) *Synopsis der mitteleuropäischen Flora* 1— 12, Leipzig

Baker, R. T. and Smith, H. G. (1902–1920) *A research on the Eucalyptus in regard to their essential oils.* Ed. 1, 2. Sydney.

(Baranov, P. A.) Баранов, П. А. (1940) *Растение и среда* (Plants and the environment) Moscow; In: Jurjev, V. J. (1952) A szántóföldi növények nemesítése és vetőmagtermesztése (Breeding of field plants and growing their sowing-seeds). Mezőgazdasági Kiadó, Budapest

Barber, H. N. and Jackson, W. D. (1957) *Nature* **179**, 1267

Bate-Smith, E. C. (1959) Plant biochemistry. In: *Vistas in Botany.* Pergamon Press, London, 100

Békésy, M. and Garay, A. (1960) Az anyarozs. Claviceps purpurea (Fr) Tul. *Culturflora of Hungary* Vol. I, No. 10. Akadémiai Kiadó, Budapest

Bell, E. A. and Fowden, L. (1962) *Intern. Conf. Taxon Biochem. Serol.* 5

Benedek, L. (1960) *Kisérletügyi Közlemények.* (Rec. Hung. Agr. Exp. St.) 52 C, 33

Berry, Ph. A., Macbeth A. K. and Swanson T. B. (1937) *J. Chem. Soc.* 1443, 1448

Blagovescsenski, A. V. (1950) *A növények evolúciós folyamatainak biokémiai alapjai* (Biochemical bases for the evolution process of plants). Akadémiai Kiadó, Budapest

(Blagoveshchensky, A. V.) Благовещенский, А. В. (1960) *Бот. Ж.* (Bot. J.) **45,** 480

(Bobrov, E. G.) Бобров, Е. Г. (1959) *Бот. Ж.* (Bot. J.) **44.** 1553

(Bobrov, E. G.) Бобров, Е. Г. (1961) *Бот. Ж.* (Bot. J.) **46,** 313

Böcher, T. W. (1960) *Planta Med.* **8,** 224

Bredemann, G., Schwanitz, F. and Sengbuch, R. (1956) *Bull. Narcot.* **8,** 31

Brehm, B. G. (1962) *Am. J. Bot.* **40,** 674

Brehm, B. G. and Alston, R. E. (1962) *Intern. Conf. Tax. Biochem. Serol.* 10

Brehm, B. G., and Alston, R. E. (1964) *Am. J. Bot.* **51,** 644

Bremekamp, C. E. B. (1959) *Kon. Ned. Ak. Proc. Ser.* **62,** 91

Briggs, L. H. (1946) *J. Roy. Soc. N.S.W.* **80,** 151

Brückner, K. (1960) *Dtsch. Gartenbau* 7, 178

Brückner, K. (1965) *Wiss. Z. Karl Marx Univ.* **14,** 463

Buchanan, R. E. (1960) *Int. Bull. Bact. Nomencl. Tax.* **10,** 16

Camerarius, R. J. (1699) *De convenientia Plantarum in Fructificatione et Viribus.* Tubingae

Candolle, De A. P. (1804) *Essai sur les propriétés médicales des plantes et leur classification naturelle.* Paris

Candolle, De A. P. (1872) *Tentative d'expériences sur la question de modification dans les espèces végétales.* Arch. Sci. Genève

Carlsson, G. (1959) *Meddelande Gullakers Vaxtför.* Hammenhög, 169

Cesalpino, A. (1583) *De Plantis Libri*, Firenze

Chakravarty, K. (1963) *Indian J. Gen. Plant. Breed.* **23,** 185

Chládek, M. (1963) *Wiss. Z. Karl Marx Univ.* **12,** 426

Chládek, M. and Kosova, V. (1957) *Sborn. Cesk. Akad. Zemed.* **30,** 1099

Clausen, I. (1921) *Bot. Tijdskr.* 37

Cortes-Latorre, C. (1951) *An. Inst. Bot. A. J. Cavaillo* **10,** 81

Culberson, W. L. (1961) *Rev. Bryol. et Lichen.*, **20,** 321

Culberson, W. L. and Culberson, C. F. (1956) *Am. J. Bot.* **43,** 678

Cuzin, J. (1957) *Pharm. Weekbl.* **92,** 775

Czabajska, W., Duchnowska, A., Pavelczyk, E. and Wrocinska, V. (1959) *Biul. Inst. Rosl. Leczn.* **5,** 252

Daday, H. (1954) *Heredity* **8,** 61, 376

Daems, W. F. (1963) *Chemische Courant* **62,** 838

Danert, S. (1958) *Kulturpflanze* **6,** 61

Danert, S. (1959) *Kulturpflanze* **7,** 73

Danser, R. H. (1929) *Genetica* **11,** 399

Darwin, C. (1955) *A fajok eredete* (Origin of species). Akadémiai Kiadó, Budapest

Dass, H. and Nybom, N. (1967) *Canad. J. Gen. Cyt.* **9,** 880.

Daubenmire, R. F. (1959) *Plants and environment.* Wiley, New York

Davis, P. H. and Heywood, V. H. (1963) *Principles of angiosperm taxonomy.* Oliver-Boyd, Edinburgh–London

Dillemann, G. (1957) *Pharm. Weekbl.* **92,** 805

Dillemann, G. (1959) *Ann. Pharm. France* **17,** 214

Dillemann, G. (1960) *Planta Medica* **8,** 263

Dillemann, G. (1961) *Bull. Soc. Bot. France* **108,** 30

Dillemann, G. (1963) Private communication

Doroganyevszkaja, E. A. (1953) *A növények földrajzi elterjedésének és anyagcseréjének összefüggése* (Relationship between metabolism and geographical distribution of plants). Akadémiai Kiadó, Budapest

(Dragendorf, G. G.) Драгендорф, Г. Г. (1879) *Фармацевтический Ж.* (Pharm. J.) No. 14—17; in Sokolov 1952

Duchnowska, A. and Pavelczyk, E. (1960) *Biul. Inst. Rosl. leczn.* **6,** 31

Edwards, G. J. (1954) *Systematic Zool.* **3,** 1

Ehrendorfer, F. (1963) *Planta Med.* **11,** 234

Ehrendorfer, F. (1965) Systematik und Evolution der Spermatophyta. Bericht über die Jahre 1963 und 1964, in *Fortschritte der Botanik* **27,** 347

Elzenga, G. J. (1954) *Pharm. Weekbl.* **92,** 767

Endlicher, S. L. (1836—40) *Genera Plantarum Secundum Ordines Naturales Disposita,* Vindobonae

Engler, A. and Prantl, K. (1897) *Die natürlichen Pflanzenfamilien.* Leipzig

Erdtman, H. (1963) *Pur. and Appl. Chemistry* **6,** 679

Essery, J. M., McCaldin, D. J. and Marion, L. (1962) *Phytochemistry* **1,** 209

Evans, W. C. and Partridge, M. W. (1953) *J. Pharm. Pharm.* **5,** 772

Fauconnet, L. (1960) *Bull. Soc. Vaud.* **67,** 299

(Fejginson, N. I.) Фейгинсон, Н. И. (1958) *О дискретности в наследственн. Достиж. биол. науки* (Discontinuance and heredity). Sel'hozgiz. Moscow

Florkin, M. (1949) *Biochemical evolution.* Academic Press, New York

Flück, H. (1954) *J. Pharm. Pharm.* **6,** 361

Flück, H. (1957) *Pharm. Weekbl.* **92,** 762;

Flück, H. (1960) *Planta Med.* **8.** 297

Forde, M. B. and Blight, M. M. (1964) *N. Z. J. Bot.* **2,** 44

Fujita, Y. (1957) *J. Chem. Soc. (Japan)* **80,** 770

Fujita, Y. (1960) *Acta Phytotax. Geobot.* **18,** 183

Fujita, Y. (1962) *Acta Phytotax. Geobot.* **20,** 132

Fujita, Y. (1965) *Bot. Mag.* Tokyo **78,** 212

Fujita, Y. (1967) *J. Jap. Bot.* **42,** 91, 278

Garber, E. D. and Strømnaes, O. (1964) *Bot. Gaz.* **125,** 96

Gaudin, J. F. G. (1828) *Flora Helvetica III.* Turici

Gibbs, R. D. (1958) *Proc. Linn. Soc.* London **169,** 216

Gibbs, R. D. (1963) History of Chemical Taxonomy. In: *Chemical Plant Taxonomy.* Ed. T. Swain,

Gildemeister, E. and Hoffmann, F. (1956–1961) Die ätherischen Öle. vol. I–VII. *Akad. Vlg.* Berlin.

Gilmour, J. S. L. (1960) *Scottish Plant Breeding Report* 99

(Goldovsky, A. M.) Гольдовский, А. М. (1947) *Вестн. Ломоносов Г. Унив.* (Rec. Lomonosov Univ.) 7. In: Doroganyevszkaja 1953

Grant, W. F. (1960) *Rev. Canad. Biol.* **19,** 240

Grebensčikov, I. (1949) *Züchter* **19,** 302

Grebensčikov, I. (1953) *Kulturpflanze* **1,** 121

(Grebinsky, S. O.) Гребинский, С. О. (1940) *Биохимия культурных растений* (Biochemistry of cultivated plants) **7,** 1

Greshoff, M. (1893) *Ber. Dtsch. Pharm. Ges.* **3,** 191

Grew, N. (1673) *An idea of a phytological history propounded.* London

Grillot, G. (1959) La classification des Orges cultivées *Ann. Amélioration d. Plantes* **4,** 445

(Grossheim, A. A.) Гроссгейм, А. А. (1949) *Бот. Ж.* (Bot. J.) **34,** 3

(Grubov, V. I.) Грубов, В. И. (1955) *Бот. Ж.* (Bot. J.) **40,** 815

(Grubov, V. I.) Грубов, В. И. (1958) *Валерианна, Флора СССР* (Valeriana, Flora USSR) **23,** 594

Guenther, E. (1956) *Ind. Parfum* **11,** 407

Guillaumin, A. (1930) *Bull. Sci. Pharmacol.* **37,** 431

(Gurvich, N. L.) Гурвич, Н. Л. (1936) *Докл. АН СССР* (Rep. Ak. Sci. USSR) **12,** 141

(Gurvich, N. L.) Гурвич, Н. Л. (1938) *Тр. Бот. Инст. Изд. Аз.* АН ССР, Баку (Works of Bot. Inst. Acad. Sci. Azerb. SSR, Baku) **7,** 185

(Gurvich, N. L.) Гурвич, Н. Л. (1940) *Тр. Бот. Инст. Изд. Аз.* АН ССР, Баку (Works of Bot. Inst. Acad. Sci. Azerb. SSR, Baku) **9,** 137

(Gurvich, N. L.) Гурвич, Н. Л. (1958) *Краткий Отчет ВНИИМЕМК* (Short report of St. Sci. res. Inst. of Oil- and Aromatic-plants) 1957, 108

(Gurvich, N. L.) Гурвич, Н. Л. (1960) *Растительное сырьё* (Raw material of plant origin) **6, 7**

Hall, M. T. (1952) *Ann. Mo. Bot. Gard.* **39,** 1

Hallier, J. (1913) Cpt. Rend. *XI. Cong. Int. Pharm.* **2,** 969

Hanover, J. W. (1966) *Hered.* **21,** 73

Hänsel, R. (1956) *Arch. Pharm.* **289,** 619

Hänsel, R., Leuchert, C., Rimpler, U. and Scharf, K. D. (1965) *Phytochemistry* **4,** 19

Harrison, G. A. (1964) In: *Phenetic and Phylogenetic Classification.* (Ed. V. H. Heywood and J. McNell) Syst. Ass. Publ. No. 6. p. 161 London

Hawkes, J. G. (1968) *Chemotaxonomy and Serotaxonomy.* Academic Press, London

Hegglin, A. (1957) *Untersuchungen über Selektionierung von Datura innoxia.* (Promotionsarbeit), Zürich, Nr. 2653

Hegnauer, R. (1948) *Ber. Schweiz. Bot. Ges.* **58,** 391

Hegnauer, R. (1951) *Pharm. Weekbl.* **86,** 805

Hegnauer, R. (1952) *Pharm. Weekbl.* **87,** 641

Hegnauer, R. (1954) *Pharm. Acta Helv.* **29,** 203

Hegnauer, R. (1955) *Planta Med.* **3,** 17

Hegnauer, R. (1956) *Pharmazie* **11,** 638

Hegnauer, R. (1957) *Pharm. Weekbl.* **92,** 810

Hegnauer, R. (1958) *Pharm. Acta Helv.* **33,** 287

Hegnauer, R. (1959) *Pharm. Ztg.* **104,** 382

Hegnauer, R. (1960) *Planta Med.* **8,** 240

Hegnauer, R. (1960a) *Pharmazie* **15,** 634

Hegnauer, R. (1961) *Planta Med.* **9,** 37

Hegnauer, R., (1963) The taxonomic significance of alkaloids. In: *Chemical Plant Taxonomy.* Ed. T. Swain

Hegnauer, R. (1962–66) *Chemotaxonomie der Pflanzen.* Birkhäuser Verlag, Basel, Vol. 1–4

Helm, J. (1957) *Züchter* **27,** 203

Herout, V. (1965) *Herba Hungar.* **4,** (Ed. Spec.) 19

Heslop-Harrison, J. (1960) *Planta Med.* **8,** 208

Heslop-Harrison, J. (1963) Species concepts; Theoretical and Practical Aspects. In: *Chemical Plant Taxonomy.* Ed. T. Swain

Heywood, V. H. (1966) Phytochemistry and taxonomy. In: *Comparative Phytochemistry*

Hillis, W. E. and Hasegawa, M. (1962) *Biochem. J.* **83,** 503

Hirota, N. (1951–53) *Mem. of Ehine Univ. Sci. Sect. II;* **1,** 5; **2,** 99

Hirota, N. (1953) *Perfum and Ess. Oil Rec.* **44,** 167, 201, 236

Hochreutiner, B. P. G. (1937) *Boissiera* **2,** 1

Hoffmann, F. (1961) *Pharm. Acta Helv.* **36,** 30

Hohmann, J. (1936) *Biochemische Merkmale in Scrophulariaceae* (Dissertation), Braunschweig

(Hotin, A. A.) Хотин, А. А. (1958) *Состояние научноисследовательской работы с эфиро масличными культурами* (State of scientific research work in the field of essential oil plants). Ed. Sel'hozgiz. Moscow

Hörhammer, L. and Hänsel, R. (1955) *Arch. Pharm.* **60,** 153

Huxley, J. (1938) *Nature* **142,** 3587

Ihloff, M. L. (1966) *Fette, Seifen, Waschmitt.* **58,** 122

Ilieva, S. (1963) *Wiss. Z. Karl Marx Univ.* **12,** 378

Ilinskaya, T. N. and Yosifova, M. G. (1956) *Bull. Narcot,* **8,** 38

(Ivanov, N. N.) Иванов, Н. Н. (1926) *Тр. по прикл. Бот. Ген. Сел.* (Works of applied Bot. Gen. Sel. 13), Vol. 16, Ed. 3

(Ivanov, S. L.) Иванов, С. Л. (1915) *Соодщ. Бюро по растениеводства* (Rep. of plant-growing bureau). Vol. 7

Jámbor, B. (1964) Doktori értekezés oppozíciója (Opposition on Tétényi's doctoral dissertation, manuscript). Library of Hung. Acad. Sci. Budapest

James, W. O. (1950) Alkaloids in the plant. In: Manske and Holmes (1950–1960) *The alkaloids* **1**, 16 Academic Press, New York

Jaminet, F. (1960) *Planta Med.* **8**, 275

Jaretzky, R. (1925) *Feddes Report Spec. Nov. Regn. Veg.* **22**, 49

(Jermakov, A. I.) Ермаков, А. И. (1961) *Физиол. Раст.* (Physiol. of Plants) **7**, 447

Jirásek, V. (1958) *Index Seminum Univ. Carol.* Prague, 9

Jirásek, V. (1959) *Index Seminum Univ. Carol.* Prague 6

Jirásek, V. (1961) *Taxon*, **10**, 34

Jirásek, V. (1965) *Preslia* **38**, 267

Jordan, A. (1873) *Remarques sur le fait de l'existence en société à l'état sauvage des espèces végétales affines et sur d'autres faits à la question de l'espèce.* Lyon

(Junusov, S.) Юнусов, С. (1950) *Ж. Общ. Хим.* (J. of Gen. Chem.) 20

Jurjev, V. J. (1952) *A szántóföldi növények nemesítése és vetőmagtermesztése* (Breeding of field plants and growing their sowing-seeds. Mezőgazdasági Kiadó, Budapest

(Juzepchuk, S. V.) Юзепчук, С. В. (1948) *Бот. Ж.* (Bot. J.) **33**, 150

(Juzepchuk, S. V.) Юзепчук, С. В. (1958) *Проблемы вида в ботанике* (Problems of species in botany) **1**, 130

Kalitzki, M. (1954) *Pharmazie* **9**, 61

Kárpáti, Z. (1961) A kultúrnövények rendszerezésének problémái (Problems in the taxonomy of cultivated plants). *Culturflora of Hungary*

Karrer, W. (1958) Konstitution und Vorkommen der organischen Pflanzenstoffe. *Birkhäuser Verlag*, Basel

Keller, E. F. (1952) *Növény és környezet* (Plant and environment) **2**, 86

(Kiryalov, N. P. and Konovalov, I.N.) Кирьялов, Н. П. — Коновалов, И. Н. (1959) *Интрод. Раст. Зел. Строит.* (Introd. Horticult. Building) **7**, 40

Klein, G. (1921) *Sitzungsberichte Akad. Wiss. Wien*, 295

(Klishchev, L. K.) Клищев, Л. К. (1961) *Биохим. Конгр. Реф. Секц. Сообщ.* Москва (V. Congr. Biochem. Ref. Sect. Communication. Moscow) **2**, 199

Koch, B. (1960) *Agrobotanika* **2**, 115

Kohlmünzer, S. (1961) *Wiadomosc. Botaniczn.* **5**, 47

(Komarov, V. L.) Комаров, В. Л. (1940) *Избр. Соч.* **1**, 125 (Collected works). Acad. Sci. USSR, Moscow

(Konstantinov, P. N.) Константинов, П. Н. (1946) *Тимирь. Сельскохоз. Акад.* (Timirj. Agricult. Acad. Nr. 39

(Koroleva, A. S.) Королева, А. С. (1948) *Тадж. Фил. АН СССР* (Tadzh. Fil. Acad. Sci. USSR) 10, 38

Korte, F. (1963) *Arch. Pharm.* **296**, 403

(Korzhinsky, S. V.) Коржинский, С. В. (1892) *Флора востока европейской России* (Flora of East-European Russia), vol. I, Tomsk

Kozma, P. (1964) Doktori értekezés bírálata (Opposition on Tétényi's doctoral dissertation. Manuscript). Library of Hung. Acad. Sci. Budapest

(Kozo–Polyansky, B. M.) Козо-Полянский, Б. М. (1950) *Пробл. бот.* (Probl. Bot.) **1**, 55

(Krachkovskaya, L. P.) Крачковская, Л. П. (1958) *Краткий отчет ВНИИМЕМК за 1957* (Short report of St. Sci. Res. Inst. of Oil and Aromatic Plants for 1957), 83

(Krachkovskaya, L. P.) Крачковская, Л. П. (1962) *Краткий отчет ВНИИМЕМК* (Short report of St. Sci. Res. Inst. of Oil and Aromatic Plants for 1959, 1960), 94

Lam, H. S. (1959) Taxonomy, general principles and angiosperms, in: *Vistas in Botany*. Pergamon Press, London, 3

Lamprecht, H. (1959) *Agric. Hortique Genetica* **17**, 103

Lanjouw, J. (1958) *Taxon* **7**, 43

Latuszinsky, J. (1960) *Nemzetközi Mg. Szemle* (International Agricult. Rev.) 52

Lehman, O. (1955) Das morphologische System der Kulturtomaten. *Züchter*, Sonderheft

Lemli, J. A. (1955) *De vluchtige olie van Mentha piperita L.* (Dissertation) Groningen

Leone, C. A. (1964) *Taxonomic Biochemistry and Serology*, Ronald Press Comp. New York

6*

Leroy, J. F. (1958) *J. Agr. Trop. et Bot. Appl.* **5**, 173

Ligeti, G. (1958) *Acta Pharm. Hung.* **28**, 237

Ligeti, G. (1959) *Pharmazie* **14**, 164

Lindley, J. (1836) *An Introduction to the Natural System of Botany*, London

Linné, C. (1751) *Philosophia botanica.* Stockholm–Amsterdam

Linstedt, G. (1951) *Acta Chem. Scand.* **5**, 129

(Lysenko, T. D.) Лысенко, Т. Д. (1928) *Вляние термического фактора на продолжитель-ности фаз развитии растений* (Influence of thermal factors on the development of plants). Baku

Lysenko, T. D. (1950) *Agrobiologia.* Mezőgazdasági Kiadó, Budapest

(Lysenko, T. D.) Лысенко, Т. Д. (1958) *Тр. Инст. Ген.* (Works of Gen. Inst.) **24**, 5

Lőve, A. (1965) *Taxon.* **14**, 69

(Luks, J. A.) Лукс, Й. А. (1958) *Интрод. раст. зел. троит.* (Introd. Horticult. Building) **6**, 11

Luten, D. B. (1964) *Lloydia* **27**, 135

Luyendijk, E. N. (1956) *Over de vorkommen van vluchtige olie.* (Dissertation), Leiden

(Maichenko, Z. G. and Shalimov, V. N.) Майченко, З. Г. и Шалимов, В. Н. (1962) *Маслоб и жиров. пром.* (Cream and fats industry) No. 6, 23

Mándy, Gy. and Bócsa, I. (1962) A kender. Cannabis sativa. *Culturflora of Hungary*, vol. VII, No 14. Akadémiai Kiadó, Budapest

Mansfeld, R. (1949) *Die Technik der Wissenschaftlichen Pflanzenbenennung.* Akademie Verlag, Berlin

Mansfeld, R. (1953) *Kulturpflanze* **1**, 138

Mansfeld, R. (1954) *Kulturpflanze* **2**, 30

Mansfeld, R. (1958) *Taxon.* **7**, 41

Mansfeld, R. (1959) Vorläufiges Verzeichnis landwirtschaftlich oder gärtnerisch kultivierter Pflanzenarten. *Kulturpflanze*, Beiheft 2, Akademie Vlg. Berlin

Manske, R. H. F. and Holmes, H. L. (1950–1960) *The alkaloids.* 7 vols. Acad. Press, New York

Marker, R. E. and Lopez, J. (1947) *J. Am. Chem. Soc.* **69**, 2383

Mason, L. (1950) *Madrono* **10**, 193

Máthé, I. and Földesi, D. (1965) Solanum laciniatum. Medicinal nightshade. *Culturflora of Hungary*, vol. V, No 17. Akadémiai Kiadó, Budapest

(Matvejev, N. D.) Матвеев, Н. Д. (1959) *Основы сортоводства и семенного дела по лекарственными культурами* (Bases of variety-breeding and seed-growing in the case of medicinal plants). Sel'hozgiz, Moskva

McAtee, W. L. (1952) *Science* **116**, 400

McNair, J. B. (1929) *Amer. J. Bot.* **16**, 832

McNair, J. B. (1935) *Bull. Torr. Bot. Club* **62**, 219, 515

McNair, J. B. (1945) *Lloydia* **8**, 145

Merxmüller, H. (1967) *Ber. Dtsch. Bot. Gesschft.* **80**, 608

Mez, C. (1924) Abderhaldens Arbeitsmethoden. Abt. 9, 1059. In: Molisch, H. (1933) Pflanzenchemie und Pflanzenverwandtschaft. Fischer Verlag, Jena

Michalszky, T. (1960) *Biul. Inst. Rosl. Leczn.* **6**, 167

Michaluk, A. and Oswiecimska, M. (1959) *Diss. Pharm.* **11**, 191

Micke, A. (1962) *Z. Pfl. Zücht.* **48**, 1

Mirov, N. T. (1956) *Canad. J. Bot.* **34**, 443

Mirov, N. T. (1958) Distribution of turpentine components among species of the genus Pinus. In: *Physiology of Forest Trees*, by K. V. Thiemann, New York, Ronald Press Co. p. 251

Mirov, N. T. (1961) *Techn. Bull.* No 1239 USDA Forest Service

Mirov, N. T. (1963) *Lloydia* **26**, 117

Moens, J. C. B. (1882) *De Kinacultur in Asia.* Evans and Co. Batavia

Moldenhawer, K. (1963) *Wiss. Z. Karl Marx Univ.* **12**, 415

Molisch, H. (1933) *Pflanzenchemie und Pflanzenverwandtschaft.* Fischer Verlag, Jena

Moritz, O. (1958) In: *Handbuch der Pflanzenphysiologie* **8**, 375, **10**, 24. Springer Verlag

REFERENCES

Moritz, O. (1962) *Allgemeine Pharmakognosie* VEB G. Fischer Verlag, Jena

Mothes, K. (1954) *Planta Med.* **2**, 200

Mothes, K. (1957) *Pharm. Weekbl.* **92**, 818

Mothes, K. (1962) *Az alkaloidok biogeneziséről* (On the biogenesis of alkaloids). Lecture in the Hungarian Academy of Science, Budapest

Mothes, K. and Romeike, A. (1958) Die Alkaloide. In: *Hdbch. d. Pflanzenphysiologie*, vol. 8, 989. Springer Verlag

Mothes, K., Romeike, A. and Schröter, H. B. (1955) *Naturwiss.* **41**, 214

(Nevstrueva, R. I.) Невструева, Р. И. (1959) *Тр. Гос. Никитск. Бот. Сада* (Works of Nikitsk. St. Bot. Garden) **29**, 345

Nigam, M. C., Nigam, I. S. and Levi, L. (1965) *J. Soc. Cosm. Chem.* (USA) **16**, 155

(Nikolaev, A. G.) Николаев, А. Г. (1960) *Кишневск. унив. Тр. Прикл. Химии Природных Соединений* (Univ. of Kisinev. Appl. Chem. of Natural Compounds) **3**, 11

(Nikolaev, A. G., Nikolaeva, D. A., Gogol, O. N. and Kubrak, M. N.) Николаев, А. Г., Николаева, Д. А., Гоголь, О. Н. и Кубрак, М. Н. (1961) *V. Int. Congr. Biochem. Ref.* vol. 2, 121

(Nilov, V. I.) Нилов, В. И. (1934) *Соц. Раст.* (Soc. Plant) **11**, 21

(Nilov, V. I.) Нилов, В. И. (1936) *Тр. по Прикл. Бот. Ген. Сел.* Works on Appl. Bot. Gen. of Agricult.) **3**, 3, 5

(Nilov, V. I.) Нилов, В. И. (1937) *Изд. АН СССР, Сер. Биол.* (Rep. Acad. Sci. USSR) Ser. Biol. **6**, 1709

(Nilov, V. I.) Нилов, В. И. (1938) *Биохим. Культ. Раст.* (Biochem. Cult. Plants), Vol. **6**, 145

(Nilov, V. I.) Нилов, В. И. (1938) *Биохим. Культ. Раст.* (Biochem. Cult. Plants), Vol. **6**, 5

Nowinski, M. (1957) *Biul. Inst. Rosl. Leczn.* **3**, 169

Ohta, Y. (1960) *Szikken Jiho Rep. Kihara Inst. Biol. Res.* (11), 63

(Oparin, A. I.) Опарин, А. И. (1937) *Изв. АН СССР, Сер. Биол.* (Rep. Acad. Sci. USSR, Ser. Biol.) **6**, 1733

Os, van F. H. L. (1957) *Pharm. Weekbl.* **92**, 846

Os, van F. H. L. (1968) *Plantes Méd. Phytothérapie* 2, (in press)

(Pangalo, K. I.) Пангало, К. И. (1948) *Бот. Ж.* (Bot. J.) **33**, 151

Penfold, A. R. (1922) *Ess. Oil. Perf. Rec.* **13**, 273

Penfold, A. R. (1929) *J. Proc. Roy. Soc.* N.S.W. 62, 225

Penfold A. R. (1950) *Ess. Oil. Perf. Rec.* **41**, 359

Penfold, A. R., McKern, H. H. G. and Willis, J. L. (1953) *Res. Ess. Oils Austral. Flora* **3**, 15

Penfold, A. R., Morrison, F. R., Willis, J. L. and McKern, H.H.G. (1950) *Res. Ess. Oils. Austral. Flora* **2**, 8

Penfold, A. R., Morrison, F. R., Willis, J. L., McKern, H. H. G. and Spies, M. C. (1951) *J. Proc. Roy. Soc. N.S.W.* **85**, 123

Persoon, Ch. H. (1805) *Synopsis plantarum I*. Paris

Petiver, J. (1699) Some attempts ... *Phil. Transactions*, London 21, 289

Pirie, N. W. (1962) *Perspect. Biol. Medic.* **5**, 446

Plouvier, V. (1962) *Rev. Gén. Sci. Pures et Appl.* **69**, 331

Priszter, Sz. and Tétényi, P. (1963) *Acta Biol. Acad. Sci. Hung.* **13**, 27 (Suppl.)

(Prohanov, J. I.) Проханов, Й. И. (1949) *Бот. Ж.* (Bot. J.) **34**, 4

Reinouts van Haga, P. (1958) Techn. Hochschr. *Bijdrage de Kennis van alkaloiden Atropa bella-donna* (Dissertation). Delft

Reznik, H. (1955) *Z. Bot.* **43**, 499

Rickett, W. H. (1958) *Taxon* **7**, 37

Rimpler, H. (1965) *Planta Med.* **13**, 412

(Rabinin, A. A. and Ilina, E. N.) Рябинин, А. А. и Ильина, Е. Н. (1951) *Докл. АН СССР* (Rep. Acad. Sci. USSR) **76**, 851

Roberts, J. E., Brady, L. R. and Tyler, V. E. (1964) *Lloydia* **27**, 192

Rochleder, F. (1854) *Phytochemie* Leipzig. In: Molisch (1933) *Pflanzenchemie und Pflanzenverwandtschaft*. Fischer Verlag, Jena

Rosenthal, C. (1943) *Pharm. Ind.* **10,** 22

Rosenthaler, L. (1907) *Beih. bot. Zentralblatt* 21, 1. Abt.

Ross, R. (1958) *Taxon* **7,** 65

Roth, A. W. (1810) Preisschrift über die Varietäten im Pflanzenreich. In: *Botan. Taschenbuch* by Hoppe

Rothmaler, W. (1950) *Allgemeine Taxonomie und Chronologie der Pflanzen,* Jena

Rothmaler, W. (1954) VIII. *Bot. Congr. Rapports et Comm.* IV, 67, Paris

Rouy, G. and Foucaud, J. (1893) *Flore de France* I, Tome, Imprim. Deslis. Tours

Rovesti, P. (1957) *Pharm. Weekbl.* **92,** 792, 843

Rovesti, P. (1958) *Riv. Ital. Ess. Profumi* **40,** 215

Rowson, J. M. (1958) *Proc. Linn. Soc. London* **169,** 212

(Rubin, B. A.) Рубин Б. А. (1937) *Изв. АН СССР, Сер. Биол.* (Inform. of Acad. Sci. USSR, Ser: Biol.) **6.** 1755

Rubin, B. A. (1951) *A micsurini biológia biokémiai problémái* (Biochemical problems of Michurin's biology). Akadémiai Kiadó, Budapest, 98.

Rubin, B. A. (1953) Pflanze und Umwelt, *Kultur und Forschr. Vlg.* Berlin.

(Rubin, B. A.) Рубин, Б. А. (1958) *Некоторые вопросы обмена веществ света учения. Достиж. биол. науки Сельхозгиз.* (Some problems of metabolism.) Sel'hozgiz. Moscow, 49.

(Rubin, B. A. and Trupp, V. E.) Рубин, Б. А. и Трупп, В. Е. (1936) *Т. Лабор. агрохимии и биохимии овощей* (Works of the Agrochem. and Biochem. Labor. Sci. Res. Inst. of Vegetables)

Ruijgrok, K. (1963) *Naturwissenschaften* **50,** 620

Sabalitschka, T. (1925) *Heil- und Gewürzpflanzen* **8,** 73

Sacco, T. (1953) *Ind. Parfum.* **8,** 449

Sacco, T. (1959) *Alliona.* Torino 5, 185

Sági, F., Zatykó, J., Kollányi, L. and Szilágyi, K. (1960) *Kísérletügyi Közlemények* (Rec. Hung. Agr. Exp. Stat.) **52/C,** 19

Sahov, A. A. (1952) *Növény és Környezet* (Plant and Environment) **2,** 44

Sander, H. (1963) *Bot. Jahresberichte* **82,** 404

Schratz, E. (1957) *Pharm. Weekbl.* **92,** 781

Schratz, E. (1960a) *Planta Med.* **8,** 282

Schratz, E. (1960b) *Arzneipflanzen. Hdbch. d. Pflanzenzüchtung,* V. 383

Schratz, E. (1963) *Planta Med.* **11,** 278

Schreiber, K. and Rönsch, H. (1963) *Tetrahedron letters* 5, 329

Sengbusch, R. (1932) *Züchter* 55. In: Bredemann, G. Schwanitz, F. and Sengbusch (1956) *Bull. Narcot* **8,** 31

Sennikov, A. P. (1953) *A növények ökológiája* (Ecology of Plants). Akadémiai Kiadó, Budapest

Sgarbieri, V. C., Gupta, M. S., Kramer, D. E. and Whitaker, J. R. (1964) *J. biol. Chem.* **239,** 2171

(Shakhov, A. A.) Шахов, А. А. (1959) *Насл. Измен. Раст. Жив. Микроорг.* (Heredity and Variability of Plants, Animals and Microorganism). T. 2, 164

(Shavrov, L. A.) Шавров, Л. А. (1961) *Изв. АН СССР, Сер. Биол.* (Rec. of Acad. Sci. USSR, ser. biol.) **30,** 582

(Shilykalnova, K.I.) Шилыкальнова, К. И. (1958) *Краткий Отчет ВНИИМЕМК за 1957— 58* (Short rep. of St. Sci. Res. Inst. of Oil and Aromatic Plants)

Sievers, A. F. (1938) *J. Am. Pharm. Ass.* **27,** 1221

Silva, F. (1966) *Planta Med.* **14,** 302

(Sinskaya, E. N.) Синская, Е. N. (1948) *Бот. Ж.* (Bot. J.) **33,** 148

(Sisakyan, N. M. and Filipovich, I. I.) Сисакян, Н. М. и Филипович, И. И. (1951) *Докл. АН СССР* (Rec. of Acad. Sci. USSR) **76,** 3

Sokal, R. R. and Sneath, P. H. A. (1963) *Principles of Numerical Taxonomy.* Freeman Co. San Francisco—London

(Sokolov, V. S.) Соколов, В. С. (1952) *Алкалоидоносные Растения СССР* (Plants with alkaloid contents in the Soviet Union). Acad. Moscow—Leningrad

Soó, R. (1926) *MTA Math. Term. Tud. Értesítője* (Rec. of Mathematics and Natural Sciences of Hung. Acad. Sci.) **43**, 20

Soó, R. (1953) *Fejlődéstörténeti növényrendszertan* (Phylogenetical taxonomy). Tankönyv-kiadó, Budapest

Soó, R. (1956) *Magy. Tud.* (Science of Hung) **4**, 173

Soó, R. (1964) Doktori értekezés oppozíciója (Opposition on Tétényi's doctoral dissertation). Manuscript, Library of Hung. Acad. Sci. Budapest

Soó, R., Greguss, P., Martos, L. et al. (1955) *Bot. Közl.* (Bot. Records) **46**, 1

Souèges, R. (1938 *Embryogénie et classification* Paris

Stahl, E. (1957) *Pharm. Weekbl.* **92**, 829

Stapf, O. (1906) *Kew. Bull.* **8**, 297

Stary, F. (1965) *Res. Trav. XXV, Congr. FIP*, Prague

Stearn, T. W. (1952) Historical Introduction. In: *Int. Code Nomencl. Cult. Plants. Regn. Veg.* No 10

Stebbins, L. (1950) *Variation and Evolution on Plants*. Oxford Univ. Press, London

Steenis, van C. G. J. (1957) *Flora Malesiana*, ser. I. **5**, 157

Steinegger, E. (1957) *Pharm. Weekbl.* **92**, 820

Steinegger, E. (1958) *Pharm. Acta Helv.* **33**, 357

Steinegger, E. and Bernasconi, R. (1963) *Pharm. Acta Helv.* **38**, 375

Steinegger, E. and Bernasconi, R. (1965) *Pharm. Acta Helv.* **40**, 246

Steinegger, E. and Hänsel, R. (1963) *Lehrbuch d. allgemeinen Pharmacognosie*. Springer Verlag. Berlin-Göttingen

Steinegger, E. and Steiger K. E. (1959) *Pharm. Acta Helv.* **34**, 521

Straub, F. B. (1965) *Biokémia*. Medicina, Budapest

Swain, T. (1963) *Chemical Plant Taxonomy*. Academic Press, London and New York

Swain, T. (1966) *Comparative Phytochemistry*. Academic Press, London and New York

(Takhtadzhyan, A. L.) Тахтаджьян, А. Л. (1955) *Бот. Ж.* (Bot. J.) **40**, 789

Targé, A. and Lambinon, J. (1965) *Bull. Soc. Roy. Bot. Belge* **98**, 295

Taylor, A. O. (1963) *New Phytol.* **63**, 135

Tétényi, P. (1958) *Taxon.* **7**, 40

Tétényi, P. (1959) *Pharmazie* **14**, 690

Tétényi, P. (1960a) *Taxon.* **9**, 241

Tétényi, P. (1960b) *Oléagineux* **15**, 471

Tétényi P. (1961) *Pharmazie* **16**, 273

Tétényi, P. (1962) *Herba Hung.* **1**, 267

(Tétényi, P.) Тетени, П. (1962) *Бот. Ж.* (Bot. J.) **47**, 1731

Tétényi, P. (1963) *Planta Med*, **11**, 287

Tétényi, P. (1964) *Bot. Közl.* (Bot. Rec.) **51**, 187

Tétényi, P. (1965) *Gyógyszerészet* (Pharmacy) **9**, 201

(Timofejev, N. N.) Тимофеев, Н. Н. (1960) *Общая селекция. Селекция и семеноводства овощных культур* (Breeding. Breeding and seedgrowing of vegetables). Sel'hozgiz. Moscow

(Timofejev-Ressovsky, N. V.) Тимофеев-Рессовский, Н. В. (1958) *Бот. Ж.* (Bot. J.) **43**, 317

Törő, I. (1966) *Az élet alapjai* (Bases of life). Gondolat, Budapest

(Trinkler, J. G.) Тринклер, Й. Г. (1962) *Бот. Ж.* (Bot. J.) **47**, 17

Troll, M. J. (1961) *Dtsch. Akad. Landw. Wiss.* **32**, 53

Tschirch, A. (1930–32) *Handbuch der Pharmacognosie*, Leipzig

Turesson, G. (1922) *Heredity* **3**, 211

Turner, B. and Alston, R. (1959) *Am. J. Bot.* **46**, 678

Turowska, J. and Skwara, J. (1959) *Acta Biol. Cracoviens.* **1**, 79

Tyihák, E., Sárkányné, I. and Máthé, I. (1963) *Pharm. Zhalle*, **102**, 3

Tyler, V. E. and Abou-Chaar, C. I. (1960) *Pharmazie* **15**, 628

Ulmann, M. (1951) *Wertvolle Kautschukpflanzen des gemässigten Klimas*. Akad. Verlag, Berlin

Vágújfalvi, D., Tétényi, P. and Lőrincz, G. (1966) Abh. deutsch Akad. Wiss. Berlin; 3 Intern. Symp: *Biochemie und Physiologie d. Alkaloide.* Halle 1965, 349

Valentin, D. H. and Lőve, A. (1958) *Brittonia* **10**, 153

(Vasiljchenko, I. T.) Васильченко, И. Т. (1958) *Тр. Бот. Инст. Комарова АН СССР* (Works of Bot. Inst. Komarov Acad. Sci. USSR). **12**, 132

(Vavilov, N. I.) Вавилов, Н. И. (1920) *Законы хомологических рядов в наследственной изменчивости* (The rules of the homologous line in inheritance-variability). vol. III, Saratov breeding congress

Venema, H. J. (1947) Het arbeitsveld de systematiek der culturgewassen. Wageningen. In: Kárpáti, Z. (1961) *Culturflora of Hungary*

Vent, W. (1960) *Taxon.* **9**, 53

Vent, W. (1962) *Wiss. Z. Humboldt Univ.* **11**, 401

Verzár-Petri, G. and Sárkány S. (1961) *Planta Med.* **9**, 15

Vickery, R. K. and Olson, R. L. (1956) *J. Heredity* **47**, 195

(Vjazov, A. A.) Вязов, А. А. (1956) *Бюлл. Главн. Бот. Сада* (Bull. Centr. Bot. Garden) **26**, 28

(Voskresenskaya, G. S. and Shpota, V. I.) Воскресенская, Г. С. и Шпота, В. И. (1962) *Кратк. Отчет ВНИИМЕМК за 1959—60* (Short Rep. of St. Sci. Res. Inst. of Oil and Aromatic Plants for the years 1959–60) 44

(Wagner, R. P. and Mitchell, H. K.) Вагнер, Р. П. и Мичел, Х. К. (1958) *Генетика и обмен веществ.* (Genetics and metabolism) *Изд. Иностр. Лит. Москва* Intern. Lit. Moscow

Weevers, T. (1943) *Blumea* **5**, 412

Weisbach, J. A., Raffauf, R. F., Ribeiro, O., Macko, E. and Douglas, E. (1963) *J. Pharm. Sci.* **52**, 350

Wettstein, R. (1898) *Grundzüge der geographisch-morphologischen Methode der Pflanzensystematik.* Jena

Wildemann, De E. (1941) *Mém. Ac. Belg. Sci.* **18**, 146

Willamann, J. J. and Li, H. L. (1963) *Econ. Bot.* **17**, 180

Willamann, J. J. and Schubert, B. G. (1955) *Econ. Bot.* **9**, 141

Willamann, J. J. and Schubert, B. G. (1961) *Techn. Bull.* No. 1234

Willis, J. C. (1940) *The course of evolution.* Cambr. Univ. Press, Cambridge

Woodward, E. F. and Smith, E. (1962) *Lloydia* **25**, 281

(Zavadsky, K. M.) Завадский, К. М. (1961) *Учение о виде.* (Study on species). *Изд. Унив. Ленинград* Univ. Leningrad

Zenk, M. H. (1967) *Ber. Dtsch. Bot. Ges.* **80**, 573

(Zhidko, E. P.) Жидко, Э. П. (1959) *Труд. Житомир. Научн. Исслед. Селекц. Ст. Хмелев.* (Works of Zhitomir. Sci. Res. Select. St.) **6**, 73

(Zolotnickaya, S. Ya.) Золотницкая, С. Я. (1953) *Изд. АН Арм. ССР* (Rec. Acad. Sci. Arm. SSR) **6**, 17

(Zhukovsky, P. M.) Жуковский, П. М. (1949) *Ботаника* (Botany). Советска Наука, Moscow

(Zhukovsky, P. M.) Жуковский, П. М. (1950) *Культурные растении и их сороднчи* (Cultivated plants and their origin) Советска Наука, Moscow

(Zhukovsky, P. M.) Жуковский, П. М. (1957) *Бот. Ж.* (Bot. J.) **42**, 1596

SPECIAL PART

GENERAL REMARKS

For the sake of easier surveyability it was necessary to group and within this grouping also to arrange the description of the data of literature referring to the infraspecific chemical taxa of the various plant species and also our own experimental data. However, within this grouping it was impossible to separate the cultivated species from those occurring spontaneously. Namely, a distinction of this type is only relative and, besides, in principle, no essential differences exist between the chemical taxa of the two groups. All chemical taxa have been formed *spontaneously*, on the effect of natural factors, intrinsic regularities, differentiation and selection. Even in the case of cultivated species, man played only the role of a passive participant in the process, instead of deliberately directing the procedure. Thus, it appears to be more correct to distinguish spontaneously formed chemical taxa, on the one hand, and *artificially* produced taxa, on the other. The latter were formed by human participation, by breeding medicinal plants.

Our present knowledge in this field has been grouped according to the main secondary metabolites (active substances), with particular respect to the biosynthetic routes (Mentzer, 1960) and to the introduction of N (Table III).

TABLE III

SCHEME OF THE GROUPS OF ACTIVE AGENTS OF CHEMICAL TAXA

Name of active agents	Literature
1. Terpenes and related compounds	STEINEGGER–HÄNSEL, 1963
1.1. Terpene compounds; sesquiterpene lactones	MORITZ, 1962; HERZ 1968,
1.2. Terpenoids (triterpenes, steroids, saponins, cardenolids)	MORITZ, 1962
1.3. Pseudoalkaloids	HEGNAUER, 1963
2. Other compounds connected with acetate metabolism	STEINEGGER–HÄNSEL, 1963
2.1. Derivatives of resorcin, of orcellinic acid; phloroglucins; ranunculin	
2.2. Quinones	ZENK–LEISTNER, 1968
3. Derivatives of phenylpropane and flavonoids	STEINEGGER–HÄNSEL, 1963
3.1. Simple phenolics; phenylpropane compounds; coumarins; stilbenes; amidic acrids	MORITZ, 1962
3.2. Flavonoids	STEINEGGER–HÄNSEL, 1963
4. Alkaloids	STEINEGGER–HÄNSEL, 1963
4.1. Protoalkaloids	HEGNAUER, 1963
4.2. Alkaloids proper	HEGNAUER, 1963
5. Isorhodanidogenes	MORITZ, 1962

As in all types of classification, some difficulties were encountered here too, e.g. in the case of species where the active agent has not yet been identified or its structure has not been elucidated or it has been classified into various groups.

However, grouping is not intended to indicate the quantity of these substances. The primary aim was to point to the infraspecific differences of the ways of biogenesis and stimulate in this manner the elucidation of the functional causes, of the differentiated metabolistic patterns leading to this specialization. We wanted only to determine the research task involved by the manifold description (though only the groups of active agents of medicinal plants have been mentioned). Namely, we are of the opinion that in order to facilitate a better knowledge of the differentiation of functions and of phylogeny, the biological (biochemical, physiological, genetical) conditions and the causes of small metabolistic alterations and differences in the mechanism of metabolism must be cleared up. The grouping presented in Table III has been used in respect to these differences.

Within the single groups of active agents, the systematization of Soó (1953) served as the basis of the sequence for discussing the plant families, taking into account the suggestions of Abbayes et al. (1963) as well. Genera and species, respectively, are listed in alphabetical order. The species and the infraspecific morphological taxa are described by the denominations accepted by Soó and Jávorka (1951), Mansfeld (1959) or Soó (1961, 1964).

In the following part, quantitative and qualitative differences are given separately (denoted by **Qn. D.** and **Ql. D.**, respectively). Quantitative data are given only in the case when the variation is interrupted. On evaluating the data of literature in respect to the content of active agents in medicinal plants, some difficulties arise because one must frequently compare values obtained by different methods (by earlier or by recent techniques).

In the cases when the data of literature were aimed at elucidating the causes of polychemism, such values are included as point to the correlation between chemical and morphological characteristics, to the independence from ecological conditions (area), to deviations in individual development or to the localized nature of the active agents. Data of this type, together with nomenclatoric statements in respect to the heritability of chemical characteristics and to the chemical taxa proper, are given in a separate place (designed by **Ch. T.**).

ABBREVIATIONS

In the line of the name of the species

Organs

Ba	bark	Sd	seed
Bu	bulb	Sh	shoot
Fl	inflorescence	Sp	sporophyte
Fr	fruit	St	stem
Lf	leaf	Tb	terminal branchlet
My	mycelium	Th	thallus
Pl	peel	Tu	tuber
Rh	rhizome	Tw	twig
Rt	root	Wd	wood
Sc	sclerotium	Wp	whole plant above ground

Indication of physical condition

E–O	essential oil	OR	oleoresin
J	juice	PS	press-sap
LX	latex	TP	turpentine

In the column of matters

A	acid	*MA*	main alkaloid
Abs.	absent	*MC*	main component
Ac	acetate	O	olivetoric
ASP	aspidin	∅	glycoalkaloid absent
AT	atranorin	ORP	optical rotatory power
B	barbatic	P	proto
C	cetraric	Pst.	present
CA	caperate	S	sola-
E	erythric	SL	salacinic
F	fumar(ic)	SQ	squamatic
G	gyrophoric	ST	stictic
GC	gas chromatography	Tc	thamnolic
ITC	isothiocyanate	Tr.	traces
LE	lecanoric	U	usnic
LI	lichesteric	VAR	variation(s)

In the line of **Ch. T.** (Chemical taxa)

Ch.	chemical	IND	individual
CHAR	character(s)	ISP	infraspecific
CORR	correlation	MP	morphological
D	difference(s)	OG	ontogenetical
DEP	dependent	PHYS	physiological
IDP	independent		

93

In the column of origin

ABY	Abyssinia	EUR	Europe	NOR	Norway
AF	Africa	FIN	Finland	OAX	Oaxacana
AFG	Afghanistan	FRA	France	PR	Polar
ALB	Albania	GAL	Galapagos	PAK	Pakistan
ALG	Algeria	GBR	Great Britain	PHIL	The Philippines
ANG	Angola	GEO	Georgia	POL	Poland
ANT	Antilles	GER	Germany	POR	Portugal
ARG	Argentina	G-L	Greenland	P-R	Puerto Rico
ARM	Armenia	GUI	Guinea	Q-L	Queensland
ASB	Aserbaidshan	HAW	Hawai	REU	Réunion
AUL	Australia	HIM	The Himalayas	RHO	Rhodesia
AUS	Austria	HUN	Hungary	ROM	Rumania
BAL	Baltic countries	I	Island	RUS	Russia
BEL	Belgium	I-C	Ivory Coast	S/	South
BOL	Bolivia	IND	India	SAH	Sahalin
BRA	Brazil	INDO	Indonesia	SAD	Sardinia
BUL	Bulgaria	IRL	Ireland	SAR	South African
BUR	Burma	ISR	Israel		Republic
C/	Central	ITA	Italy	SEN	Senegal
CAB	Calabria	JAM	Jamaica	SEY	Seychelles
CAL	California	JAP	Japan	SIC	Sicily
CAM	Cameroon	KAB	Kabardia	SIB	Siberia
CAN	Canada	KAH	Kasahstan	SPA	Spain
CAU	Caucasia	KAS	Kashmir	SUD	Sudan
CAY	Cayenne	KEN	Kenya	SWE	Sweden
CBA	Cambodia	MAB	Malabar Coast	SWI	Switzerland
CEY	Ceylon	MAC	Macedonia	TAH	Tahiti
CHI	China	MAD	Madagascar	TAI	Taiwan
CHL	Chile	MAL	Malaysia	TAM	Tasmania
CLU	Columbia	MAR	Marocco	TAN	Tanganyika
COLL	Collection	MED	Mediterranean	TAS	Tashkent
CON	Congo	MEX	Mexico	THAI	Thailand
COR	Corea	MOC	Mozambique	TRI	Trinidad
CSR	Czechoslovakia	MOL	Moldavia	TUR	Turkey
DAL	Dalmatia	MYS	Mysore	UKR	Ukraine
DEN	Denmark	N/	North	URU	Uruguay
DOM	Dominica	N-C	New Caledonia	USA	United States
E/	East	N-G	New Guinea	USSR	Soviet Union
EGY	Egypt	N-Z	New Zealand	V-N	Vietnam
ERI	Eritrea	NED	The Netherlands	W/	West
EQU	Equador	NIG	Nigeria	YUG	Yugoslavia

1. TERPENES AND RELATED COMPOUNDS

1.1. TERPENE COMPOUNDS*; SESQUITERPENE LACTONES

GRIMALDIACEAE

Grimaldia fragrans (Balb.) Corda – Th
Ql. D. cypress-like scent; or scentless/var. *inodora*   GILDEMEISTER–HOFFMANN,
        (Wallr.) Lindb.   1958
Ch. T. MP D Abs.; IDP of substrate   SLAVIK, 1950

PINACEAE

Abies balsamea L. (Mill.) – OR
Ql. D. Δ^3-carene Pst. or Abs.   ZAVARIN, 1968

A. concolor (Gord.) Hoopes – OR
Ql. D. Δ^3-carene 15 % + camphene 15 % +   ZAVARIN–SNAJBERK, 1965
     β-pinene 38 %; or β-pinene 69 %, both other
     components only 0·5 % /var. *lowiana*
     (Gord.) Lemmon

A. lasiocarpa (Hook.) Nutt. – OR
Ql. D. Δ^3-carene 18 %; or only in Tr.   ZAVARIN–SNAJBERK, 1965
     MC: limonene 79 %; or phellandrene 52 %   ZAVARIN, 1966
Ch. T. MP D. Abs.; separate races within species   ZAVARIN, 1966

A. pindrow (Royle) Spach–Lf/E–O
Ql..D. terpineol + terpineol-nonylate + sesquiter-   SIMONSEN, 1922
     pene alcohol
     Δ^3-carene + dipentene + cadinene + bor-   RAO–SOOD, 1962
     nyl Ac

Picea abies (L.) Karst. — Lf/E–O
Ql. D. cadinene 17–26% + borneol-bornyl-Ac 8·5%   MAISIT, 1935
     borneol-bornyl-Ac 15% + camphene 13%+   BRADISHEV–CHERCHES,
     limonene-dipentene 12 %, cadinene Abs.   1959
     limonene 25 % + borneol-bornyl-Ac 17·5%   SCHANTZ–JUVONEN,
     + camphene 9·7 % + cadinene 1·4 %   1966

P. engelmanni (Parry) Engelm. – Lf/E–O
Ql. D. camphor 16% + borneol-bornyl-Ac 13% +   RUDLOFF, 1964
     myrcene 4 %
     camphor 0·4 % + borneol-bornyl-Ac 2 % +   SCHANTZ–JUVONEN, 1966
     myrcene 25% + limonene 7% + δ-cadi-
     nene 9 %

---

* Including also the E–O bearing species if specialized by differences between terpenic and phenylpropane compound components.

P. pungens Engelm. – Lf/E–O
Ql. D. bornyl-Ac. 23–47 % + limonene 16–19 %
  bornyl-Ac. 16 % + limonene 36 %
Ch. T. DEP on season

RUDLOFF, 1962
SCHANTZ–JUVONEN, 1966
RUDLOFF, 1962

Pinus contorta Dougl. – TP
Ql. D. β-phellandrene 90 % + Δ^3-carene 4 %   N–Z
  β-phellandrene 61–77 % + Δ^3-carene 5–14 %   USA

SMITH, 1964
WILLIAMS–BANNISTER, 1962

P. elliottii Engelm. – TP
Ql. D. various ORP of individuals
  α-pinene 39 % + β-pinene 55 %
  α-pinene 76 % + β-pinene 21 % + phellandrene 3 %; or α-pinene 61 % + β-pinene
  34 % + phellandrene 3 %; or phellandrene 19 %/var. *densa* Little et Dorman
Ch. T. phellandrene content DEP on origin

HERTY, 1908
ANONYMOUS, 1961
MIROV et al., 1965

MIROV et al., 1965

P. khasya Royle – TP
Ql. D. β-pinene 46–71 % + α-pinene 12–54 %
  α-pinene 94 %   IND
  α-pinene 76 % + β-pinene 19 %
  β-pinene 52 % + longifolene 10 % + phel-   BUR
  landrene 2 %; or β-pinene 2 % + longi-   V–N
  folene 0·1 % + phellandrene 17 %
Ch. T. MP D Abs.; 2 Ch. races

DUPONT, 1937
GUHA–ROY, 1942
FISCHER, 1963
ZAVARIN et al., 1966

ZAVARIN et al., 1966

P. longifolia Roxb. – TP
Ql. D. Δ^3-carene 37–60 % + longifolene 5–30 % +   IND
  pinene 8–39 %; or pinenes 70 %; or   USA
  pinenes + Δ^3-carene, longifolene Abs.   USSR

VERGHESE, 1966

P. montezumae Lamb. – TP
Ql. D. dl-α-pinene 98 %; or dl-α-pinene 72 % + li-   MEX
  monene 7 %; or l-β-pinene 62 % + dl-α-
  pinene 32 %/var. *rudis* Endl.; or limonene 56 % + Δ^3-carene 5 % + dl-α-pi-
  nene 28 %/var. *hartwegii* Lindl.
  Δ^3-carene 59–86 % + α-pinene 13 %   N–Z
Ch. T. the 2 var. are separated species

ILOFF–MIROV, 1953
ILOFF–MIROV, 1954

BLIGHT–McDONALD, 1964
GILDEMEISTER–HOFFMANN, 1956

P. monticola Dougl. – TP
Ql. D. various ORP, limonene Pst. or Abs.
  MC: pinenes; or Δ^3-carene; or limonene
Ch. T. strong genetic control of inheritance of
  Ch. CHAR

MIROV, 1956
HANOVER, 1966
HANOVER, 1966

P. muricata D. Don – TP
Ql. D. α-pinene 97–99 %, Δ^3-carene Abs.   USA
  Δ^3-carene 59–86 % + α-pinene 13 %   N–Z
  sabinene + terpinolene   N–Z
  sabinene 50–60 % + terpinolene 20–40 %;   USA
  or sabinene 9–62 % + terpinolene 3–33 %
  + pinene 12–60 %; or phellandrene 15 %

MIROV, 1958
BLIGHT–McDONALD, 1963
FORDE–BLIGHT, 1964
MIROV et al., 1966

Ch. T. inheritance of Ch. CHAR; 3 Ch. races   FORDE–BLIGHT, 1964
phylogenetical suggestions   MIROV et al., 1966

P. michoacana Martinez — TP
Ql. D. α-pinene 70–96%; or only 40%   MANJARREZ–GUZMÁN,
but β-pinene 56%/var. *procera*   1964

P. nigra Arn. – TP
Ql. D. ORP (–11° – –48°) various   FRA   DUPONT–BARRAUD, 1925
ORP (–10° – –44°) various   AUS   SCHEUBLE, 1933

P. palustris Mill. – TP
Ql. D. various ORP   HERTY, 1908

P. pinaster Solander ap. Ait. – TP
Ql. D. ORP (–90° – –16°) various   OUDIN, 1939
some IND dextrarotatory; α-pinene 4–40 %   SANDERMANN, 1962
+ β-pinene 57–90 %
α-pinene 90 % + β-pinene 7 %   WILLIAMS–BANNISTER,
     1962
Ch. T. selfing plants F_1 proved inheritance of Ch.   GUINIER, 1961
CHAR

P. pityusa Stev. – TP
Ql. D. 1-α-pinene 70 % + Δ^3-carene 24 %   USSR   ARBUSOV, 1932
d-α-pinene 93–99%/*P. halepensis* Mill.   ITA   PALAZZO et al., 1917

P. ponderosa Douglas – TP
Ql. D. various ORP   HAAGEN–SMIT et al., 1950
limonene, terpinolene, cadinene and longi-   USA   MIROV, 1956
folene Pst. or Abs.; β-pinene from very
little to much
GC VAR proved   N-Z   WILLIAMS–BANNISTER,
     1962
β-pinene 50–60 % + Tr. of Δ^3-carene or Δ^3-   SMITH, 1964c
carene 83 % + Tr. of β-pinene
Ch. T. DEP on area-D; PHYS forms   MIROV et al., 1965
IDP of age   SMITH, 1964b

P. pseudo-strobus Lindl. – TP
Ql. D. α-pinene only; or   USA   MIROV, 1958
α-pinene 51 % + limonene 16 % + longi-   MEX
folene 7 %/var. *oaxacana* Martinez
Ch. T. hybridisation barrier Abs., not two IDP species   HEGNAUER, 1962

P. radiata D. Don – TP
Ql. D. dl-α-pinene 75 % + 1-β-pinene 22 %   USA   MIROV, 1958
α-pinene 41 % + β-pinene 57 %   USSR   ARBUSOV et al., 1932
α-pinene 34 % + β-pinene 62 %   FRA   BARRAUD, 1950
α-pinene 67–89 % + β-pinene 18–33 % with   N-Z   BANNISTER et al., 1962
continuous VAR
α-pinene 36 %; camphere 35 %;   CHL   BIANCHI, 1960
limonene 26 %; β-pinene in Tr.
Ch. T. no *P. attenuata* Lemmon introgression   BANNISTER et al., 1962

P. silvestris L. – TP

Ql. D. ORP (–17° – –32°) various   GER   SCHEUBLE, 1953
pinene 68–81 % + Δ^3-carene 14–19 %   USSR   ARBUSOV et al., 1931
pinene 64 % + limonene 6 %   BUL   IVANOV–IVANOV, 1949
Δ^3-carene; or 1-β-phellandrene   USA   MIROV, 1956
Δ^3-carene 46 % + pinenes 30 %   FIN   HIRSJÄRVI-PIRILA, 1964
    –Lf
pinene 10–58 % + Δ^3-carene 0·5 %   FIN   JUVONEN, 1966
    or 11–39%

Ch. T. PHYS varieties   MIROV, 1956
Phellandrene content DEP on age   PIGULEVSKI–MAKSIMOVA,
                                                              1960

DEP on area, IDP of total E–O content, or   JUVONEN, 1967
on Lf length; CORR with terpinolene
content

P. washoensis Masson et Stockw. – TP

Ql. D. dextrorotatory with Δ^3-carene component, or   HAAGEN–SMIT, 1949
laevorotatory with l-β-pinene

Pseudotsuga menziesii (Mirb.) Franco – TP

Ql. D. sabinene 9·5 %; or Abs./var. *glauca* (Beissn.)   ZAVARIN–SNAJBERK, 1965
Franco
Ch. T. IND VAR, IDP of localization

TAXODIACEAE

Cunninghamia lanceolata (Lamb.) Hook. – TP

Ql. D. β-pinene + phellandrene Pst.,   CHI   FUJITA, 1960
or Abs./var. *konishii* Fuj.   TAI

Sciadopytis verticillata (Thunb.) S. et Z. – Lf/E–O

Ql. D. kaurene + isophyllocladene   KAWAMURA, 1931
phyllocladene; kaurene Abs.   UOTA, 1937
Ch. T. DEP on origin   NISHIDA-UOTA, 1931

PODOCARPACEAE

Dacrydium biforme Pilger – Lf/E–O

Ql. D. phyllocladene 13 % + biformene   AITKEN, 1928
myrcene 12 % + β-terpinene   CORBETT–WONG, 1955
Ch. T. distinct varieties *A* and *B*   FUJITA, 1962 a, b, c

D. colensoi Hook. – Tw/E–O

Ql. D. phyllocladene 67 % + cadinene 20 %   BLACKIE, 1929
phyllocladene 35 % + pinene 17 % + iso-   BRIASCO–MURRAY, 1952
phyllocladene + limonene
Ch. T. distinct varieties *A* and *B*   FUJITA, 1965

D. laxifolium Hook. – Wp/E–O
Ql. D. phyllocladene only, kaurene Abs.   MURRAY, 1960a
            kaurene only, phyllocladene Abs.   APLIN–CAMBIE, 1964

Podocarpus macrophyllus (Thunb) D. Don – Lf/E–O
Ql. D. (-)kaurene only, phyllocladene Abs.   NISHIDA–UOTA, 1931
            phyllocladene + isophyllocladene +   BRIGGS–CAWLEY, 1948
              (+) kaurene
Ch. T. VAR DEP on origin and/or MP CHAR

P. spicatus R. Br. – Lf/E–O
Ql. D. (+)kaurene 23–34 % + oxyterpene 4 %,   N–Z   BUTLER–HOLLOWAY, 1939
            (phyllocladene Abs.)   S/I
            phyllocladene 2 % + oxyterpene (kaurene N/I   BRIGGS–LOE, 1950
            Abs.)
            kaurene only, phyllocladene Abs.; or phyllo-   APLIN et al., 1963
            cladene only, kaurene Abs.
Ch. T. MP D Abs.   McGIMPSEY–MURRAY,
                                                             1960

P. totara D. Don. – Lf/E–O
Ql. D. totarene 45 %   AITKEN, 1929
            rimuene 30 %, phyllocladene Abs.   BEATH, 1933
            kaurene + isokaurene + rimuene (little)   BRIGGS–LOE, 1950
            phyllocladene only, rimuene Abs./var. *hallii*
              Pilger
            phyllocladene   MURRAY, 1960a
Ch. T. DEP cn origin   APLIN–CAMBIE, 1964
            systematic degree of var. *hallii*   BRIGGS–LOE, 1950

CUPRESSACEAE

Chamaecyparis obtusa (S. et Z.) Endl. – Lf/E–O
Ql. D. hinoki A + one diterpene 5 %   JAP   UCHIDA, 1928
            sabinene 17 % + chamene + terpinene-4-ol TAI   KAFUKU et al., 1931
            /var. *formosana* (Hay) Rend.
Ch. T. var. *formosana* as distinct species   ERDTMAN, 1959

Juniperus virginiana L. – Wd/E–O
Ql. D. cedrene 80% + cedrol 14%   DUBENCHIEK, 1955
            cedrene 35% + thujopsene 30%   RUNEBERG, 1960
Ch. T. clinal intergradation   FLAKE et al., 1968

Libocedrus bidwillii Hook. – Tw/E–O
Ql. D. one rimuene-like dipentene   BIRELL, 1932
            isophyllocladene   APLIN et al., 1963

Thujopsis dolabrata (L. f.) S. et Z. – Wd/E–O
Ql. D. carvacrol + thujaplicines   NOZOE et al., 1951
            carvacrol 65 % + isopropylphenol 22 %   YOSHIKOSI, 1960

LAURACEAE

Aniba rosaeodora Ducke – Wd/E–O
Ql. D. 1-linalool 80 %;   CAY   MORS et al., 1962
          or dl-linalool 85–90 %/var. *amazonica* Ducke BRA

Cinnamomum camphora (L.) Sieb. – Wd/E–O
Ql. D. camphor; or cineol; or borneol; or safrol;   GILDEMEISTER–HOFMANN,
          or sesquiterpene; or sesquiterpene alcohol;   1959
          or linalool (at 86 % or at 71 % level)
Ch. T. MP D Abs.; inheritance of Ch. CHAR   HIROTA, 1951, 1953
          OG changes; localization   FUJITA, 1937
          PHYS separated taxa (Sippe)   MANSFELD, 1959
          Chemotypes; parallel mutations   HEGNAUER, 1965

C. glanduliferum (Wall.) Meissn. – Lf/E–O
Ql. D. cineol 34 % + terpineol 10 % + camphor   IND   ANONYMOUS, 1910
          various components predominants   CHI   CAI SJAN–JUAN et al.,
Ch. T. more Ch. types   1964

C. molle H. W. Li – Lf/E–O
          camphor 50 %; or other components as pre-   CAI SJAN–JUAN, et al.,
          dominants   1965

C. parthenoxylon Meissn. – Lf/E–O
Ql. D. cineol 60 %; or cadalene + terpineol +   CAI SJAN–JUAN et al.,
          phellandrene   1965

C. zeylanicum Blume – Lf/E–O
Ql. D. caryophyllene 62 % + eugenol 15 %   IND   GILDEMEISTER– HOFFMANN,
          eugenol 50 % + benzyl benzoate 27 %   MOC   1959
          eugenol 90 %–70 %   SEY   GUENTHER, 1956
          eugenol Abs.   INDO
Ch. T. intra IND localization of Ch. CHAR   GILDEMEISTER–HOFFMANN,
                                                                   1959
          Ch. races   HEGNAUER, 1966

Litsea zeylanica C. et T. Nees – Lf/E–O
Ql. D. ocimene 60 % + bicyclicsesquiterpenes 27 %   RAO, 1923
          ocimene 35 % + terpinene 20 % + alcohol   SHARMA et al., 1953
          25 %

Persea gratissima Gaertn. – Lf/E–O
Ql. D. d-α-pinene + methylchavicol   USA   RABAK, 1912
          anise-like scent   MEX   ANDERSON, 1950
          scentless   ANT

MYRISTICACEAE

Myristica fragrans Houtt. – Fr/E–O
Ql. D. geraniol 12 % + linalool 8 % + terpinolene   BEJNAROVITZ–KIRCH, 1963
          1·4 %; or linalool 11 % + safrol 6 %
          /terpinolene Abs.; or safrol 6 %/linalool
          and geraniol Abs.; or camphor 4 %/terpi-
          nolene, eugenol Abs.
Ch. T. DEP on origin

100

ARISTOLOCHIACEAE

Asarum europaeum L. – Rh/E–O
Ql. D. sesquiterpenealcohols 90–98 %; or asaron   STAHL-JORK, 1966
      48–89 %; or trans-isoeugenolmethylether
      42–58 %; or unknown phenylpropane
Ch. T. inheritance of Ch. CHAR, Ch. races

Asiasarum heterotropoides (F. Schmidt) Maekawa
    – Rh/E–O
Ql. D. *MC*: eucarvone; eucarvone + safrol; or   JAP   NAGASAWA, 1961
      safrol 47 %
      MC: eucarvone; or methyleugenol;   CHI
      or safrol/var. *mandshuricum* Maekawa

A. sieboldii (Miq.) Maekawa – Rh/E–O
Ql. D. cineol, eucarvone Abs.; or *MC:* safrol; or   JAP   NAGASAWA, 1961
      methyleugenol; or methyleugenol + eucar-
      vone
      methyleugenol 47 % + safrol + little eucar-   COR   KAKU-KONDO, 1931
      vone/var. *seoulense* Nakai
Ch. T. geographical gradient in composition   HEGNAUER, 1964
      var. *cineoliferum* Fuj.   FUJITA, 1966

MYRTACEAE

Baeckea gunniana Schauer – Lf/E–O
Ql. D. pinene 50 % + cineol 9 %, baeckol Abs.   SMITH, 1922
      eudesmol 60 % + baeckol/var. *latifolia*   PENFOLD, 1925
      F. Muell.

Backhousia angustifolia F. Muell. – Lf/E–O
Ql. D. dehydroangustione; or dehydroangustione +   CANNON-CORBETT, 1962
      angustifolionol; or angustione + angusti-
      folionol
Ch. T. Ch. forms, or races   MCKERN, 1965

B. citriodora F. Muell. – Lf/E–O
Ql. D. citral 90–95 %; or citronellal 62–80 %   PENFOLD et al., 1951
Ch. T. as "type", or "var. *A*"
      Ch. forms   MCKERN, 1965

Blepharocalyx tweediei (H. et A.) Berg – Lf/E–O
Ql. D. terebenthene   ARG   FESTER et al., 1958
      australene   URU

Calythrix tetragona Labill. – Lf + Tw/E–O
Ql. D. pinenes 49–53 % + sesquiterpenes 6–11 %   JONES et al., 1949
      citronellol + citronellylformiate   PENFOLD et al., 1935
Ch. T. as "type" and "var. *A*"   PENFOLD et al., 1950

Eucalyptus amygdalina Labill. – Lf + Tb/E–O
Ql. D. cineol 65–72 %; or piperitone 36–46%   PENFOLD et al., 1950
Ch. T. as "type", or "var. *A*"

E. andreana Naudin – Lf/E–O
Ch. T. 3 varieties ("piperitone form" and others)   HILLIS, 1966

E. andrewsi Maiden – Lf/E–O
Ql. D. in Ch. composition of oil   McKERN, 1965

E. camaldulensis Dehnh. – Lf + Tw/E–O
Ql. D. p-cymol + phellandrene + cineol   8–10 %;   PENFOLD, 1950
    or cineol 45 % + pinene/var. *borealis*
      Bak. et Smith
Ch. T. var. *borealis* morphologically inseparable   McKERN, 1965

E. citriodora Hook. – Lf + Tw/E–O
Qn. D. 1·7–4 0 % E–O content   IND   KAPUR et al., 1967
Ql. D. citronellal 45–86 %; or citronellylesther 42 %   AUL   PENFOLD et al., 1950
    + citronellol 34 %; or hydrocarbons
    citronellol 50–75 %; or 78–86 %   IND   KAPUR et al., 1967
Ch. T. MP D, or area D Abs.; inheritance of Ch.   PENFOLD et al., 1953
    CHAR of "type", or "var. *A*", or
    "form"
    criticism of conclusions   SCHRATZ, 1960b
    Qn. D: DEP on ecological factors   NEYBERGH, 1953

E. dives Schauer – Lf + Tw/E–O
Ql. D. piperitone 40–52 %; or phellandrene   PENFOLD–MORRISON, 1954
    60–80%; or cineol 25–45 % + piperitone
    12–18%; or cineol 68–75 %
Ch. T. as "type", or "var. *A, B* and *C*"

E. flocktoniae Maiden – Lf/E–O
Ql. D. torquatone 25 %; or Abs.
Ch. T. substance detected only in a form having   BOWYER–JEFFERIES, 1962
    ribbed fruits from   W/AUL   McKERN, 1965

E. numerosa Maiden – Lf + Tb/E–O
Ql. D. phellandrene 60–80 %; or piperitone 40–52 %   PENFOLD–MORRISON, 1953
    or piperitone 20–30 % + piperitolesther
      + cineol 12–15 %/E. *lindleyana* (Blake) DC.
Ch. T. as "type", or "var. *A* and *B*"

E. oleosa F. Muell. – Lf/E–O
Ql. D. cineol 52 % + pinenes
                              GARTNER–WATSON,
                              1947/48
    cineol 45 % + geraniol 20 %; or cineol   PENFOLD, 1950
    84–88 %/var. *borealis* Marsh. et Wats.

102

E. ovalifolia Bak. – Lf/E–O
Ql. D. phellandrene + sesquiterpenes; or cineol 45 %   PENFOLD–MORRISON,
          + pinene/var. *lanceolata* Bak. et Smith   1953

E. pauciflora Sieb. – Lf + Tb/E–O
Ql. D. *MC:* pinene; or phellandrene   WILLIS et al., 1963
Ch. T. 2 forms, not *E. phlebophylla* F. Muell. and
          E. coriacea A. Cunn.

E. piperita Sm. – Lf + Tw/E–O
Ql. D. piperitone 40–50 %; or cineol 10–20 % +   PENFOLD, 1950
          eudesmol + phellandrene
Ch. T. as "type", or "var. *A*" mountain form

E. punctata DC. – Lf + Tw/E–O
Qn. D. cineol 46–64 %; or only 10–15 %   PENFOLD, 1950

E. racemosa Cav. – Lf + Tb/E–O
Ql. D. cineol 33 %; or piperitone 41–47 % +   PENFOLD–MORRISON, 1950
          phellandrene; or piperitone + cryptone
Ch. T. as "type", or "var. *A*, and var. *B*"

E. radiata Sieber – Lf + Tb/E–O
Ql. D. cineol 65–72 %; or terpinene + β-phelland-   PENFOLD–MORRISON, 1953
          rene; or α-phellandrene 35 % + cineol
          20–50 %; or piperitone + α-phellandrene;
          or eudesmol/var. *nitida* Benth.

E. sparsifolia Blakely – Lf + Tw/E–O
Ql. D. eudesmol 60–90 %; or only 1 %   WILLIS et al., 1963
Ch. T. Ch. CHAR inherited

E. spathulata Hook. – Lf/E–O
Ql. D. torquatone Pst./var. *grandiflora* Benth. one   BOWYER–JEFFERIES, 1962
          sample; or Abs.

E. tereticornis Sm. – Lf + Tw/E–O
Ql. D. phellandral + p-cymane + cuminal/var.   BAKER–SMITH, 1902
          linearis Bak. et Smith; or cineol 45–58 %
          + α-pinene/var. *cineolifera* Smith et
          Bak.

E. viminalis Labill. – Lf/E–O
Ql. D. cineol 43–65 % + benzaldehyde; or cineol   PENFOLD, 1950
          25–41 % + α-phellandrene
Ch. T. as "type", or "var. *A*"
          hybridize freely, some caution necessary   WILLIS et al., 1963

Leptospermum citratum Penf. – Lf + Tb/E–O
Ql. D. citral 75–85 % + citronellal; or d-α-pinene+   AUL   PENFOLD et al., 1953
          γ-terpinene; or citral 16–20 % + citro-   PENFOLD et al., 1950
          nellol + geraniol
          citral 46 % + citronellol 34 % + geraniol   CON   MATHEWS–PICKERING,
          3 %   1950
Ch. T. as "type", or "var. *A, B*", PHYS forms   PENFOLD et al., 1948

L. lanigerum Sm. – Lf + Tw/E–O
Ql. D. eudesmene 70–75 % + α-pinene 16–20 %;   GILDEMEISTER–HOFFMANN,
       or α-pinene 40–60 % + darwinol 40–43 %   1957

L. liversidgei Bak. et Sm. – Lf + Tw/E–O
Ql. D. citral 70–80 %; or α-pinene 50–60 % + cit-   PENFOLD, 1922, 1950
       ronellal 30–40 %; or citral 35–50 % +
       geraniol 10 %
       citral 35–50 % + linalool   McKERN–WILLIS, 1957

Melaleuca alternifolia Cheel – Lf + Tb/E–O
Ql. D. α-pinene 50–60 % + cineol 3–8 %; or cineol   AUL   PENFOLD et al., 1948
       31–45 %; or cineol 54–69 %
       pinenes + terpinene   INDO   HULSSEN–MEIJER, 1940
       terpinolene 25 % + terpineol-4 33 % +   AUL   LAAKSO, 1965
       terpinene 12 %; or *MC:* p-cymene
Ch. T. as "type", or "var. *A, B*"   PENFOLD, 1950

M. ericifolia Sm. – Lf + Tb/E–O
Ql. D. α-terpineol   BAKER–SMITH, 1922
       cineol 21 % + terpenes 15 %   HELLYER, 1957
       cineol 40–60 %   PENFOLD, 1959
       linalool 30–40 % + sesquiterpenes 25 %   McKERN–WILLIS, 1957

M. leucadendra L. – Lf/E–O
Ql. D. cineol 45–65 %   AUL   GUENTHER, 1953
       eugenolmethylether 78 %   CON   NEYBERGH, 1953

M. linariifolia Sm. – Lf + Tw/E–O
Ql. D. cineol 61–66 %   JONES, 1937
       alcohol 52 % (borneol?)   DAVENPORT et al., 1949
       terpinene 40 % + terpinenol 4–37 %   PENFOLD, 1953
       cineol 16–20 % + terpenes 27–60 %   LAAKSO, 1965

M. quinquenervia (Cav.) S. T. Blake – Lf/E–O
Ql. D. cineol 45–60 %   MAL   PENFOLD–MORRISON, 1953
       nerolidol 40–70 % + linalool 30 %; or nero-   AUL   HELLYER–McKERN, 1955
       lidol 88–95 %; or limonene + cineol +
       viridiflorol
Ch. T. as "type", or "var. *A*" and "forma"; no hy-
       brid tendencies

RUTACEAE

Boronia ledifolia Gay – Lf + Tw/E–O
Ql. D. sesquiterpenes + terpenes (oxygeneless); or   PENFOLD–MORRISON, 1953
       methyl-n-heptyl- + nonylketone 75 %
Ch. T. as "type", or "var. *A*"

B. pinnata Smith – Lf + Tw/E–O
Ql. D. terpenes + sesquiterpenes/var. *pinnata*   PENFOLD–WELCH, 1921
       citronellol + citronellylesther/var. *citrio-*   PENFOLD, 1926
       dora Gunn.; elemicine 90 %/var. *muelleri*   PENFOLD, 1929
       Cheel; safrol/var. *safrolifera* Cheel   TAM   PENFOLD, 1925

B. thujona Penf. et Welch – Lf/E–O
Ql. D. $\alpha + \beta$-thujone   PENFOLD–WELCH, 1921
    safrol 80 %   PENFOLD, 1929
Ch. T. as "type" and "var. *A*"

Citrus aurantifolia (Christm.) Swingle – Pl/E–O
Ql. D. furfurol + borneol + geraniol   MEX   SLATER, 1961
    cineol + camphene + p-cymol   DOM

C. hystrix DC. – Pl/E–O
Ql. D. citral 40 %   INDO   SACCO, 1955
    citronellol + terpenes 26 %/var. *torosa*   PHIL   TANHICO–WEST, 1933
    Webst.
    citronellal   MAD   IGOLEN, 1958

C. limon (L.) Burman f. – Pl/E–O
Ql. D. more citral, than linalool   SIC   SLATER, 1961
    more linalool, than citral   CAL+NIG
    in citral, pinene, terpinene content   USA   SWISMER, 1966
    octanal 14 %, octanol Abs./cv. 'Halle';   CAMERON–SCORA, 1968
      or octanal 3 % + octanol 22 %/cv. 'Royal'
Ch. T. some D of 2n–4n form

C. paradisi Macf. – Lf/E–O
Ql. D. terpinenol-4 much/cv. 'Duncan'; terpine-   ATTAWAY et al., 1966
    nol-4 little + α-terpineol/cv. 'Marsh'

C. reticulata Blanco – Lf/E–O
Ql. D. thymol + thymilmethylether + ocimene   ATTAWAY et al., 1966
    /cv. 'Dancy'; pinene + terpinenol-4 +
    sabinene/cv. 'Murcott'
    terpenes 39 % + alcohols 29 %   ZAIDI–GUPTA, 1962
        – Pl(E–O) excluded terpenes
Ql. D. terpineol 36 % + nonanol 15 %/cv. 'Owari'   CAMERON–SCORA, 1968
    octanal 18 % +linalool 11 % +
    nonyl Ac 11 %/cv. 'Dancy'

C. sinensis (L.) Osbeck – Lf/E–O
Ql. D. ocimene much + citronellal/cv. 'Valencia';   ATTAWAY et al., 1966
    ocimene little + γ-terpineol/cv. 'Ham-
    lin'; ocimene much + citronellal little
    /cv. 'Pineapple'
    in linalool, geranial, neral content   SCORA–TORRISI, 1965
        – Pl (E–O) excluded terpenes
Ql. D. linalool 16 % + nonyl Ac. 4 %/cv. 'Wash-   CAMERON–SCORA, 1968
    ington' or 'Navel'; linalool 9 % + nonyl
    Ac. 21 %/cv. 'Ruby'
Ch. T. entranglement of genetic and climatic effects   SCORA–TORRISI, 1965

Geijera parviflora Lindl. – Lf + Tw/E–O
Ql. D. linalool 50 % + geijerene; or geijerene +   PENFOLD–MORRISON, 1953
    azulenes; or camphene 80 % + limonene
Ch. T. as "type", and "var. *A*", and "form"

Murraya koenigii (L.) Spreng. – Lf/E–O
Ql. D. caryophyllene 26 % + cadinene 18 % +   DUTT, 1958
      cadinol 13 %
      sabinene 34 % + pinene 27 % + dipentene 16 %   NIGAM–PUROHIT, 1961

Poncirus trifoliata L. – Pl/E–O
Ql. D. limonene 52 % + myrcene 20 %/cv. 'Rubidoux'   SCORA et al., 1966
      limonene 30 % + myrcene 34 %/cv. 'Kryder'

Ruta graveolens L. – Wp/E–O
Qn. D. obtained freshly 0·051–0·084 %   DAL   VERNAZZA, 1959
          0 07–0·12 %   GER   SPRECHER, 1958
          0 064–0·168 %   HUN   TÉTÉNYI, 1963
          obtained from drugs 0·55 %   GER   LANGERFELDT, 1954
          0·75–1·2 %   MAR   GUENTHER, 1938
Ql. D. methyl-n-nonylketone 85 %   FRA   GILDEMEISTER–HOFFMANN,
                                       1959
      methyl-n-heptylketone 67 %   ALG
Ch. T. IDP of place of culture   SPRECHER, 1958
      IDP of annual climatic conditions, chemo-   TÉTÉNYI, 1963
      cultivars

Zanthoxylum budrunga Wall. – Fr/E–O
Ql. D. *MC:* sabinene   RAU–SIMONSEN, 1922
      sabinene + α-terpinene + β-phellandrene   RAO et al., 1925
      δ-terpinene + α-phellandrene + pinene   RAO–BHAVE, 1959

BURSERACEAE

Bursera microphylla A. Gray – Tw
Ql. D. in terpene composition
Ch. T. north-south relationship of populations   MOONEY–EMBODEN, 1968

APIACEAE / UMBELLIFERAE

Anethum graveolens L. – Fr/E–O
Ql. D. carvone 47 % + dillapiol 40 %   IND   MALAVIYA–DUTT, 1939
      carvone 42 % + dillapiol 19 %   GUPTA et al., 1955
      MC: carvone 40–60 %; or dillapiol UAR   STAHL, 1968
Ch. T. 2 Ch. races
               – Wp/E–O
      carvone 30 % + limonene 35 %   CHAKRAVARTI–
                                  BHATTACHARRYYA, 1954
      carvone 14 % + phellandrene 45 % (no GUPTA et al., 1955
      limonene at all)

Carum copticum Benth. et Hook. – Fr/E–O
Qn. D. 3–11 %   COLL   MICHELSON, 1938
      3–5 %; or 7–11 %   COLL   JOSHI–JOSHI, 1963
Ql. D. thymol 28–52 %   COLL   MICHELSON, 1938
    thymol 50–60 %; or p-cymol 50 % + thymol USSR LIBIZOV, 1938
      24 %
      thymol 40–86 %   IND   KARTHA–KIDWAY, 1965

thymol 43% + carvacrol 9% terpinene 17% IND BHARGAVA–HAKSAR, 1962
p-cymol 40 % + thymol 32 % + USSR GORIAYEV–IGNATOVA,1959
 terpinene 7 %/carvacrol Abs.
Ch. T. CORR Abs. between MP and Ch. CHAR   MICHELSON, 1938
 OG changes in composition   NILOV, 1938
 inbreeding preserves the level of E–O   JOSHI–JOSHI, 1963

Coriandrum sativum L. – Fr/E–O
Qn. D. 0·2–1·0 %   COLL WASICZKY, 1929
 0·35–1·41 %   COLL LŐRINCZ, 1962
Ql. D. linalool 50–58 %   AFG OBUHOV–KONDRATZKI,
             W/EUR 1946

Ch. T. DEP on 1000 grain weight   AUGUSTIN et al., 1948
                 HARROD, 1960
 DEP on gradient of origin   IVANOV, 1961
 IDP on grainsize   OS, 1950; LUKIANOV, 1963
 IDP on 1000 grain weight   TÉTÉNYI, 1963

Crithmum maritimum L. – Wp/E–O
Ql. D. dillapiole 60 %   FRA DELÉPINE, 1910
 dillapiole+phellandrene   ITA FRANCESCONI–
                 SERNAGIOTTO, 1913
 terpinene much, dillapiole little   GER RICHTER–WOLFF, 1927
 p-cymene 90 %, dillapiole Abs.   USSR NILOV, 1934
Ch. T. the last taxa is a separated species   NILOV, 1934

Cuminum cyminum L. – Fr/E–O
Ql. D. ketone Abs.   GILDEMEISTER–HOFFMANN,
                 1959
 ketone Pst./cryptone   EL-HAMIDI–RICHTER, 1965
Ch. T. chemical races   EL-HAMIDI–RICHTER, 1965

Daucus carota L. – Fr/E–O
Ql. D. b e t w e e n c u l t i v a r s
 carotol + pinene + cymol   NED SORM et al., 1951
 carotol 48–63 %; or carotol 12–16 % + COLL STAHL, 1964
  geranylacetate 40–48 %
 sesquiterpene 35 % + pinene 14 %; or   MURRI, 1961
  daucol + carotol + bizabolol + asaron JAP
 carotol 12 % + bizabolene (?) 80 % IND GUPTA–GUPTA, 1958
 ester/alcohol = 3–4   COLL TÉTÉNYI, 1963
 b e t w e e n s p o n t a n e o u s p o p u-
  l a t i o n s
 carotol 70 % + daucol 11 %   HIM NIGAM–RADHAKRISHNAN,
                 1963
 carotol 51 % + daucol 13 %   IND TALWAR et al., 1963
 carotol 80 %   ARM PIGULEVSKY–KOVALEVA,
 carotol 45 % + bizabolene   TAS 1955a, b, 1959, 1964
 geranylacetate 75–85 %   MOL
 geranylacetate 67 % + sabinene   CAU
 geranylacetate 36 % + sabinene 30 % UKR
 geranylacetate 30 % + sabinene 20 % KAB
 sabinene 39 % + α-pinene 16 %   POL PARCZEWSKY–
                 RAJKOWSKI, 1962

Daucus carota (continued)

pinene 55 % + geraniol 27 %	C/RUS	MAKAROVA–BORISIUK, 1957
terpene-esters + caryophyllene	COLL/EUR	STAHL, 1964
carotol 20–30 % + asaron 8 %	EGY+CHI	
carotol 27 % + geranyl Ac 22 % + limo-nene 15 %	USA	ZALKOW et al., 1963
MC: trans-iso-asarone/var. *maximus*	MED	STAHL, 1968
ester/alcohol = 0·1–3·2	COLL	TÉTÉNYI, 1963

Ch. T. Ch. differentiated botanical forms

PIGULEVSKY–KOVALEVA, 1961

Ch. races with carotol or geranylacetate   STAHL, 1964

taxa at chemovarietas level   TÉTÉNYI, 1963

Foeniculum vulgare Mill. – Fr/E–O

Ql. D. fenchone 51 % + estragole 46 %/ssp. *piperitum* (Ucria) Coutinho	SIC	PELLINI–MORANI, 1923
fenchone, – anethole Abs./ssp. *piperitum*	USSR	NILOV, 1938
phellandrene 35 % + estragole 33 %	CAL	GUENTHER, 1938
anethole 40–60 % + fenchone 7–20 %/var. *panmorium* DC.	IND	TSCHIRCH, 1917
estragole much, anethole Tr./var. *vulgare*	ALG	TARDY, 1872
anethole 39 % + fenchone 6 %	POR	COSTA–VALE, 1959
anethole 60 % + fenchone 22 %	YUG	NAVES–TUCAKOV, 1959
anethole 75 % + fenchone 10 % + borneol	JAP	GURVICH, 1960
anethole 60–80 %	GER	TSCHIRCH, 1917
anethole 83–86 % + fenchone 1–4 %/var. *dulce* (Mill.) Thell.	COLL	KÜCHLER et al., 1965
anethole 88–92 %, fenchone Tr./var *dulce*	MAC	NAVES–TUCAKOV, 1959
anethole 90–98 %, fenchone Abs.	FRA	TSCHIRCH, 1917
anis-like smell Pst. or Abs./var. *azoricum* (Mill.) Thell.	COLL	GAGNEBIN, 1964

Ch. T. OG changes at maturation   NILOV, 1936

PHYS varietates   TSCHIRCH, 1917

inheritance of Ch. CHAR; CORR Abs.   NILOV, 1938
between Ch. and MP CHAR

Libanotis transcaucasica Schischk. – Fr/E–O

Qn. D. 1·35–2·05 %; or 4·24 %   LUTKOV, 1960

2·3 %   PIGULEVSKY, 1943

Ql. D. geraniol 10 % + phellandrene + sesquiter-penes   PIGULEVSKY, 1943

geraniol 38 % + phellandrene 20 % + ses-quiterpenes 18 %   ZARAISKAIA–BORISIUK, 1957

geraniol 50 % + sesquiterpenes 30 %; or geraniol 47–54 % + phellandrene 11–20 % + sesquiterpenes 5 %   LUTKOV, 1960

geraniol Abs.   FODOROV, 1961

bisabolol 50 %; or *MC:* isoelemicine   PIGULEVSKI–BAKINA, 1965

Ch. T. MP and Ch. differentiated taxa   SHISHKIN, 1950

D in growth season, in area above sea-level   LUTKOV, 1960
inheritance of Ch. CHAR

Ch. races   FODOROV, 1961

Petroselinum crispum (Mill.) Nym. – Fr/E–O

Ql. D. myristicine much, apiol little — FRA — THOMS, 1908

myristicine 50 %; or apiol 50 %; or apiol — COLL — RAJKOWSKI, 1962
18 % + pinenes 36 %

apiol 60–80 %; or myristicine 55–75 %; or — COLL — STAHL et al., 1964
allyltetramethoxybenzene 50–60 %

Ch. T. IDP of MP CHAR; Ch. races; IND D — STAHL et al., 1964

VALERIANACEAE (see p. 143)

VERBENACEAE

Lantana camara L. – Lf + Fl/E–O

Ql. D. caryophyllene 80 % — IND, Tra- MUDGILL–VRIDHACHALAN,
vancore   1922

caryophyllene 67 % + phellandral 5 % + — IND, Al- DUTT, 1960
linalool 4 %; or caryophyllene 41 % + ca- — lahabad
dinene 8 % + pinene 7 % + dipentene — IND, Delhi
6 % + cineol 5 % + terpinene 5 % +
cymene 5 %

Lippia alba (Mill.) N. E. Br. – Wp/E–O

Ql. D. piperitone + lippione; or pinene + dihydro- — FESTER et al., 1955
carvone; or limonene, lippion Abs. (cul-
tivated forms);
or citral as *MC;* or citral + cineol — FESTER et al., 1961

Ch. T. PHYS varieties, with D in area

L. seriphioides (Mold.) A. Gray – Wp/E–O

Ql. D. thymol(?) 60–65 %; or phenols only 12 % — FESTER et al., 1955
citral + geraniol

Ch. T. PHYS varieties, MP D Abs., but D in area

LAMIACEAE / LABIATAE

Agastache formosana Hay. – Wp/E–O

Ql. D. pulegone 80 % — TAI — FUJITA, 1951
pulegone 32 % + isomenthone 35 % — JAP — FUJITA et al., 1964

Elsholtzia ciliata Hyl. – Wp/E–O

Ql. D. elsholtziaketone 85 %; or only 1–8 % + — UEDA–FUJITA, 1959
naginataketone 35–66 %; or elsholtzia- — FUJITA et al., 1965
ketone 27–61 % + isovaleric A 8–35 % — FUJITA et al., 1967

E. oldhami Hemsley – Wp/E–O

Ql. D. elsholtziaketone 45 % + dehydroelsholtzia- — NAVES–OCHSNER, 1960
ketone 20 %

elsholtziaketone   45 % + naginataketone — FUJITA, 1960
18–20 % /var. *Argyi* (Léveil.) Miq.; or elsholtziaketone 80 % + naginataketone 15%;
or elsholtziaketone 85 %, naginata-ketone
Abs./*E. ciliata* (Thunb.) Hyl.; or p-cymol
30 %-geraniol   35 %/var. *nipponica* Ohwi

Ch. T. vicariation between *E. Oldhami* and *E. ciliata*   FUJITA, 1960
     chemotypes   HEGNAUER, 1965

Galeopsis ladanum L. – Lf.
Ql. D. acetylharpagid Pst. or Abs./ssp. *intermedia*   WIEFFERING, 1966
     (Vill.) Briq.

Hyptis suaveolens (L.) Poit. – Wp/E–O
Ql. D. sabinene 31 % + sesquiterpenes 56 %   IND   GILDEMEISTER–HOFF-
     menthol much, as *MC*   PHIL   MANN, 1961

Hyssopus officinalis L. – Wp/E–O
Qn. D. 0·2–1·3 % f. *ruber<albus<cyanaeus*   YUG   SOLDATOVIC, 1957
     0·6–1·2 % f. *albus<ruber<cyanaeus*   CSR   FELKLOVA, 1958
     ruber more E–O content than *cyanaeus*   YUG   TUCAKOV, 1960
Ch. T. possibility of Ch. races   ANONYMOUS, 1961

Lavandula angustifolia Mill. – Fl/E–O
Qn. D. 0·04–2·3 %   GILDEMEISTER, 1961
     0 05–0·6 %; or 0·65–1·3 %   COLL   TÉTÉNYI, 1963
Ql. D. linalylacetate 11–87 %   COLL   NILOV, 1937, 1938
     linalylacetate 11–78 %   COLL   STAICOV-TCHIGOVA, 1965
     linalylacetate 33–56 %   COLL   TÉTÉNYI, 1963
     linalylacetate 37–41 %   COLL   TUROWSKA et al., 1940
Ch. T. inheritance of Ch. CHAR   NILOV, 1938
     DEP on Fl colour   SCHRATZ, 1947
     IDP of Fl colour   TUROWSKA et al., 1940
     taxa at chemoconculta level, IDP of Fl colour   TÉTÉNYI, 1963

Majorana hortensis Moench – Wp/E–O
Ql. D. sabinene hydrate 9 %/geraniol, eugenol   NICOLETTI–BAIOCCHI,
     Abs.   1961
     geraniol 19 % + eugenol 8 %   VASHISTA et al., 1963
     sabinene hydrate 32–40 %/geraniol, eugenol   LOSSNER, 1967a
     Abs.
Ch. T. IDP of cultivation place   LOSSNER, 1967b

Mentha aquatica L. – Wp/E–O
Ql. D. linalyl Ac 33–74 %   USA   KREMERS, 1922
     linalyl Ac 65 % + linalool 8 %   ITA   SACCO, 1960
     MC: linalool; or limonene; or carvone; or   USSR   GURVICH, 1960
     menthol
     menthofurane + menthol 7 %   NED   HEGNAUER-JONG, 1956
     menthofurane 51 % + cineol 22 %   USA   HANDA et al., 1964
     menthofurane 40 % + limonene 18–21 %   GER   BAQUÀR-REESE, 1965
     menthofurane; or linalool; or isopino-   COLL   SHIMIZU, 1966
     camphene
Ch. T. chemotypes   HEGNAUER, 1965

M. arvensis L. – Wp/E–O
Ql. D. pulegone 90 %; or Abs.   USA   KREMERS, 1925
     pulegone 30 %   SAH   GUNTHER, 1953
     pulegone 65 % + isomenthone 30 %   CAL   VARIATI, 1954
     pulegone 48 % + menthone 21 %/var. *praecox*   ITA   SACCO-SHIMIZU, 1965

pulegone/ssp. *austriaca* Briq.; or menthone; or linalool	SWI NED	HEGNAUER–DE JONG, 1956
menthone 30 % + pulegone 12 %	ITA	ROVESTI, 1925
menthone 40–50 % + menthol 30 %/ssp. *haplocalyx* Briq.	JAP	SHINOSAKI–NAGASAWA, 1929
menthone 81 %/var. *nilgiris*	IND	CHOPRA et al., 1964
mint-like scent, menthol Abs.	IND	DINGHRA et al., 1951
menthofurane 50 % + linalool 30 %	UKR	CHAGOVEC–BORISIUK, 1957
menthol 46 % + menthone 15 %/var. *Jawarances*	IND	TALWAR et al., 1964
MC: menthol; or linalool; or carvone, menthone Abs.	CHI	CHIANG–HSI CHANG, 1958
carvone 81 %	IND	DUTT, 1940
piperitone	TAI	PING–HSIEN, 1960
Δ^3-octanone 90 %	JAP	SHIMIZU et al., 1961
Δ^3-octanol 90/var. *praecox* Sole	JAP	SACCO–SHIMIZU, 1965
linalool-like smell	FRA	ANONYMOUS, 1910
limonene 22–30 %; various piperitone content; or ethylamylcarbinol 17–21 % + pinene 10–16 %/ssp. *agrestis* (Sole) Briq.	GER	BAQUAR–REESE, 1965

Ch. T. DEP on origin (above see level) Ch. races; chemotypes
PHYS races

KREMERS, 1925
HEGNAUER, 1955, 1965
CHIANG–HSI–CHANG, 1958

M. canadensis L. – Wp/E–O

Ql. D. pulegone 80–90 %; or menthone 50 %	USSR	GURVICH, 1960
pulegone as *MC*, or Abs.		GILDEMEISTER–HOFFMANN, 1961

Ch. T. Ch. CHAR as taxonomic superior values · GURVICH, 1960

M. longifolia (L.) Nath. – Wp/E–O

Ql. D. pulegone	FRA	ANONYMOUS, 1910
pulegone 29 % + menthofurane	ALB	SALGUES, 1954
pulegone 52–66 %; or carvone 50–73 %; or piperitone 43–46 %; or piperitone-oxide; 60–75 %; or piperitenone-oxide 37–80 %; piperitone 33 % + menthone 43 %; or linalool 90 %; or menthone 70 %; or hydrocarbons	COLL	SHIMIZU et al., 1961
carvone 50 % + dihydrocarveol 25 %	CAB	LAFACE, 1953
carvone 58–62 % + limonene 10–16 %	USA	SMITH et al., 1963
carvone 70 %/var. *crispa* Benth. cv.-s		SCHICK–REIMANN, 1957
carvone + linalool	MOL	BOGONINA et al., 1965
dihydrocarvone, as *MC*, carvone Abs.	COLL	SMIMIZU–UEDA, 1962
piperitone or piperitenone as *MC*	USA	REITSEMA, 1956
piperitenone oxide 31–68 %	USA	REITSEMA–VARNIS, 1956
piperitone oxide 66 %	IND	HANDA et al., 1964
piperitone 49–57 %	GER	BAQUAR–REESE, 1965
piperitol 40 % + menthol 10 %	IND	CHOPRA et al., 1964
menthol 24–58 %	ARM	HRIMLIAN, 1948, 1951
menthol 58 %; or	KAH	GORIAYEV–SHVAKINA, 1948
menthol 70 –80 %	ASB	

M. longifolia (continued)

linalool 73–85 %	USSR	LUTKOV, 1955
limonene	ARM	GURVICH, 1960
MC: nerol; or citral; or thymol	COLL	TÉTÉNYI–VÁGUJFALVI, 1962

Ch. T. IDP of MP CHAR — GURVICH, 1961
    IDP of pilosity of Lf, of athocyanate degree — TÉTÉNYI–VÁGUJFALVI,
      of stem; chemoconvars and chemovars — 1962
    IDP of number of chromosomes and of MP D — SHIMIZU–IKEDA, 1958
    IDP of origin; D in required daylight — HRIMLIAN, 1959
    Ch. races — HRIMLIAN–MINASIAN, 1955
    Ch. taxa in the flora of Hungary — HRIMLIAN–TÉTÉNYI, 1965

M. pulegium L. – Wp/E–O

Ql. D.

pulegone 40–92 %	USSR	GURVICH, 1960
pulegone 9–16 %/var. *hirsuta* Guss; or		GILDEMEISTER–HOFMANN,
MC: piperitone	SIC	1961
pulegone 71–84 %	IND	CHOPRA et al., 1964
pulegone 74 % + isopulegone	IND	HANDA et al., 1964

Ch. T. isomenthone, menthone, piperitenone types — NAVES, 1943
    7 Ch. races — HRIMLIAN, 1965a, b

M. rotundifolia (L.) Huds. – Wp/E–O

Ql. D.

pulegone 85–92 %	ITA	ROVESTI, 1925
pulegone 80–85 %/ssp. *timija* Coss	MAR	SFIRAS, 1952
carvone 50 %	USSR	LIBIZOV, 1938b
carvone 40 % + limonene	BRA	FESTER et al., 1955
piperitenone oxide 50 %	USA	REITSEMA, 1958
MC: piperitenone oxide; or neoiso-isopu-	COLL	SHIMIZU–IKEDA, 1958
legol 52 % + piperitenone 13 %	FRA	
piperitenone oxide 87 %; or	ITA	HANDA et al., 1964
isopiperitenone	FRA	
piperitone oxide 53–60%; or only 33%	SWI	STICHER–LÜCK, 1968

Ch. T. biochemical varieties — ROOTH–HEGNAUER, 1955
    Ch. races — SHIMIZU–IKEDA, 1958
      HRIMLIAN, 1965a, b
    Chemotypes — HEGNAUER, 1966

M. sachalinensis (Briq.) Kudo – Wp/E–O

Ql. D. menthol 10–90 %, or menthone 10–50 % — NIKOLAEV–NEREVJAN-
    CHENKO, 1961

Ch. T. inheritance of Ch. CHAR — NIKOLAEV, 1960

M. satureioides R. Br. – Wp/E–O

Ql. D.

menthol 40–70 %	USSR	GURVICH, 1960
pulegone 40 % + menthenone 30 %		GILDEMEISTER–HOFFMANN, 1961
menthone 20–30 % + menthol 12 %		HEGNAUER, 1966

Ch. T. necessity of Ch. taxonomy — GURVICH, 1960

M. spicata L. – Wp/E–O

Ql. D.

carvone 59–72 % (cultivars)	HUN	İRK, 1911
carvone 20 %	IND	HANDA et al., 1957
pulegone + menthone	USA	REITSEMA, 1954

112

pulegone 32 %	ARG	FESTER et al., 1958
pulegone 60 % + piperitenone-oxide	TAI	PING-HSIEN, 1964
piperitenone 55 % + cineol 31 %	IND	CHAKRAVARTI–BHATTA-
		CHARRYYA, 1955
menthone 43 % + piperitone 33 %; or pipe-	USA	MURRAY–REITSEMA, 1954
ritone oxide; or piperitenoneoxide		
piperitone 58 % + limonene 10 %	GER	BAQUAR–REESE, 1965
isopulegone 69 %/var. *laciniata*	IND	CHOPRA et al., 1963
linalool 56–65 %	USSR	KUSNER–GRINBERG, 1935
linalool 38–55 %	ITA	SACCO, 1959
linalool 32 % + carvacrol	SAR	RATTU–FALQUI, 1953

Ch. T. inheritance of Ch. CHAR   MURRAY, 1960b
biochemical varieties   ROOTH–HEGNAUER, 1955
4 Ch. races   HRIMLIAN, 1965

Monarda fistulosa L. – Lf/E–O
Ql. D. carvacrol 67 %   HENDRICKS–KREMER, 1899
thymol scent; or lemon-like scent/one clone   SCORA, 1966
    of var. *mollis*
thymol 67 % + p-cymene 12 %/var. *brevis*   SCORA, 1967
thymol 60 % + cineol 11 %/var. *mollis*
thymol 50 % + cineol 16 %-cymene 14 %-
    sabinene/var. *menthifolia*
cymene 33 % + terpinolene 22 %-terpineol
    11 %/Arkansan segregate
Ch. T. chemodemes, IDP of soil, MP CHAR,   SCORA, 1966
    geographical varieties

M. mexicana Epling – Lf/E–O
Ql. D. thymol 83 % + cineol 1 %   SCORA, 1967
thymol 63 % + cineol 6 %-bornyl Ac
    /ssp. *austromontana*

M. punctata L. – Lf/E–O
Ql. D. thymol 92 %/var. *coryi*   SCORA, 1967
thymol 75 % + cymene 10 %/var. *inter-*
    media
thymol 72 % + cineol 10 %/var. *villicaulis*
thymol 68 % + cineol 20 %/var. *lasiodonta*
thymol 65% + cymene 11 %/var. *fruticulosa*
thymol 30 % + cymene 50 %/var. *arkansana*
thymol 22 % + carvacrol 41 %/var. *punctata*
thymol 20 % + cineol 23 %/var. *maritima* Cory

Mosla carvonifera (Huang.) Fuj. – Wp/E–O
Ql. D. carvone 32 % + carvacrol 9 %; or carvone   FUJITA, 1955
    12 % + thymol 6 % + carvacrol 15 %
    /*M. minoris-carvoniferum* Huang

M. chinensis Maxim. – Wp/E–O
Ql. D. carvacrol 65 % + carvacryl Ac. 6 % + bor-   FUJITA, 1965a, b, c
    neol; or carvacrol + small thymol 59 %,
    borneol Abs./var. *albiflora* Fuj.

8   113

M. formosana Maxim. – Wp/E–O
Ql. D. dillapiol 65–78 % + caryophyllene 5 %; or   TAI   Fujita, 1955
    dillapiol 55–65 % + caryophyllene 25 %   JAP
    /var. *okinavaense* Fuj.; or carvacrol 47–   TAI
    53 % + dillapiol in Tr./*M. lysimachiflora*
    Kudo

M. grosseserrata Maxim.
Ql. D. methyleugenol 90 %; or methylchavicol;   Fujita, 1965a, b, c
    75 %; or myristicine 70 %; or methyliso-
    eugenol 55 %
Ch. T. last three as *M. methylchavicolifera* Fuj. etc.

M. hadai Nakai – Wp/E–O
Ql. D. carvacrol 72–75 %   TAI   Fujita, 1955
    carvacrol 58 % + γ-terpinene 15 %   JAP

M. hirta Hara – Wp/E–O
Ql. D. thymol 46 %; or carvacrol 48–55 %; or thy-   Fujita, 1955
    mol 22 % + carvacrol 6 %   Fujita, 1965a, b, c
Ch. T. last two as separated species: *M. pseudo-*   Fujita, 1965a, b, c
    hirta and *M. goshinanensis* Fuj.

M. lanceolata Maxim. – Wp/E–O
Ql. D. cineol 60–80 %; or geranyl Ac 80 %; or cit-   Fujita, 1965a, b, c
    ral 30 % or dihydrocarvone 60 %; or sabi-
    nol 65–72 %
Ch. T. last four as *M. citralifera*, *M. sabinolifera*, etc.

M. linaloolifera Fuj. – Wp/E–O
Ql. D. d-linalool   75–82 % + limonene   5–12 %;   Fujita, 1943
    or l-linalool 78 % + limonene 3 % + caryo-   Fujita–Ueda, 1957
    phyllene 10 %
Ch. T. last as var. *laevo-linaloolifera* Fuj.

M. punctulata (Maxim.) Nakai – Wp/E–O
Ql. D. thujone 75 %; or elemicine 10–40 % +   Fujita, 1965a, b, c
    methyleugenol 25–65 %; or bisabolene
    55 %; or asarone 23–25 %
Ch. T. last two as *M. asaronifera*, *M. bisabolenifera* Fuj.

M. tenuicaulis (Koidz.) Fuj. – Wp/E–O
Ql. D. thymol 50 %; or thymol 34 % + thymol-   Fujita, 1965a, b, c
    methylether 16 %
Ch. T. the last as forma *taikeiensis* Fuj.

Nepeta cataria L. – Wp/E–O
Ql. D. citral 18–75 %/var. *citriodora* (Beck) Balb.   HUN   Páter, 1924/25
    citronellal 22–80 %   USSR   Gurvich, 1960
    nepetalic acid 40 %   USA   Guenther, 1953
    carvacrol   ITA   Liotta, 1923
    citronellol + geraniol   USA   Waller–Regnier, 1966
    geraniol 27 % + citronellol 17 %   POL   Kulesza et al., 1961
    citronellal 48 %; or nepetalactone 78 %   USA   Regnier et al., 1967

Ch. T. DEP on chromosomal pair number   KACZMAREK, 1957
        continuous VAR of Ch. CHAR   GURVICH, 1960

N. mussinii Spreng. – Wp/E–O
Ql. D. menthol, or aldehydes as *MC*   USSR   HRIMLIAN, 1948, 1951
        menthol 48 %   FRA   SALGUES, 1953
        citral(?) 17 %   POL   SAWICKA, 1956
        epinepetalactone   USA   REGNIER et al., 1967
Ch. T. 4 Ch. races   HRIMLIAN, 1965

N. transcaucasica Grossh. – Wp/E–O
Qn. D. 0·15–0·4 %   USSR   GURVICH, 1960
Ql. D. geranyl acetate 85–90 %; or citronellol
        75–88 %; or citral 30–40 %
        1–5 different components   MISHUROVA, 1966
Ch. T. IDP of place of culture, Ch. forms   MAKOVKINA, 1962

Ocimum basilicum L. – Wp/E–O
Ql. D. linalool 70 %   POL   TUROWSKA et al., 1956
        linalool 48 % + methylcinnamate   IND   RAKSHIT, 1938
        linalool 40–48 % + methyl chavicol 33 % +   ITA   BONACCORSI, 1936
          methyl cinnamate 15–21 %
        linalool 40 % + methylchavicol 50 %   FRA   CAMUS–CAMUS, 1910
        methylchavicol 65–80 %   SEY   GUILLAUMIN, 1930
        methylcinnamate 57 % + terpinene   IND   NIGAM–DUTT, 1946
        ocimene as *MC*, linalool little   IND   HANDA et al., 1957
Ch. T. IDP of MP CHAR   TUROWSKA–SKWARA, 1958
        camphor and eugenol containing forms   GILDEMEISTER–HOFFMANN,
          are presumably hybrids   1961
        Ch. races, or forms   STAHL, 1957

O. canum Sims. – Wp/E–O
Ql. D. citral 60–70 %/var *citrata*   IND   DUTT, 1940
                                  ERI   BURNS–RUNGE, 1948
        camphor 80–99 %   USSR   NESTERENKO, 1934
        methylcinnamate 87 %   CON   NILOV, 1936
Ch. T. Ch. D at the level of the species   KIRIALOV–KONOVALOV,
                                     1959; DILLEMANN, 1960
        Ch. D as var. *citrata*   ROVESTI, 1957
        chemotypes   HEGNAUER, 1966

O. gratissimum L. – Wp/E–O
Ql. D. citral 66–70 %   IND   NIGAM–DUTT, 1944
        bisabolene 54 %   USSR   NILOV, 1937
        eugenol 60 % + ocimene 15–21 %   INDO   DULOU–PÉTARD, 1947
        thymol Abs./var. *suavis* Hook.   TAI   PING–HSIEN, 1960
        thymol 44–50 %, eugenol Abs.   CON   GUILLAUMINE, 1930
Ch. T. IDP of place of culture   NAYAK–GUHA, 1952
        Ch. races, PHYS varieties   GUENTHER, 1956
        chemotypes   HEGNAUER, 1966

O. menthaefolium Hochst. – Wp/E–O
Ql. D. citral 56 %; or methylchavicol 73 %; or   ERI   ROVESTI, 1957
        camphor 23 %; or anethol 39 %

Ch. T. as var. *anisata, citrata, camphorata* etc.
inheritance of Ch. CHAR

O. sanctum L. – Wp/E–O
Ql. D. aldehydes (citrale) 68 %; or eugenol 71 %   IND   TAYAL–DUTT, 1938
/var. *allahabad*
methylchavicol 60 %   PHIL   BACON, 1910
chavibetol 23 % + cineol 15 %   IND   ANONYMOUS, 1937
Ch. T. chemotypes   HEGNAUER, 1966

O. viride Willd. – Wp/E–O
Ql. D. citral 75 %; or thymol 65 %   USSR   GURVICH, 1960
thymol much; or phenols little   GILDEMEISTER–HOFFMANN,
1961

Origanum vulgare L. – Wp/E–O
Ql. D. thymol 55–76 %/var. *formosanum* Hay. +   GILDEMEISTER–HOFFMANN,
var. *viride* Boiss.   1961
carvacrol 74 % + thymol 3–24 %   YUG   SALGUES, 1953
linalyl Ac/phenols Abs. or sesquiterpenes   USSR   GURVICH, 1960
Pst., blue oil
Ch. T. DEP on origin   GILDEMEISTER–HOFFMANN
ISP VAR, Ch. differentiation   GURVICH

Perilla frutescens (L.) Britt. – Wp/E–O
Ql. D. perillaaldehyde 50 %/var. *crispa* Dcne.; or   TAI   PING–HSIEN, 1960
piperitone 55 %; or naginataketone 37 %
elsholtziaketone 90 %; or citral 59 %   FUJITA–UEDA, 1959
/*P. citriodora* Ohwi
perillaketone   JAP   SEBE, 1943
naginataketone 90 %   JAP   UEDA, 1960
elsholtziaketone 49 % + naginataketone   PING–HSIEN, 1961
37 %; dillapiol 65 % + caryophyllene   TAI
24 % egomaketone 70 %/f. *discolor* Makino   UEDA–FUJITA, 1962
perillaketone + isoegomaketone   ITO, 1964
Ch. T. morphologically indistinguishable Ch. races   PING–HSIEN, 1961
P. dillapioliferum, P. naginataketoniferum
chemotypes   HEGNAUER, 1965

Pogostemon plectranthoides Hook. – Lf/E–O
Ql. D. menthol + aromadendrene + caryophyl-   KAS   CHAUDRY et al., 1959
lene
cadinene 21 % + guajol 15 %   IND   NIGAM–PUROHIT, 1966

Prunella vulgaris L. – Wp/E–O
Qn. D. E–O only in Tr.   EUR   HEGNAUER, 1965
0·5 % E–O (camphor 50 %)   IND   BASLAS, 1955

Rosmarinus officinalis L. – Wp/E–O
Ql. D. ORP from 23·5° to –14°   USSR   NESTERENKO, 1934
ORP + in general, but – in →   FRA   GILDEMEISTER–HOFFMANN,
1961

Ch. T. DEP on area of origin   HEGNAUER, 1965

Salvia apiana Jepson – Wp/E–O
Ql. D. cineol 40–46% + camphor-borneol 30–40%;　　　　EMBODEN–LEWIS, 1967
　　　or cineol 68 % + camphor-borneol
　　　10%/ssp. *compacta*

S. officinalis L. – Fl/E–O
Ql. D. thujone 50 %; or Abs./ssp. *lavandulifolia*　SPA　BRIESKORN–FUCHS, 1962
　　　(Vahl) Gams

S. sclarea L. – Wp/E–O
Qn. D. 0·03–0·84 %　　　　　　　　　　　　COLL　ILIEVA, 1965
Ql. D. linalyl Ac + linalool 58–85 %

Satureja abyssinica (Hochst.) Briq. – Wp/E–O
Ql. D. pulegone 48 % + isomenthone 42 %　　　TAN　NAVES, 1948
　　　citral 30–35 % + limonene 23 %; or men-　ERI　ROVESTI, 1957
　　　thone 60–65 %
Ch. T. DEP on origin (above sea level); inheritance　　　ROVESTI
　　　of Ch. CHAR; as var. *citrata*, etc.
　　　chemotypes　　　　　　　　　　　　　　HEGNAUER, 1966

S. biflora (Benth.) Briq. – Wp/E–O
Ql. D. pulegone 56–60 %; or citral 56–63 %; or　ERI　ROVESTI, 1952, 1957
　　　menthone 57 %; or camphor 25 %
Ch. T. DEP on origin (above sea-level) D; CORR　　　ROVESTI, 1957
　　　Abs. between MP and Ch. CHAR; as
　　　var. *citrata*, etc.
　　　chemotypes　　　　　　　　　　　　　　HEGNAUER, 1966

S. odora (Griseb.) Epl. – Lf/E–O
Ql. D. pulegone 70–75 % + lippione 10 %　　　　FESTER, 1950
　　　MC: lippione; or piperitenone oxide; or　　FESTER et al., 1959, 1961
　　　piperitone oxide

Thymus armeniacus Klok. et Schost. – Wp/E–O
Ql. D. *MC:* limonene; or camphor; or geraniol; or　ARM　GURVICH, 1960
　　　linalool; or thymol
Ch. T. IDP of indentation of flower calyx　　　　GURVICH, 1940
　　　Ch. races　　　　　　　　　　　　　　SHOSTENKO et al., 1936

T. austriacus Bernh. – Wp/E–O
Ql. D. terpineol, borneol, thymol Pst. or Abs.　　SCHRATZ et al., 1968

T. eriophorus Ronn. – Wp/E–O
Ql. D. citronellol; or citral　　　　　　　　　GURVICH, 1965

T. fedtschenkoi Ronn. – Wp/E–O
Ql. D. composition and scent various　　　　　GURVICH, 1965

T. froelichianus Opiz – Wp/E–O
Ql. D. linalool, terpineol, nerolidol, borneol　　SCHRATZ et al., 1968
　　　eucalyptol, thymol, terpinyl Ac Pst. or Abs.

T. hadzhievii Grossh. – Wp/E–O
Ql. D. citral; or camphor; or borneol; or geraniol;　GURVICH, 1965
　　　or linalool

117

T. karamarianicus Klok. et Schost. – Wp/E–O
Ql. D. citral; or borneol; or camphene; or carvacrol   GURVICH, 1965

T. karjagini Grossh. – Wp/E–O
Ql. D. citral; or camphor; or borneol; or geraniol;   GURVICH, 1965
or linalool

T. kjapazi Grossh. – Wp/E–O
Ql. D. various composition and scent   GURVICH, 1965

T. kotschyanus Boiss. et Hohen. — Wp/E–O
Ql. D. citronellal 51 %; or thymol 65 %   CAU   GURVICH, 1936, 1938
linalylacetate   ARM   HRIMLIAN et al., 1941
limonene; or borneol; or citral; or camphor;   HRIMLIAN, 1951
or thymol + limonene   HRIMLIAN–MINASIAN,
1955
thymol 20 %; + carvacrol 16 %   HRIMLIAN, 1965
Ch. T. inheritance of Ch. CHAR; IDP of place of   GURVICH, 1960
culture
IDP of flower colours, 10 chemoraces   HRIMLIAN, 1965

T. marschallianus Willd. — Wp/E–O
Ql. D. citral; or borneol; or terpineol; or phenols   USSR   KASAKEVICH–SOBO-
LEVSKAIA, 1928
thymol 33 % + p-cymene 29 %   FUJITA, 1965
geraniol, linalool, nerolidol, eucalyptol   SCHRATZ et al., 1968
Pst. or Abs.
Ch. T. MP D Abs.   GURVICH, 1940
26 types of E–O   SCHRATZ et al., 1968

T. nigricus Klok. et Schost. — Wp/E–O
Ql. D. citronellol; or linalool   GURVICH, 1960

T. oenipontanus H. Braun — Wp/E–O
Ql. D. linalool, geraniol, borneol, citral, thymol,   SCHRATZ et al., 1968
carvacrol, geranyl Ac, neryl Ac Pst. or Abs.

T. polytrichus Kerner — Wp/E–O
Ql. D. linalool, terpineol, borneol, thymol,   SCHRATZ et al., 1968
carvacrol Pst. or Abs.

T. pulegioides L. — Wp/E–O
Ql. D. citral; or carvacrol; or thymol 34—42 %   HEGNAUER, 1948
citral much. phenols little   MESSERSCHMIDT, 1965
borneol, citral, carvacrol, thymol Pst. or Abs.   SCHRATZ et al., 1965
Ch. T. Ch. races   HEGNAUER, 1957
citral race must be excluded from pharmaco-   FLÜCK, 1960
poeia
58 types of E–O   SCHRATZ et al., 1968

T. serpyllum L. — Wp/E–O
Ql. D. carvacrol 50—55 %   FRA   SALGUES, 1945
carvacrol 53 % + p-cymene 17 % + γ-ter-   IND   SING-RAO, 1935
pine 8 %

thymol 35 %	JAP	Schantz–Ivars, 1964
linalool + linalylacetate 39—57 % myr-	N/FIN	Schantz–Luens, 1964
cene 15—22 %; or sesquiterpene 22—30 %	C/FIN	
ssp. *tanaënsis* (Hyl.) Jalas		
caryophyllene 19—27 % + cineol 18—28 %	S/FIN	
/ssp. *angustifolius* (Pers.) Vollm.		
geraniol, borneol, citral Pst. or Abs. sensu		Schratz et al., 1968
stricto plants		

Ch. T. Ch. races   Tucakov–Savin, 1960
        IND of MP D; 7 scent types   Gurvich, 1960
        chemotypes   Hegnauer, 1966

T. serrulatus Hochst.

Ql. D. *MC* carvacrol 60 % + thymol	ERI	Rovesti
MC linalool		

Ch. T. DEP on height above sea level

T. sudeticus Opiz — Wp/E–O

Ql. D. borneol, citral, thymol, geranyl Ac Pst. or Abs.		Schratz et al., 1968

T. tiflisiensis Klok. et Schost. – Wp/E–O

Ql. D. citral; or camphor; or borneol; or linalool;	USSR	Gurvich, 1960
or geraniol		

T. transcaucasicus Ronn. – Wp/E–O

Ql. D. linalool 80–90 %; or geranylacetate 62 %;	USSR	Gurvich, 1936, 1938
or terpinene 36 % + thymol 35 %		
Ch. T. CORR Abs. between Ch. and MP CHAR		Gurvich, 1960
Ch. races		Stahl, 1957

T. trautvetteri Klok. et Schost. – Wp/E–O

Ql. D. geraniol; or citronellol; or citral		Gurvich, 1960

T. vulgaris L. – Wp/E–O

Ql. D. citral; or p-cymol	MAR	Guenther, 1953
thymol/carvacrol at various rates	ITA	Pellini–Morani, 1923
cineol		Stahl, 1957
linalool; or thymol; or citral	FRA	Igolen, 1963
terpinene; or linalool 50 %; or linalool +	FRA	Granger et al., 1963
borneol + phenol; or linalool + p-cymene		
+ phenol; or phenols 53 %		
MC: carvacrol; or thymol; or p-cymol; or		Kerdilès, 1967
linalool + linalyl-Ac 80 %; or terpineol +		
terpenyl-Ac; or terpineol-4 + terpinene		
bornyl Ac Pst. or Abs.		Schratz et al., 1968
Ch. T. IDP of ecological factors		Messerschmidt, 1965
Ch. D taxa with MP uniformity		Igolen, 1963
Ch. races		Tucakov–Savin, 1960
DEP on area, IDP of OG changes		Granger et al., 1964
IDP of Fl colour, on height above sea level,		Kerdilès, 1967
DEP on area of origin		
chemotypes		Hegnauer, 1966
3 types of E-O		Schratz et al., 1968

MYOPORACEAE

Myoporum deserti Cunn. – Wp/E–O
Ql. D. in sesquiterpene composition   SUTHERLAND–PARKS, 1967
Ch. T. No CORR between chemistry, geography
    or morphology, 9 Ch. forms

GERANIACEAE

Pelargonium roseum Willd. – Wp/E–O
Ql. D. citronellol 98 % + geraniol 2 %; or citro-   PRAVDOLJUBOVA, 1936
    nellol 48 % + geraniol 52 %
    citronellol 38 %   MAR   ANONYMOUS, 1961
    menthone 5–20 %   USSR   KRACHKOVSKAIA, 1958
Ch. T. inheritance of Ch. CHAR   MASLOVA, 1957
    morphologically indistinguishable Ch. mutant   KUCHULORIA, 1964
    with much menthone in E–O

ERYTHROXYLACEAE

Erythroxylum monogynum Roxb. – Wd/E–O
Qn. D. 1·15 %   RAO et al., 1926
    0·09–0·17 %   GUPTA–MUTHANA, 1954
Ql. D. bisabolene + cadinene as *MC*   RAO et al., 1926
    pinene 40 %+monogynol as *MC* of the diter-   GUPTA–MUTHANA, 1954
    penes 50 %

DIPTEROCARPACEAE

Dipterocarpus appendiculatus Scheffer – OR
Ql. D. caryophyllene 75 % + humulene 20 %; or   BISSET, 1966
    caryophyllene 30 % + humulene 65 %

D. baudii Korth. – OR
Ql. D. gurjunene 60 % + calarene 20 %; or gurju-   THAI   BISSET, 1966
    nene 10 %/calarene Abs.   MAL

D. geniculatus Vesque – OR
Ql. D. humulene 60 % + caryophyllene 40 %; or   BISSET, 1966
    humulene 15 % + caryophyllene 80 %
    /var. *grandis* Ashton; or humulene 10 %
    + caryophyllene 20 % + aromadendrene
    65 %/var. *grandis*

D. grandiflorus Blanco – OR
Ql. D. alloaromadendrene 95 %;   MAL   BISSET, 1966
    or alloaromadendrene 50 % + gurjunene   PHIL
    20 % + humulene 20 %

D. obtusifolius Teysm. – OR
Ql. D. humulene 60 %, cyperene Abs.; or humu-   V–N   BISSET, 1966
    lene 15 % + cyperene 15 %

120

D. turbinatus Gaertn. f. – OR
Ql. D. calarene Pst., humulene Abs.; or humulene   Bisset, 1966
    Pst., calarene Abs.; gurjunene 0–75 %,
    or only 20 %

D. warburgii Brandis – OR
Ql. D. alloaromadendrene 55 % + copaene 35 %;   Bisset, 1966
    or caryophyllene 30 % + copaene 30 % +
    humulene 15 % + cyperene 10 %

D. zeylanicus Thw. – OR
Ql. D. farnesane 50 % + caryophyllene 20 %; or   Bisset, 1966
    caryophyllene 65 % + humulene 35 %

ERICACEAE

Ledum palustre L. – Lf/E–O
Ql. D. myrcene + ledol + palustrol   EUR   Gildemeister–Hoffmann,
                                                                1961
    p-cymol 30 % + sesquiterpenes + p-cresol/   JAP   Uota–Kondo, 1943
     var. *dilatatum* Wahlenb.;
    ledol Pst./var. *vulgare*, var. *dilatatum*;   USSR   Berezovskaya, 1962
     or Abs./var. *angustatum* E. Busch
    p-cymol + pinene + germacrone, ledol Abs.   SIB   Naugolnaja, 1963
Ch. T. morphologically no D   Naugolnaja, 1963

ASTERACEAE / COMPOSITAE — I. TERPENES

Achillea asplenifolia Vent. Fl/E–O
Ql. D. prochamazulenes Pst. or Abs.   CSR   Kucera–Mackova, 1955
Ch. T. polychemism verified   Tyihák et al., 1963

A. ageratum L. – Wp/E–O
Ql. D. prochamazulenes Pst. or Abs.   COLL   Kosova, 1959

A. clypeolata Sieb. – Wp/E–O
Ql. D. prochamazulenes Pst. or Abs.   COLL   Kosova, 1959

A. depressa Janka – Wp/E–O
Ql. D. prochamazulenes Pst. or Abs.   COLL   Kosova, 1959

A. distans W. et K. – Wp/E–O
Ql. D. prochamazulenes Pst.   GER   Stahl, 1952
    prochamazulenes Abs.   ROM   Kotilla, 1959

A. grandiflora Flod. – Wp/E–O
Ql. D. prochamazulenes Pst. or Abs.   COLL   Kosova, 1959

A. microphylla L. – Wp/E–O
Ql. D. prochamazulenes Pst. or Abs.   COLL   Kosova, 1959

121

A. millefolium L. – Fl/E–O
Qn. D. azulenes 0·1–16 %   GILDEMEISTER–HOFFMANN,
    1961

Ql. D. prochamazulenes Pst. or Abs.   GER   KOCH, 1940
  3 prochamazulenes at different rate   GER   STAHL, 1953
  various prochamazulenes;   POL   MICHALUK–OSWIECZIM-
    SKA, 1959
  prochamazulenes Pst. or Abs./*A. collina* Becker   OSWIECZIMSKA, 1968
Ch. T. IDP of ecological factors   GRAHLE, 1952
  inheritance of Ch. CHAR   STAHL, 1952
  correlation Abs. between Ch. and MP CHAR   ROSENTHAL, 1941
  DEP on ploidy degree   OSWIECZIMSKA, 1968
  Ch. races   STAHL, 1957
  4 Ch. races   MICHALUK–OSWIECZIMSKA,
    1959
  14 Ch. taxa   TÉTÉNYI et al., 1964

A. nobilis L. — Wp/E–O
Ql. D. prochamazulenes Pst.   GER   STAHL, 1952
                            COLL   KOTILLA, 1959
  prochamazulenes Abs.   COLL   KOSOVA, 1959
  prochamazulenes Abs./ssp. *neilreichii*   COLL   LENKEY, 1961
  (Kern.) Jáv.

A. odorata Koch – Wp/E–O
Ql. D. prochamazulenes Pst.   GER   STAHL, 1952
  prochamazulenes Abs.   COLL   KOSOVA, 1959

A. stricta Schleich. – Wp/E–O
Ql. D. prochamazulenes Pst.   COLL   KOTILLA, 1959
  prochamazulenes Abs.   GER   KOCH, 1942

A. setacea W. et K. – Wp/E–O
Ql. D. prochamazulenes Pst.   COLL   KOSOVA, 1959
  prochamazulenes Abs.   GER   STAHL, 1952

A. tanacetifolia All. – Wp/E–O
Ql. D. prochamazulenes Pst. or Abs.   COLL   KOSOVA, 1959

Artemisia absinthium L. – Wp/E–O
Qn. D. 0·2–3·1 %   USSR   GURVICH–GADSHIEV, 1938
Ql. D. thujone + thujylalcohol   GER   STAHL, 1953
  myrcene 40 % + sabinene 33 %   CSR   HEROUT, 1952
  myrcene 39 % + isothujyl Ac. 38 %   USSR   GORIAYEV et al., 1962
  cadinene (azulenes Abs.)   COCKER et al., 1958
  cadinene + s-guajazulene 13 %   IND   SINGH et al., 1959
  proartemazulene   GILDEMEISTER–HOFFMANN,
    1961
  various azulenes   COLL   TYIHÁK–MÁTHÉ, 1963

A. arborescens L. – Wp/E–O
Ql. D. azulenes 50 % + thujene   SIC   PELLINI–MORANI, 1923
  thujone 16 % + thujylalcohol 22 %   ITA   RATTU–MACCIONI, 1953

thujone + borneol; azulenes Abs.	USSR	GURVICH, 1960
camphor 14 % + arborescine	ISR	WEIZMANN, 1952

A. austriaca Jacq. – Wp/E–O
Ql. D. cineol 30 % + thujone 29 %   USSR   HOLMOV et al., 1948
      camphor + aldehydes + azulenes   KAH   GORIAYEV et al., 1962
      camphor 27 % + cineol 18 % + thujone   GORIAYEV–GIMADDINOV,
      31 %   1964

A. balchanorum Krasch. – Sh/E–O
Ql. D. linalool 40 % + geraniol 25 % + citral   JAP   COCKER et al., 1958
      linalool 50 %; or geraniol 90 %; or citral   USSR   KOVERGA, 1959
      20 %
Ch. T. CORR Abs. between Ch. and MP CHAR   GURVICH, 1960

A. cina (Berg) Willk. – Fl/E–O
      cineol 78–82 %   USA   GUENTHER, 1953
      cineol 30 + camphor 13 %   USSR   RIBALKO–BANKOVSKI, 1959

A. dracunculus L. – Wp/E–O
Ql. D. sabinene 80–85 %   KIRIALOV–KONOVALOV,
                             1959
      sabinene 37 % + pinene 10 % + myrcene   GORIAYEV–SATDAROVA,
      10 %   1959
      methylchavicol 60–80 % (cultivars)   GILDEMEISTER–HOFFMANN,
                             1961
Ch. T. leaf-index correlated with Ch. CHAR   ROSENTHAL, 1954
      D in growing season and fertility   GILDEMEISTER–HOFFMANN,
                             1961
      2 separated species   IVANOV, 1937

A. ferganensis Krasch. – Wp/E–O
Ql. D. sesquiterpene-alcohol 40 % + terpenes 20 %   GORIAYEV–GIMADDINOV,
                             1954
      camphor 85 % + cineol 9 %   GORIAYEV et al., 1962

A. herba-alba Asso – Wp/E–O
Ql. D. camphor + camphene   GILDEMEISTER–HOFFMANN,
                             1961
      thujone + phenols 30 %   SPA   FESNEAU, 1950
      thujone + camphor + camphene; sesqui-   CAMUS–CAMUS, 1920
      terpenes Abs /var. *genuina* Batt. et Trab.
      thujone + sesquiterpenes/var. *densiflora* Boiss.   GILDEMEISTER–HOFFMANN,
                             1961

A. lercheana Web. – Wp/E–O
Ql. D. camphor 91 %   KASAKEVICH, 1928
      camphor 6 % + borneol 23 %/var. *astra-*   GORIAYEV et al., 1962
      chanica Poljak

A. macrocephala Jacq. – Wp/E–O
Ql. D. guajazulenes 30 %; or Abs.   FODOROV, 1961
Ch. T. Ch. races

123

A. pallens Wall. – Wp/E–O
Ql. D. in composition of 2 taxa   IND   SRINATH–RAMASWAMY,
                                                                              1964
          ORP from 35° to –26°   GILDEMEISTER–HOFFMANN,
                                                                              1961

A. porrecta Krasch. – Wp/E–O
Ql. D. cineol 47 % + camphor 37 %   GORIAYEV et al., 1962
          thujone 30 % + linalylbiturate 28 %/var.   GORIAYEV–GIMADDINOV,
          coerulea Pol.   1964

A. santolinifolia Turcz. – Wp/E–O
Ql. D. cineol 26 % + phenols 16 %   CHISTOVA, 1935
          thujone 26 % + thujylalcohol 20 %   GORIAYEV et al., 1962

A. scoparia W. et K. – Wp/E–O
Ql. D. scoparylene 79 %; or Abs.   IND   PARIHAR–DUTT, 1947
          eugenol + pinene + cadinene   IND   DAKSHINAMURTI, 1953
          pinene 20 % + agropyrenes 42 %   USSR   HOLMOV–AFANASIEV, 1957
          pinene + myrcene; cadinene Abs.   USSR   GURVICH, 1960

A. scoparioides Grossh. – Wp/E–O
Ql. D. eugenol from 3 % to 27 %   GURVICH, 1960

A. sieversiana Willd. – Wp/E–O
Ql. D. pinene 25 % + cineol 13 % + myrcene   PROHOROVA–LEBEDEV,
          10 % + sesquiterpenes   1932
          azulenes 30 %; or little   GORIAYEV et al., 1962
          azulenes 15 % + myrcene as *MC*   NAZARENKO, 1965
          borneol(?)28 % + camphor 16 % + cineol   FAVORSKAYA, 1963
          12 %

A. terrae-albae Krasch. – Wp/E–O
Ql. D. camphor 37 % + cineol 8 % + artemisia-   GORIAYEV et al., 1962
          ketone 14 %; or camphor 96 %/var.
          massagetovii Krasch.; or cineol 60 %
          /var. *kurdaica* Pol.

A. tridentata Nutt. – Wp/E–O
Ql. D. cineol 29 % + camphor 26 % + artemisol   USA
          21 %;   Utah   COCKER et al., 1958
          or camphor 40 % + pinene 20 %   USA
          + methacroleine 9 %   Nevada
          thujone + camphene + artemisol + meth-   USSR   GURVICH, 1960
          acroleine
          deoxymatricarine much/ssp. *parishii*   USA   GEISMANN et al., 1967

Chrysanthemum cinerariaefolium (Trev.) Vis. – Fl
Qn. D. 0·7–1·7 % pyrethrines   COLL   BORKOWSKY et al., 1959
          2·0 % pyrethrines   KEN   ANONYMOUS, 1962
          pyrethrines Abs.   USSR   VETCHININA, 1948
Ql. D. pyrethrine I or II as *MC*   COLL   MARTIN, 1960
Ch. T. inheritance of Ch. CHAR   MARTIN, 1960

124

C. vulgare (L.) Bernh. – Lf/E–O

Ql. D.	crystallizable camphor	GBR	BRUYLANTS, 1878
	camphor; or thujone; or borneol	IND	HANDA et al., 1957
	camphor 59–62 %; or thujone 66–69 % or borneol 20–28 %; or cineol 27–29 %	FIN	SCHANTZ–JÄRVI, 1965
	isothujone 61 %	USSR	KARPENKO et al., 1952
	isothujone 73–87 %; or thujone 80–90 %	CAN	RUDLOFF–UNDERHILL, 1965
	thujone 28 % + cineol 12 % + camphor 10%	IND	TALWAR et al., 1961
	isothujone 98 %; or umbellulone 70 %; or camphor 75%; or monoterpene hydrocarbons 50 %; or monoterpene ester 75 %; or sesquiterpene derivatives 71 %; artemisiaketone 91 %; or chrysanthemum epoxide 51 %	COLL	STAHL–SCHEU, 1966
	MC: α-pinene; or β-pinene; or γ-terpinene		SCHANTZ et. al., 1966
Ch. T.	DEP on MP CHAR Abs., geographical D		STAHL–SCHMITT, 1964
	influence of ecological factors Abs.,		SCHANTZ–JÄRVI, 1965
	Ch. races; segregation in S_1 generation		STAHL–SCHEU, 1966
	IDP of MP CHAR; OG changes of Fl		SCHANTZ et al., 1966

Matricaria chamomilla L. – Fl

Qn. D.	32–112 mg % azulenes	GER	KOCH, 1942
	0–125 mg % azulenes	COLL	BLAZEK–STARY, 1961
Ql. D.	prochamazulenes Pst. or Abs.	GER	HAGENSTRŐM–SCHMERSAHL, 1954
	bisabolols + farnesol at various levels	COLL	TYIHÁK et al., 1963
Ch. T.	DEP on area D	HUN	MÁTHÉ–TYIHÁK, 1960
	DEP on origin	SWI	LENKEY, 1961
	inheritance of Ch. CHAR; IDP of ecological factors, of MP CHAR or of ploidic level; chemoforma – chemovars		TÉTÉNYI, 1961
	chemoconculta		TYIHÁK et al., 1963

ASTERACEAE / COMPOSITAE – II. SESQUITERPENE LACTONES

Ambrosia acanthicarpa (Hook.) Cav. - Wp

Ql. D.	confertiflorin; or chamissonin; or artenovin		GEISSMAN–MATSUEDA, 1968

A. ambrosioides (Cav.) Payne/*Franseria ambrosioides* Cav. — Wp

Ql. D.	damsin + franserin	MEX	ROMO et al., 1968
	hispidulin	USA	HERZ, 1968

A. artemisiifolia L. — Wp

Ql. D.	coronopilin	USA	HERZ–HÖGENAUER, 1961
	psilostachyin	AUL	BIANCHI et al., 1968
	artemisiifolin; or cumanin + peruvin		PORTER–MABRY, 1968

A. chamissonis (Less.) Green — Wp

Ql. D.	in composion of sequiterpene lactones		GEISMANN–MATSUEDA, 1968

A. confertiflora DC./*Franseria tenuifolia* Harvey et
    Gray – Wp

Ql. D. confertiflorin + desacetylconfertiflorin; or   USA,   MABRY et al., 1966
    other germacranolides   Texas
    psilostachyin + psilostachyin C   Arizona   HERZ, 1966

A. cumanensis H. B. et K.
    cumanin 100 %; or psilostachyin 50 % +   GEISMANN et al., 1967
    psilostachyin B 50 %; or psilostachyin
    50 % + psilostachyin B 35 % + psilo-
    stachyin C 15 %; or psilostachyin 20 % +
    psilostachyin B 60 % + psilostachyin C
    20 %
    psilostachyin B + C + cumanin;   MEX   MILLER et al., 1968
    ambrosin + coronopilin
    ambrosin + damsin + psilostachyin   CLU   HERZ, 1968

A. dumosa Gray – Wp
Ql. D. coronopilin + ambrosiol; or burrodin +   GEISSMAN–MATSUEDA,
    apulodin   1968
Ch. T. DEP on ploidy degree

A. peruviana Willd. — Wp
Ql. D. psilostachyin C + tetrahydroambrosin   P–R   KAGAN et al., 1966
    or peruvin + peruvinin   MEX   JOSEPH-NATHAN-ROMO,
                                              1966

A. psilostachya DC. – Wp
Ql. D. coronopilin   HERZ–HÖGENAURER, 1961
    coronopilin + ambrosiol; or ambrosiol; or   MABRY et al., 1966
    psilostachyin; or damsine+3-hydroxydamsin
    coronopilin; or coronopilin +cumanin;
    or cumanin
    ambrosiol 100 %; or coronopilin 100 %; or   MILLER et al., 1968
    ambrosiol 60 % + coronopilin 40 %; or
    coronopilin 45 % + parthenin 55 %; or
    psilostachyin 70 %; or ambrosiol 50 % +
    cumanin 50 % or psilostachyin B 65 %
Ch. T. no MP D; D in geographical distribution   GEISSMAN–MATSUEDA,
                                            1968
    IDP of ploidy; dilactone and monolactone   MILLER et al.
    races

Artemisia brevifolia Wall. – Sh
Ql. D. santonin 0·6–1·4 %; or Abs.   IND   QAZILBASH, 1951

A. coerulescens L. – Wp
Ql. D. santonin Pst. or Abs.   YUG   VODOPIVEC et al., 1952
    β-santonin Pst.   YUG   MARKOVIC et al., 1952

A. cina (Berg) Willk. — Fl
Ql. D. santonin 0·7—2·1 %; or Abs.   JAP   NAKAMURA–OHTA,
                                           1933–34

126

A. gallica Willd. – Wp
Ql. D. santonin Pst. or Abs. WICHMANN, 1958

A. kurramensis Qaz. – Fl
Qn. D. 1·1–2·8 % santonin QAZILBASH, 1951, 1954
Ql. D. santonin Pst. or Abs. COLL KAWATANI et al., 1958
   α; or β-; or α + β santonin KURODA–KAWATANI, 1962
Ch. T. MP D insignificant KURODA–KAWATANI

A. maritima L. – Fl
Qn. D. 0·2–1·2 % santonin HUN TÉTÉNYI, 1963
   1·3 % santonin/var. *boschniakiana* Bess. USSR RIBALKO et al., 1963
Ql. D. santonin Pst. or Abs. WEHMER, 1931
   1-β-santonin IND OELSSNER, 1951
   1-β-santonin + pseudosantonine POL BORSUTZKI, 1955
   α- or β-santonin as *MC;* or both Abs. HUN TÉTÉNYI
   TOMOWA, 1955
Ch. T. IDP of soil D, or DEP? WICHMANN, 1958
   MP D Abs. OELSSNER, 1951
   Ch. races KLEIN, 1921
   Ch. differentiated species KAWATANI, 1953

A. tenuisecta Nevski – Fl
Ql. D. santonin Pst. or Abs. GORIAYEV et al., 1962

Cnicus benedictus L. – Wp
Ql. D. cnicin; or cnicin + benedictin KORTE–BECHMAN, 1958

Chrysanthemum parthenium (L.) Pers. – Wp
Ql. D. parthenolide CSR SOUCEK et al., 1961
   santamarin MEX ROMO–JIMENEZ, 1965

Gaillardia pulchella Foug. – Wp
Ql. D. helenalin + pulchellin/coast race; HERZ–INAYAMA, 1961
   or pulchellin B + C + D/plains race
   gaillardin Texas KUPCHAN et al., 1965
Ch. T. MP identical KUPCHAN et al.

Helenium amarum (Rafin.) H. Rock. – Wp
Ql. D. tenulin HERZ et al., 1962
   tenulin + aromaticin + amaralin LUCAS et al., 1964b

H. autumnale L. – S
Ql. D. helenalin; or LUCAS et al., 1964a
   dehydromexicanin E

H. mexicanum H. B. K. – Wp
Ql. D. helenalin MEX/ ROMO–ROMO, 1959
   OAX
   mexicanins MEX DOMINGUEZ–ROMO, 1963

127

Iva axillaris Pursh — Wp
Ql. D. ivaxillarin; or anhydro-ivaxillarin + axivalin   HERZ, 1968
     + ivaxilin/ssp. *robustior* (Hook.) Bassett
     or ivaxillarin + anhydroivaxillarin
     + axivalin/ssp. *robustior*

I. microcephala Nutt. — Fl + Lf
Ql. D. ivalin; or microcephalin + pseudoivalin   HERZ–HÖGENAUER, 1962
Ch. T. geographical D; as var. *A* and *B*

Parthenium hysterophorus L. — Wp
Ql. D. parthenin   USA   HERZ et al., 1962
     hysterin + ambrosin   MEX

Petasites albus (L.) Gaertn. – Rh
Ql. D. petasins; of furoeremophilanes   NOVOTNY et al., 1966
Ch. T. chemovars 'petasin', or 'furan' differing in
     enzyme system

P. hybridus (L.) G. M. et Sch. – Rh
Ql. D. petasol + petasines   SWI   AEBI–DJERASSI, 1959
     eremophilanes + sesquiterpenes   CSR   NOVOTNY et al., 1962
     eremophilanes derivatives; or furoeremophi-   CSR   HEROUT, 1966
     lanes; or petasin
Ch. T. chemovarieties; DEP on origin   HEROUT

Xanthium strumarium L. – Wp
Ql. D. in composition of E–O   GEISMANN–MATSUEDA,
                            1968

CHENOPODIACEAE

Chenopodium ambrosioides L. – Wp/E–O
Ql. D. ascaridol 36–81 %   CSR   KOSOVA et al., 1958
     ascaridol 57–86 %; or ascaridol + pinene;   USSR   NIKOLAEV, 1960
     or ascaridol 8–36 % + phellandrene;
     pinocarvone 50–57 % + pinene + aritasone   JAP   TAKAMOTO et al., 1953
Ch. T. Ch. races   NIKOLAEV

C. botrys L. – Wp/E–O
Ql. D. ascaridol 8–18 %   COLL   KOSOVA et al., 1958
     ascaridol Abs., esther Pst.   USSR   NIKOLAEV, 1960
     ascaridol Abs.   CSR   DUSINSKY–TYLLOVA, 1962

C. integrifolium Worosch. – Wp/E–O
Ql. D. ascaridol 25–36 % + p-cymol + limonene   USSR   NIKOLAEV, 1960
     p-cymol 50 % + ascaridol 20 %   ARG   FESTER et al., 1951

C. schraderianum Roem. et Schult. – Wp/E–O
Ql. D. ascaridol 3–4 %   COLL   KOSOVA et al., 1958
     ascaridol Abs.   USSR   NIKOLAEV, 1960

C. suffruticosum Willd. – Wp/E–O
Ql. D. ORP laevo- or dextrarotatory   USSR   NIKOLAEV, 1959
     E–O Abs./ssp. *remotum* Worosch.   AELLEN, 1960

Roubieva multifida Moq. – Wp/E–O
Ql. D. ascaridol much + p-cymol; or *MC* phell-   BRA   GILDEMEISTER–HOFFMANN,
      andrene + anethol   USA   1961
      ascaridol + limonene + carveol   ARG   FESTER et al., 1958

CANNABIACEAE / CANNABINACEAE

Cannabis sativa L. – Wp/OR
Ql. D. tetrahydrocannabinol/cannabidiol Abs.;   INDO   FARMILO, 1955
      or cannabidiol 95–97 %;   ROM+ITA
      or cannabinol as *MC*   NIG+BRA KORTE–SIEPER, 1964
Ch. T. DEP on areal D   GRLIC–ANDREC, 1961
      IDP of MP CHAR   STAHL, 1957
      PHYS varieties   NOVÁK et al., 1962
      genetical observations, possibilities   BREDEMANN et al., 1956

Humulus lupulus L. – Fr/OR
Qn. D. acrid matter content 13–24 %   GARBUZOVA, 1964
Ql. D. myrcene; or myrcene + farnasene; or oci-   COLL   HOWARD–SLATER, 1957
      mene + myrcene + caryophyllene
      myrcene + caryophyllene; or posthumu-   COLL   ROBERTS, 1962
      lene much
      β-selinene   COLL   STEWENS, 1964
Ch. T. clonal inheritance of Ch. CHAR   GARBUZOVA
      Ch. CHAR DEP on variety   HOWARD–SLATER

CYPERACEAE

Cyperus rotundus L. – Tu/E–O
Ql. D. camphor-like scent   SUD   JOSEPH–WHITEFELD, 1922
      cyperol 49 % + cyperene 38 %   JAP   KIMURA–OHTAINI, 1928
      cyperone 30–54 %   IND   HEDGE–RAO, 1935

GRAMINEAE

Bothriochloa decipiens (Hack.) Hubbard — Fl/E—O
Ql. D. extremely variable/var. *cloncurrensis* Hubb.   WET–SCOTT, 1965
Ch. T. two basic Ch. types

B. glabra (Roxb.) A. Camus — Fl+Lf/E—O
Ql. D. variable   WET–SCOTT, 1965
Ch. T. three Ch. types

B. insculpta (Hochst.) A. Camus — Fl + Lf/E—O
Ql. D. variable hexaploid as pentaploid races   WET–SCOTT, 1965
Ch. T. three Ch. types

B. intermedia (R. Br.) A. Camus — Fl/E—O
Ql. D. extremely variable in composition   WET–SCOTT, 1965

B. ischaemum (L.) Keng. — Fl+Lf/E—O
Ql. D. variable in composition   WET–SCOTT, 1965

Cymbopogon coloratus (Nees) Stapf – Wp/E–O
Ql. D. citral 40 % + geraniol 30 % + geranyl Ac   GOULDING–EARL, 1914
    camphene 15 % + sesquiterpenes 35 %;   PILLAY et al., 1928
    citral Abs.
Ch. T. Ch. varieties   FUJITA, 1960

C. connatus (Hochst.) Chiovenda – Wp/E–O
Ql. D. perillaalcohol 30–35 % + unknown alde-   ROVESTI, 1927, 1959
    hyde + phellandrene; or *MC:* perilla-
    alcohol 44 % + carvone 7 %; phelland-
    rene Abs.; or *MC:* phellandrene + peril-
    laalcohol 7 %; aldehyde Abs.

C. flexuosus (Nees) Wats. – Wp/E–O
Ql. D. citral 75–80 %; geranylsalycylate Abs.   IND   GUENTHER, 1952
    cineol 4–30 % + geranylsalycylate Pst.   TAI   PING–HSIEN, 1961

C. martinii (Roxb.) Wats. – Wp/E–O
Ql. D. geraniol 75–95 %; perillaalcohol Abs./var.   NAVES–GRAMPOLOFF,
    motia Burk.   1959, 1961
    menthadienols 32 %; geraniol Abs./var. *sofia*   NAVES, 1960
    Burk.
    perillaalcohol 54 % + geraniol   CHAUDHARY et al., 1958
Ch. T. PHYS varieties, MP indistinguishable, with   STAPF, 1906
    some D in area

C. nardus (L.) Rendle – Wp/E–O
Ql. D. citronellal 38–54 % + geraniol 22–27 %; or   INDO   GUENTHER, 1952
    citronellal 5–16 % + terpenes 10–15 %   CEY
    (both cultivars); or geraniol 39–64 % +   CEY
    citronellal/var. *confertiflorus* (Steud.) Stapf
    geraniol 35 % + alcohols 20 %   IND   PAUL–HANDA, 1960
    camphene 22 % + dipentene/f. *albescens*   IND   VARIER, 1946
    Stapf
Ch. T. PHYS varieties, without any MP D   STAPF, 1906

Elyonurus viridulus Hack. – Wp/E–O
Ql. D. citral a + citral b 95 %; or camphene +   FESTER et al., 1959, 1960
    pinene + sesquiterpenes 55 %
Ch. T. Ch. variant

Vetiveria zizanioides (L.) Nash – Rh/E–O
Ql. D. ORP from –22° to –89°   IND   ANONYMOUS, 1961
    ORP from –55° to +35°   IND   SADGOPAL, 1960
    ORP from +15° to +45°   INDO   KOOLHAAS–ROWAAN, 1937
Ch. T. MP D Abs.; ORP DEP on origin   SADGOPAL

ZINGIBERACEAE

Alpinia galanga Willd. – Rh/E–O
Ql. D. cinnamic A methylester 48 % +   JAVA   NIGAM–RADHAKRISHNAN,
    campher–cineol 20–30 %   1963
    cinnamic A methylester 2·6 % +   IND
    cineol 5·6 % + *MC:* sesquiterpenes

A. nutans (Andr.) Roscoe – Lf/E–O
Ql. D. camphor 30 % + camphene 17 %   JAP   KAFUKU, 1917
    pinenes + cineol; camphor Abs.   INDO   ULTÉE, 1937
Ch. T. possibility of Ch. taxa   HEGNAUER, 1963

Elettaria cardamomum (Roxb.) Maton – Sd/E–O
Ql. D. cineol 62 % + terpinyl Ac 27 % + borneol   MAB   GILDEMEISTER–HOFFMANN,
    /var. *minor* Watt   1956
    cineol 31 % + limonene 14 %/var. *minor*   IND   NIGAM et al., 1965
    cineol 41–45 % + linalool-l-Ac 2 %/var.   MYS   LEWIS et al., 1966
    minor; or cineol 27 % + linalool-l-Ac.   MAB
    12 %/var. *minor;* or cineol 36 % + lina-
    lool + linalyl Ac 6 %/var. *major* (Smith)
    Thwaites

ARACEAE

Acorus calamus L. – Rh/E–O
Qn. D. 1·4–3·1 %   IND   HANDA et al., 1957
    1·5–4·8 %   COLL   CHOPRA et al., 1958
    2·3 %   USSR   PIVNENKO et al., 1957
    2·1–6·8 %   COLL   WULFF–STAHL, 1960
    3·5–4·3 %   POL   KOZLOWSKIJ, 1960
Ql. D. asarone 82 %   IND   DANDIYA et al., 1959
    asarone 20–83 %   COLL   CHOPRA et al., 1958
    asarone 77–80 % + camphor 18 % (4 x);   IND   JANAKI–AMMAL et al.,
    or asarone 5 % + camphor 58 % (6 x)   1964
    asarone 76 % + calamene 4 % (4 x)   Jammu   VASHIST–HANDA, 1964
    asarone 5 % + calamene 19 % (6 x)   Kashmir
    asarone 50–65 % (3 x); or geranylacetate   EUR   WULFF–STAHL, 1960
    65 % + geraniol 20 % (2 x)
    camphene 70 % + asaron + pinene   USSR   PIVNENKO et al., 1957
    camphene + sesquiterpenes   HUN+FIN   SCHANTZ, 1958
Ch. T. DEP on ploidity degree   WULFF, 1954
    IDP of ploidity degree, but DEP on origin   WULFF–STAHL, 1960
    systematics insufficient on MP ground   MANSFELD, 1959

1.2. TERPENOIDS (TRITERP ENES, STEROIDS, SAPONINS, CARDENOLIDS)

ROSACEAE

Potentilla rupestris L. – Rt   STEINEGGER–PETERS, 1966
Ql. D. tormentoside Pst.; or Abs./var. *typica* Th. W.

FABACEAE / LEGUMINOSAE

Trigonella foenum-graecum L. – Sd
Ql. D. diosgenin alone   MARKER et al., 1943
    diosgenin + tigogenin + gitogenin   MARKER–LOPEZ, 1947
    diosgenin + gitogenin   SANNIÉ–LAPIN, 1952

APIACEAE / UMBELLIFERAE

Hydrocotyle asiastica L. – Sh
Ql. D. centelloside   CEY   Battacharryya, 1956
       indocentoic A   IND
       asiaticoside + madecassoside   MAD   Boiteau–Ratsimamanga, 1957
       brahmozide + brahminozide as Mu   IND   Rastogi et al., 1960
       thankuniside + isothankuniside   IND   Dutta–Basu, 1962
Ch. T. Ch. races   Hegnauer, 1957

DIPSACACEAE

Succisa inflexa (Kluk.) Beck – Sh   Aurich et al., 1965
Ql. D. saponins Pst.; or Abs.

APOCYNACEAE

Acocanthera schimperi DC. – Sd
Ql. D. acovenoside A 85 % + ouabain 5 %   KEN   Bally et al., 1952
       acovenoside A 60 % + ouabain 27 %   ABY   Thudim et al., 1958
       ouabain 40 %; acovenoside Abs.   ERY   Thudim et al., 1959
Ch. T. Ch. races   Abisch–Reichstein, 1960
       some MP D   Reichstein, 1965

Cerbera manghas L. – Ba   Abisch–Reichstein, 1960
Ql. D. cardenolids Pst. or Abs.

C. venenifera (Poir.) Steud. – Sd
Ql. D. tanginin + tangiferin; or cardenolids Abs.   MAD   Helfenberger–Reichstein, 1952
       tanginoside   SEY   Flury et al., 1965

Strophantus sarmentosus DC. – Sd   SUD   Tamm, 1957
Ql. D. 0·5 % sarmutoside + 0·2 % musaroside   I-C
       0·2 % sarveroside + 0·4 % panstroside 1 %   MAL
         sarmentocymarin + 0·4% sarnovide
       cardenolids in Tr. only   GUI   Richter et al., 1953
Ch. T. inheritance of Ch. CHAR; Ch. races   Reichstein, 1963

ASCLEPIADACEAE

Parquetina nigrescens (Afzel.) Bullock – Wd
Ql. D. nigrescigenin + strophantidol; or strophan-   Schenker et al., 1954
        tigenin + convallatoxin   Mauli–Tamm, 1957
Ch. T. morphologically insufficiently differentiated   Berthold et al., 1965
       2 variants
       morphologically identical Ch. races   Brandt et al., 1966

Sarcostemma viminale (L.) R. Br. – St
Ql. D. cardenolids Abs.   NIG   Abisch–Reichstein, 1962
       cardenolids Abs./prostrate form; or meta-   Schaub et al., 1968

plexigenins + vimolon + sarcostins/   S/RHO
climbing and tree-forms

POLEMONIACEAE

Phlox paniculata L. – Lf
Ql. D. in number and R_{st} of the sterin components   COLL   AURICH et al., 1965
     Pst.

Polemonium coeruleum L. – Wp, or L, or Rt
Ql. D. saponin Pst. or Abs.   USSR   SARAEVA, 1952
     3 saponin   COLL   AURICH et al., 1965
Ch. T. D in localization   SARAEVA, 1952
     inheritance of Ch.   D   MATVEIEV, 1959

CONVULVULACEAE

Ipomoea hederacea (L.) Jacq. – Lf
Ql. D. in number and in colour reaction of the   AURICH et al., 1965
     sterin-components Pst.   COLL

I. nil (L.) Roth – Lf
Ql. D. in number and in colour reaction of the   COLL   AURICH et al., 1965
     sterin-components Pst.

VERBENACEAE

Lantana camara L. – Lf
Ql. D. lantadene A + little lantadene B; or lanta-   BARTON et al., 1956
     dene A Abs.; or cardenolids Abs.

SOLANACEAE

Browallia demissa L. – Wp
Ql. D. saponins Pst. or Abs.; sterine-components   AURICH et al., 1965
     in various number and R_{st}

Cestrum parqui L'Hérit. – Wp
Ql. D. gitogenin + digitogenin   CANHAM et al., 1951
     steroids Abs.   WALL et al., 1959
     digitogenin 0·0035 %   SILVA et al., 1962
     sapogenins + sterins Pst.   AURICH et al., 1966

C. nocturnum L. – Wp
Ql. D. sapogenins Pst.   WALL et al., 1955
     sapogenins Abs.   WALL et al., 1959
     0·5 % sapogenin content   ANZALDO et al., 1957

Iochroma coccinea Scheidw. – Sh
Ql. D. in colour and R_{st} of sterin components Pst.   COLL   AURICH et al., 1965, 1966

133

Nicandra physaloides (L.) Gaertn. – Lf
Ql. D. in colour, number and R_{st} of sterin compo-   COLL   AURICH et al., 1965
   nents Pst.

Physalis ixocarpa Brot. – Sh
Ql. D. in colour, number and R_{st} of sterine compo-   COLL   AURICH et al., 1965, 1966
   nents Pst.

Solanum tripartitum Dun. – Lf
Ql. D. in number, R_{st} and colour-reactions of   COLL   AURICH et al., 1965
   sterins Pst.
   diosgenin   COLL   VÁGÚJFALVI et al., 1966
   saponins Pst. or Abs.   AURICH et al., 1966

Withania somnifera (L.) Dun. – Lf
Ql. D. somnirol + somnitol   S/AFR   POWER–SALWAY, 1911
   unsaturated lactone   IND   KURUP, 196
   Jamnagar
   somnitol + withanon   IND   DHALLA et al., 1961
   Delhi
   1 unknown withanolide; or withaferin A; or   ISR   ABRAHAM et al., 1968
   7 withanolides;
Ch. T. IDP of OG changes and of MP CHAR   ABRAHAM et al., 1968
   chemotypes with distinct area

SCROPHULARIACEAE

Digitalis cariensis Jaub. et Spach. – Lf
Ql. D. digoxin + lanatoside C/ssp. *lamarckii*   GREGG–GISVOLD, 1954
   (Werner) Ivan.
   acetyldigitoxin + lanatoside A, B   STOLL–RENZ, 1956
   MC: glucofucosids 18 % + gitorosides 15 %   KAISER, 1967
   /ssp. *lamarckii*; or digoxin – lanatoside C
   in Tr.

D. lanata Ehrh. – Lf
Qn. D. in cardenolides content   COLL   SCHWERDTFEGER, 1961
Ql. D. lanatoside A or lanatoside C as *MC*;   HUN   LIGETI, 1959
   lanatoside B little or Abs.   SUI   FAUÇONNET, 1960
   lanatoside A, or B, or A + C 100 %   ROM   SILVA, 1966
Ch. T. CORR Abs. between Ch. and MP CHAR;   SCHWERDTFEGER, 1961
   inheritance of Ch. CHAR, at chemovar   LIGETI, 1959
   level;
   discussion of level, chemocultivar   TÉTÉNYI, 1959
   IDP of ecological factors, restoring tendency   SILVA, 1966
   to the equilibrium of 3 lanatosides

D. mertonensis Buxt. et Darl. – Lf
Ql. D. acetyldigitoxin + digitoxin + gitoxin   USA   GISVOLD, 1958
   lanatoside E + strospeside + verodoxin   ROM   CALCANDI et al., 1965

D. purpurea L. – Lf
Qn. D. in cardenolide content   SWI   STOLL, 1950
Ql. D. digitoxin, or gitoxin as *MC*   SWI   STOLL, 1950
    MC: strospeside, or gitaloxin, or digipurpu-   COLL   Os, 1960, WIRTH, 1961
      rin   HENNING, 1962
    gitaloxin 79 %; or strospeside   POL   CZÁBAJSKA et al., 1959
    MC: purpurea-glycoside A   GER   NECZYPOR, 1958
Ch. T. inheritance of Ch. CHAR   MATHER–DYER, 1944
    IDP of ecological factors, CORR Abs.   Os et al., 1954, 1956
      between Ch. and MP CHAR   ROWSON, 1960
    chemovar. level   CZABAJSKA et al., 1959

GERANIACEAE

Geranium sanguineum L. – Sh
Ql. D. saponins + 4 sterins; or 6 sterins, sapo-   AURICH et al., 1965
    nins Abs.

ZYGOPHYLLACEAE

Tribulus terrestris L. – Wp
Ql. D. 0·36 % tigogenine   USA   WALL et al., 1959
                                  N/Carolina
    sapogenins Abs.   USA   WALL et al., 1961
                                  Texas
    diosgenin + gitogenin + ruscogenin   SAR   BROWN–KOCK, 1959
    diosgenin   USSR   KACHUHASHVILY, 1965

EUPHORBIACEAE

Euphorbia hirta L. – Wp
Ql. D. taraxerone + taraxerol   TAKEMOTO–INAGAKI, 1958
    friedelin + β-amyrin + β-sitosterin +   ESTRADA, 1962
      hentriakontan/var. *procumbens* (Boiss.)
      Small.

CRUCIFERAE

Erysimum canescens Roth – Sd
Qn. D. in glycoside-content   USSR   LIU JUN–LUN, 1962
Ql. D. erysimoside + erycanoside   CSR   BAUER, 1960
    helveticoside + digitoxose   HUN   NOVÁK–HÁZNAGY, 1962
    erysimin + erysimoside + cheirotoxin   USSR   LOSHKARIOV–
                                            BONDARCHUK, 1964

CUCURBITACEAE

Citrullus colocynthis (L.) Schrad. – Fr
Ql. D. cucurbitacins Pst. or Abs.   USSR   ARASIMOVICH, 1937
                                  SAR   REHM, 1960

C. lanatus (Thunb.) Mansf. – Lf
Ql. D. in number and colour reaction of sterine COLL Aurich et al., 1965
    components

Cucumis sativus L. – Lf
Ql. D. cucurbitacins Pst., or at the rate 1 : 15,000 NED Anderweg–De Bruyn,
    1959

Cucurbita pepo L. – Fr
Ql. D. cucurbitacins Pst. or Abs. SAR Joubert–Enslin, 1954

Lagenaria siceraria (Molina) Standl. – Fr
Ql. D. cucurbitacins Pst. or Abs SAR Rehm, 1960
Ch. T. MP D Abs.

ERICACEAE

Agauria salicifolia Hook. f. – Ba
Ql. D. agauriolic acetate; or agauric A + agauro- Sosa, 1951
    lene + morolic A
Ch. T. great D in Ch. CHAR Hegnauer, 1964

AMARANTHACEAE

Alternanthera denticulata R. Br. – Wp
Ql. D. saponins Abs. Simes et al., 1959
    saponins Pst. Cain et al., 1961

Celosia cristata L. – Lf
Ql. D. saponins Pst./var. *castrensis* Moq.; or Abs. Aurich et al., 1965, 1966

MORACEAE

Antiaris toxicaria Lesch. – LX
Ql. D. IND Ch. D INDO Bisset, 1957
    α-antiarin; or β-antiarin; or not toxic latex Wehrli et al., 1962
Ch. T. DEP on place of origin Greshoff, 1899

BETULACEAE

Alnus glutinosa (L.) Gaertn. – Ba
Ql. D. taraxerol + taraxerone; or GER Zellner, 1926
    taraxerol + lupeol + taraxerone + gluti- FRA Chapon–David, 1953
    none + β-sitosterol

A. viridis (Chaix) DC. – Ba
Ql. D. taraxerol + taraxerone; or GER Zellner, 1926
    taraxerone + taraxerylacetate + alnincanone USSR Domoreva et al., 1961
    alnincanone + taraxerone + taraxeryl-ace- POL Pasich–Kowalewski,
    tate; or taraxerone without taraxerol 1960

136

LILIACEAE

Bowiea volubilis Harvey – Bu
Ql. D. bovoside A Pst.; or Abs./other bovosides Pst.   HEGNAUER, 1963
Ch. T. DEP on colour of Bu   ZECHNER, 1966

Ruscus aculeatus L. – Tu
Ql. D. ruscogenin Pst.; or   MAR   BALANSARD–DELPHAUT, 1945

    Abs.   USSR   UTKIN, 1959
    ruscogenin-neoruscogenin at different rate   CON   FONTAN–CANDELA, 1954
          ITA   LAPIN, 1957

Urginea maritima (L.) Bak. – Bu
Ql. D. scillirosidin, or   STOLL–RENZ, 1942
    scillarenin   STOLL–KREIS, 1951
Ch. T. DEP on colour of Bu and of flesh   WICHTL–FUCHS, 1962
    Ch. races or varieties   ABISCH–REICHSTEIN, 1963

AGAVACEAE

Agave aurea Brand – Lf
Ql. D. hecogenin + 9-dehydrohecogenin; or   WALL et al., 1957, 1959,
    hecogenin tigogenin + manogenin   1961

A. brandegeei Trel. – Lf
Ql. D. hecogenin; or tigonenin alone or with mano-   WALL et al., 1957, 1959,
    genin; or sapogenin Abs.   1961

A. caerulata Trel. – Lf
Qn. D. 0·1–1·2 % sapogenin content   WALL et al., 1954
Ql. D. hecogenin 7–100 %; or tigogenin   Os, 1957
    MC: hecogenin; or tigogenin; or gitogenin   WALL et al., 1957
Ch. T. Ch. races   Os

A. funkiana C. Koch et Bouche – Lf
Ql. D. tigogenin + manogenin; or smilagenin +   MARKER–LOPEZ, 1947
    yuccagenin; or mexogenin + samogenin

A. marmorata Roezl – Lf
Ql. D. smilagenin; or chlorogenin 55 % + smila-   WALL et al., 1955
    genin; or sapogenins Abs.

A. nelsoni Trel. – Lf
Ql. D. manogenin; or tigogenin; or hecogenin   WALL et al., 1957

A. promontorii Trel. – Lf
Ql. D. manogenin; or tigogenin; or sapogenins Abs. MEX   WALL et al., 1957, 1959,
          USA   1961

A. roseana Trel. – Lf
Ql. D. tigogenin; or hecogenin; or sapogenin Abs.   WALL et al., 1957

A. sobria Brandegee – Lf
Ql. D. manogenin; or manogenin + gitogenin; or　　　Wall et al., 1957
　　　hacogenin + tigogenin; or sapogenins　　　　　　　1959, 1961
　　　Abs.

Furcraea guatemalensis Trel. – Lf
Ql. D. tigogenin; or sarsasapogenin　　　　　　　Wall et al., 1957

Yucca aloifolia L. – Lf
Ql. D. smilagenin　　　　　　　　　　　MEX,　　Marker et al., 1943
　　　　　　　　　　　　　　　　　　　　MED
　　　tigogenin alone or with gitogenin　　　　MED　　Heitz, 1954
　　　tigogenin + Tr. of smilagenin　　　　　　JAP　　Takeda, 1954
　　　gitogenin + chlorogenin 43 %　　　　　　BUL　　Tomowa–Panowa, 1963

Y. de-smetiana Bak. – Lf
Ql. D. tigogenin　　　　　　　　　　　　　　　　Heitz, 1954
　　　sapogenin Abs.　　　　　　　　　　　　　　　Marker et al., 1943

Y. filamentosa L. – Lf
Ql. D. gitogenin　　　　　　　　　　　MEX　　Marker et al., 1943
　　　gitogenin + tigogenin　　　　　　　　MED　　Heitz, 1954
　　　tigogenin/var. *flaccida* Haw.　　　　JAP　　Ohno et al., 1959
　　　smilagenin + tigogenin + gitogenin　BUL　　Panowa–Tomowa, 1963

Y. gloriosa L. – Lf
Ql. D. smilagenin　　　　　　　　　　　MEX　　Marker et al., 1943
　　　gitogenin + tigogenin　　　　　　　　MED　　Heitz, 1954
　　　tigogenin 80% + smilagenin　　　　　SPA　　Davila–Panzio, 1958

Y. recurvifolia Salisb. – Lf
Ql. D. smilagenin　　　　　　　　　　　MEX　　Marker et al., 1943
　　　gitogenin　　　　　　　　　　　　　JAP　　Takeda et al., 1954
　　　tigogenin + smilagenin　　　　　　　USSR　Pkheidze–Madaeva, 1961

Y. schidigera Roezl – Lf
Ql. D. sarsasapogenin 100 %　　　　　　USA　　Wall et al., 1957
　　　sarsasapogenin + manogenin　　　　　MEX　　Wall et al., 1959, 1961

DIOSCOREACEAE

Dioscorea composita Hemsl. – Tu
Ql. D. diosgenin; or diosgenin + yamogenin 40 %　　Wall et al., 1961

D. deltoidea Wall. – Tu
Qn. D. 1·8–2·4 % sapogenin content; or 5·2–5·4 %　　Chou–Yun et al., 1965
　　　sapogenin/var. *orbiculata*

D. humilis Bert. – Tu
Ql. D. sapogenins Pst. or Abs.　　　　　　　　　Ricardi, 1958

D. pusilla Hook. – Rh
Ql. D.   saponins Pst. or Abs./*Epipetrum humíle* Burk.   RICARDI, 1958

Tamus communis L. – Rh
Ql. D.   0·002 % diosgenin   SPA   LAORGA–PINAR, 1960
         sapogenins Abs.   SWI   HOLZACH–FLÜCK, 1950
         0·05 % diosgenin   HUN   HELD–VÁGÚJFALVI, 1965

CYPERACEAE

Carex arenaria L. – Rh
Ql. D.   0·15–0·2 % saponin content   BRA   FREISE, 1938
         saponins Abs.   EUR   HEGNAUER, 1957

GRAMINEAE

Miscanthus sinensis (Thunb.) Anderss. – Wp
Ql. D.   in number, R_{st} and colour reaction of ste-   COLL   AURICH et al., 1965
         rin components

1.3 PSEUDOALKALOIDS

RANUNCULACEAE

Aconitum napellus L. – Rh
Ql. D.   aconitine as *MA*, or as minor component   FAUGERAS–PARIS, 1961
Ch. T.   DEP on conditions of original area

A. soongoricum Stapf. – Rt
Ql. D.   aconitine   YUNUSOV, 1948
         songorine + acetyl-songorine   KUSUVKOV–MASSAGETOV,
                                                           1956
         norsongorine + songorinine   SAMATCOV et al., 1965

SOLANACEAE

Lycopersicon esculentum Mill. – Wp
Ql. D.   tomatidin/var. *ribesiforme* Voss.   BOIT, 1961
         tomatidin + soladulcidin(?)/var. *cerasiforme*   VÁGÚJFALVI et al., 1966
         (Dun.) Alef.; or unknown steroid-alkaloid
         /var. *pyriforme* (Dun.) Alef.

Solanum alatum (Moench) Mansf. – Wp
Ql. D.   solasonin; or Ssonin + Smargin; or ∅   SCHREIBER, 1963
         solamargin   BRIGGS–CAMBIE, 1958
         solamargin + solasonin; or ∅   BOGNÁR–MAKLEIT, 1961
         steroid-alkaloids Abs.   CERNY–LÁBLER, 1959
         solamargin + solasonin   MÁTHÉ–HELD, 1965
         solasodine + tigogenin as *MC*   VÁGÚJFALVI et al., 1966
Ch. T.   MP D Abs.   BOGNÁR–MAKLEIT, 1965

S. atropurpureum Schrank – Wp
Ql. D. β-solanigrin; or ∅   SCHREIBER, 1963
        steroid-alkaloids Abs.   PÉREZ–MEDINA et al., 1964
        steroid-alkaloids Pst.   SABER et al., 1965
        solasodine   TUZSON–KISS, 1957
Ch. T. OG changes   SABER et al., 1965

S. boerhaavii Thell. – Wp
Ql. D. solasonine + solamargin   SCHREIBER et al., 1961
        tomatine   MAKLEIT et al., 1963

S. capsicastrum Link – Wp
Ql. D. solanocapsin   SCHREIBER et al., 1961
        steroid-alkaloids Abs.   BOGNÁR–MAKLEIT, 1962

S. carolinense L. – Wp
Ql. D. steroid-alkaloids Pst.   BORKOWSKI et al., 1961
        steroid-alkaloid Abs.   SCHREIBER, 1963
        solamargin + solasonin   MAKLEIT et al., 1963
        solasodine + (diosgenin or tigogenin); or   VÁGÚJFALVI et al., 1966
           soladulcidin + tigogenin

S. cornutum Lam. – Wp
Ql. D. solasonin + solamargin   BORKOWSKI et al., 1961
        solasonin + β-solamargin   SCHREIBER, 1963
        solasodin + diosgenin as *MC;* or unknown   VÁGÚJFALVI et al., 1966
           steroidalkaloid + sapogenin; or ∅
Ch. T. infraspecific Ch. VAR   VÁGÚJFALVI et al., 1966

S. douglasii Dun. – Fr (unripe)
Ql. D. solamargin   N-Z   BRIGGS–CAMBIE, 1958
        steroidalkaloids Abs.   COLL   SCHREIBER et al., 1961

S. dulcamara L. – Wp
Ql. D. Sdulcidin; or tomatidenol; or Smarin; or   SANDER, 1963
           combinations with Ssodine
        Sdulcidin alone; or in combinations   SCHREIBER–RÖNSCH, 1965
        Ssonin + β-Smargin/var. *persicum* Willd.   TOMOWA, 1965
        tomatidenol + Ssodine   BOGNÁR–MAKLEIT, 1965
        Sdulcidin + tigogenin as *MC;* or Sdulcidin   VÁGÚJFALVI et al., 1966
           + diosgenin
        tomatidin (25 %); F_1 of tomatidenol × dul-   RÖNSCH et al., 1968
           cidin forms
Ch. T. CORR Abs. between Ch. and MP CHAR;   ALKEMEYER–SANDER, 1961
           IDP of ecological factors
        DEP on area of origin;   SANDER et al., 1962
        IDP of polyploidy level   DERSCH–SANDER, 1962
        IDP of area of origin   BOGNÁR–MAKLEIT, 1965
        Ch. strains   BOLL–ANDERSEN, 1962
        Ch. varieties   SCHREIBER–RÖNSCH, 1963
        Ch. CHAR genetically fixed, Ch. forms, che-   WILLUHN, 1966
        motypes
        chemovars   TÉTÉNYI, 1963

S. gilo Raddi – Wp
Ql. D. 0·05 % steroidalkaloid content; or ∅
    steroidalkaloids Abs.

SCHREIBER, 1963
BOGNÁR–MAKLEIT, 1965

S. gracile Otto – Wp
Ql. D. solasodine; or steroidalkaloid Abs.
    solamargin

SCHREIBER, 1963
BORKOWSKI et al., 1961

S. haematocarpum hort./*S. pyracanthum* Jacq. – Wp
Ql. D. tomatidin
    solasonin + solamargin

TUZSON et al., 1958
SCHREIBER et al., 1961

S. nigrum L. (sensu lato) – Wp
Ql. D. solasonin/*melanocerasum* Willd.
    xanthocarpum Koenig
  solasonin + solamargin/*americanum* Mill.
    astroites Forst.
    atriplicifolium (Desp.) Dun.
    memphiticum J. F. Gmel.
    nigrum sensu stricto

SCHREIBER et al., 1961
BRIGGS, 1946
BOGNÁR–MAKLEIT, 1961
SCHREIBER, 1963
SCHREIBER, 1958

TOMOWA, 1962
MAKLEIT–BOGNÁR, 1959

    schultesii (Opiz) Wirtg.
    xanthocarpum Koenig
  solasonin + β-solamargin/*quitoense* Lam.
  solasonin + solamargin + β-solamargin
    astroites Forst.
    atriplicifolium (Desp.) Dun.
    heterophyllum Balb.
    chlorocarpum (Spenn.) Boiss.
    nigrum s. str.
    nigrum s. str.
    quitoense Lam.
  solamargin *nigrum* s. str.
  tigogenin *malanocerasum* Willd.
    /*quitoense* Lam.
  unknown sapogenin/*melanocerasum* Willd.
  steroidalkaloid Tr. + tigogenin
    chlorocarpum (Spenn.) Boiss.
  solasodine/*paranense* Dusen
  steroidalkaloids Abs. *americanum* Mill.
    astroites Forst.
    atriplicifolium (Desp.) Dun.
    melanocerasum Willd.
    memphiticum J. F. Gmel.
    nigrum s. str.
    nigrum s. str.
    paranense Dusen
    quitoense Lam.
    xanthocarpum Koenig

MAKLEIT et al., 1963
SCHREIBER, 1963
SCHREIBER et al., 1961.

SCHREIBER, 1961
BOGNÁR-MAKLEIT, 1961
SCHREIBER et al., 1961
BOGNÁR-MAKLEIT, 1965
SCHREIBER et al., 1961
MAKLEIT-BOGNÁR, 1959
MAKLEIT et al., 1963
BOLL, 1958
CERNY-LÁBLER, 1959

VÁGÚJFALVI et al., 1966

SCHREIBER et al., 1961
PÉREZ-MEDINA et al., 1964

SCHREIBER, 1963
BORKOWSKI et al., 1961
SCHREIBER, 1958
SCHREIBER et al., 1961
MAKLEIT-BOGNÁR, 1959
SCHREIBER et al., 1961
CERNY-LÁBLER, 1959
SCHREIBER, 1963

S. luteum Mill. – Wp
Ql. D. Smargin + Ssonin; or Ssonin + Smargin
    + β-Smargin; or steroidalkaloids **Abs.**

SCHREIBER, 1963

141

S. luteum (continued)
    Svillin; or Smargin + Ssonin at different   MAKLEIT-BOGNÁR, 1959
      rate
    Ssonin + Smargin + 3 steroidalkaloids   BORKOWSKI et al., 1961

S. macrocarpum L. – Fr (unripe)
Ql. D. solasonin; or steroidalkaloids Abs.   SCHREIBER, 1963
    steroidalkaloids Abs.   BOGNÁR-MAKLEIT, 1965

S. melongena L. – Wp
Ql. D. steroidalkaloids Pst.   MINASIAN, 1947
    steroidalkaloids Abs.   SCHREIBER, 1963
    solasonin (Fr)   WAAL et al., 1960

S. nitidibaccatum Bitt. – Wp
Ql. D. tomatidin   GRACZA–SZÁSZ, 1962
    solasonin   SCHREIBER, 1963
    solasonin + solamargin   BOGNÁR–MAKLEIT, 1965
    solasodin + diosgenin as *MC:* 1 : 10   VÁGÚJFALVI et al., 1966

S. nodiflorum Jacq. – Wp
Ql. D. solasodine; or ø   SCHREIBER, 1963
    0·8 % steroidalkaloid + 11 $^0/_{00}$ tigogenin   VÁGÚJFALVI et al., 1966

S. radicans L. f. – Wp
Ql. D. 3 steroidalkaloids Pst.; or ø   SCHREIBER, 1963

S. rostratum Dun. – Wp
Ql. D. sclamargin 99 %; or solasonin   SCHREIBER, 1963
    solasodine + diosgenin as *MC:* 1 : 20   VÁGÚJFALVI et al., 1966

S. sinaicum Boiss. – Wp
Ql. D. steroidalkaloids Pst.; or ø   SCHREIBER, 1963
    solasodine   BOGNÁR–MAKLEIT, 1965
    solasodine + diosgenin   VÁGÚJFALVI et al., 1966

S. sisymbrifolium Lam. – Wp
Ql. D. steroidalkaloids Pst.   SCHREIBER, 1963
    steroidalkaloids Abs.   PÉREZ–MEDINA et al., 1964

S. stoloniferum Schlecht. et Boch. – Wp
Ql. D. tomatin   BITE et al., 1962
    solanin + chaconin   BOGNÁR–MAKLEIT, 1965

S. tomatillo Phil. f. – Wp
Ql. D. tomatidin alone   SCHREIBER, 1959
    tomatidin + demissidin Tr.; or tomatidin +   VÁGÚJFALVI et al., 1966
      diosgenin

S. torvum Swartz – Wp
Ql. D. steroidalkaloids Pst.   TACKIE, 1959
    steroidalkaloids Abs.   PÉREZ–MEDINA et al., 1964

S. vernei Bitt. et Wittm. – Wp
Ql. D. solanin + chaconin   SCHREIBER, 1963
    steroidalkaloids Abs.   BOGNÁR–MAKLEIT, 1965

BUXACEAE

Buxus microphylla S. et Z. – Tw
Ql. D. cyclomicrobuxin + cyclobuxomirein +   NAKANO et al., 1966
  cyclomirosin/var. *suffruticosa* Sieb. non L.
  cyclobuxophyllin + suffrobuxin +
  cyclobuxoviridin + cyclobuxosuffrin/f. *major*

Sarcococca pruniformis Lindl. – Tw
Ql. D. epipachysamin A + kurchetin   CHATTERJEE et al., 1965
  5-α-pregnane + pregn-5-ene   KOHLI et al., 1966

LILIACEAE

Veratrum album L. – Sh
Ql. D. protoveratrine Pst. or Abs.   HEGI–FLÜCK, 1956
  protoveratrine A; or protoveratrine B +   JASPERSEN et al., 1961
    veratroylzygadenine; or germine + geral-
    bine; or veratroylzygadenine
  jervine as predominant component   POETHKE–KERSTAN, 1958
            – Rh
  protoveratrine + jervine at different rate   HUN   BITE, 1960
  protoveratrine + jervine 94 %   CSR   TOMKO et al., 1962
  jervine + veratramin + zygacine/var.   JAP   TSUKAMOTO–YAGI, 1959
    grandiflorum Loes.
  jervine + germidine   USSR   SHINKARENKO–BONDAREN-
                                                                    KO, 1966
Ch. T. DEP on areal D   TOMKO et al., 1962
  necessity of Ch. approach in infraspecific   POETHKE–KERSTAN, 1962
    systematics

V. viride Ait. – Rh
Ql. D. germidine + germitrine; or   FRIED et al., 1950
  neogermitrine   FRIED et al., 1952
  protoveratrine   KLOHS et al., 1952
  protoveratridine   SEIFERLE et al., 1942
  neogermbudine + germbudine   MYERS et al., 1952
Ch. T. recognition of infraspecific Ch. D   WOODWARD–SMITH, 1962

VALERIANACEAE

Nardostachys jatamansi DC. – Rt/E–O
Ql. D. ORP + 31°   IND   CHOWDHRY et al., 1958
  ORP – 7.4°   CHI   NAVES–MARCOVICI, 1963
Ch. T. ORP D DEP on origin   BASLAS, 1968

Valeriana wallichii DC. – Rh/E–O
Ql. D. ORP – 15° to –35°   IND   GILDEMEISTER–HOFFMANN,
                                                                    1958
  ORP –13° to –56°; or +7° to +19°   COLL   SADGOPAL–GULATI, 1956
  maalioxide, ar-curcumene, patchoulenes Pst.   IND/   NARAYANAN et al., 1964
    or Abs.   COLL

143

2. OTHER COMPOUNDS CONNECTED WITH ACETATE METABOLISM

2.1.1. DERIVATIVES OF RESORCIN AND OF ORCELLINIC ACID

ASPERGILLACEAE

Aspergillus terreus Thom. – My
Ql. D. geodine + erdine; or geodoxine; or asterric   CURTIS et al., 1959
    acid

ROCELLACEAE

Rocella portentosa (Mont.) Darb. – Th
Ql. D. lecanoric A   CHL   HUNECK et al., 1957
    rocellic A + protocetraric A   GAL
Ch. T. IDP of MP CHAR; Ch. races

R. fuciformis DC.
Ql. D. acetylportentol   FRA   HUNECK et al., 1967
    rocellic A + portentol   MAR
Ch. T. "Chemovarietät"

PELTIGERACEAE

Peltigera horizontalis (Huds.) Baumg. – Th
Ql. D. scabrosin A + B Pst.;   JAP   KUROKAWA et al., 1966
    or Abs.   EUR
                        TAI

P. malacea (Ach.) Funck. – Th
Ql. D. dolichorrhizin Pst.   CAN   KUROKAWA et al., 1966
    or Abs.   EUR, JAP

P. scabrosa Th. M. Fr. – Th
Ql. D. scabrosin A + B   EUR   KUROKAWA et al., 1966
    dolichorrhizin   JAP

STICTACEAE

Lobaria pulmonaria Hoffm. – Th
Ql. D. norST A + G A   SAH   ASAHINA–SHIBATA, 1954
    squamatic A   USA, JAP

144

CLADONIACEAE

Cladonia chlorophaea (Flk.) Spreng. – Th
Ql. D. novochlorophaeic A; or novochlorophaeic +   G–L   DAHL, 1952
usnic A
FPC A; or FPC A + grayic A; or FPC A +   SHIBATA–CHIANG, 1965
cryptochlorophaeic A; or FPC A + mero-
chlorophaeic A
merochlorophaeic A + FPC A   N/AM   AHTI, 1966
Ch. T. discussion on the level of D: infraspecific   ASAHINA, 1937
or not   MACKENZIE–LAMB, 1951
chemotypes   AHTI, 1966

C. furcata (Huds.) Schrad. – Th
Ql. D. atranoric A; or FPC A   HENNIPMANN, 1967
Ch. T. varietas level/var. *subrangiformis* Sandst.

C. impexa Harm. – Th
Qn. D. in U A content 0·05–2·87 %   RAMAUT et al., 1966
Ch. T. IDP of MP and of ecological CHAR

C. nemoxyna (Ach.) Arnold – Th
Ql. D. FPC A   CSR, GER
FPC A Abs.   FIN   SUOMINEN–AHTI, 1966
Ch. T. morphologically identical 2 genotypes;
genetic control

C. pityrea Flk. – Th
Ql. D. FPC A; or   EUR   ASAHINA, 1937
FPC A + homosecicaic A; or   JAP
homosecicaic A/*subpityrea* Sandst.   JAP

C. squamosa (Scop.) Hoffm. – Th
Ql. D. squamatic A; or Tc A/*subsquamosa* Nyl.   DAHL, 1952

C. tenuis (Floerke) Harm. – Th
On. D. in U A content 0·1–2·4 %   RAMAUT et al., 1966
0·018–1·2 %/var. *leucophaea* Des Abb.   AHTI, 1966
Ch. T. IDP of MP and of ecological CHAR; two
varietas

LECANORACEAE

Haematomma puniceum (Ach.) Wainio – Th
Ch. T. 3 Ch. differentiated ssp.   ASAHINA, 1964

Lecanora caesiorubella Ach. – Th
Ql. D. monoacetyl PC A; or norST A + PC A/ssp.   IMSHAUG–BRODO, 1966
lathamii Ims.-Brodo; or norST A in low
content/ssp. *saximontana* Ims.-Brodo
or PC A.;/ssp. *glaucomodes* Nyl.;
or lacking PC A as norST A/f. *sub-
ochracea* Magnusson   HAW
Ch. T. ssp. D in Ch. and MP CHAR and in geographical distribution

L. epanora Ach. — Th
Ql. D. rhysocarpic A + pannarin; or epanorin; or
    U A   HUNECK, 1966
Ch. T. 2 Ch. differentiated taxa (Sippe)   POELT–ULLRICH, 1964
    L. hercynica and *L. handelii* at species level   HUNECK, 1966

L. pallida (Schreb.) Rabenh. – Th
Ql. D. norST A Abs.; or Pst./var. *rubescens* Ims.-
    Brodo   IMSHAUG–BRODO, 1966
Ch. T. Ch and MP D at varietas level

Ochrolechia tartarea (L.) Mass. – Th
Ql. D. LE A + E A/*californica* Vers.; or   VERSEGHY, 1962
    LE A + E A + G A/*balcanica* Vers.

Rinodina oreina (Ach.) Mass. – Th
Ql. D. PC A; or gyrophoric A; or both Abs.   HALE, 1952
Ch. T. IDP of MP CHAR; 3 Ch. strains

PARMELIACEAE

Anzia opuntiella Muell.-Arg. – Th
Ql. D. divaricatic A; or sekikaic A; or both Pst.   KUROKAWA–JINZENJI, 1965
Ch. T. Ch. populations; neither distinct distribution,
    nor MP D

A. ornata (Zahlbr.) Asah. - Th
Ql. D. sekikaic A   USA   CULBERSON, 1961
    divaricatic A; or divaricatic A + sekikaic A JAP   KUROKAWA–JINZENJI,
                                         1965

Asahinea chrysantha (Tuck.) Culb. et Culb. – Th
Ql. D. α-collatolic A Pst.; or Abs.   JAP   CULBERSON–CULBERSON,
Ch. T. DEP on geographical D; Ch. races   USSR   1965

Cetraria ciliaris Ach. – Th
Ql. D. alectoronic A; or O A; or PLI A   HALE, 1963
Ch. T. IDP of MP CHAR, of exposure, of
    height on tree, of substrate species; DEP
    on geographical D of area; 3 chemotaxa

C. crispa (Ach.) Nyl. – Th
Ql. D. FPC A + 1-PLI A;   JAP   ASAHINA, 1937
    or alloPLI A + d-PLI A   EUR
    d-PLI A + LI A   NOR   DAHL, 1952

C. islandica (L.) Ach. – Th
Ql. D. allo-PLI A/var. *tenuifolia* (L.) Ach.; or   A   ASAHINA–SHIBATA, 1954
    d-PLI A/var. *orientalis* (Retz) Howe; or JAP
    d-PLI A + U A + FPC A   EUR
    PLI A + d,1-UA   SWI
    FPC A + PLI A   EUR   STICHER, 1965

146

Parmelia arnoldii Du Rietz – Th
Ql. D. alectoronic A;   EUR   HALE, 1963
    or SL A/*P. margaritata* Hus.   USA
Ch. T. two morphologically identical taxa

P. bolliana Muell.-Arg. – Th
Ql. D. LE A + AT; or U A + LE A; or G A +   CULBERSON–CULBERSON,
    AT; or PLI A + AT   1956
Ch. T. Ch. strains

P. borreri (Sm.) Turn. – Th
Ql. D. LE A + AT; or LE A + U A; or G A +   CULBERSON–CULBERSON,
    AT/*P. pseudoborreri* Asah.   1956
Ch. T. Ch. strains morphologically identical   CULBERSON–CULBERSON,
                         1956

    IDP of area; chemovar. *pseudoborreri*   TARGÉ–LAMBINON, 1964

P. conspersa (Ehrh.) Ach. – Th
Ql. D. SL A; or SL A + FPC A + PC A; or   JAP   ASAHINA, 1937
    ST A   IRL
    ST A; or SL A; or FPC A   USA   HALE, 1956

P. caperata (L.) Ach. – Th
Ql. D. CA A + caperine + caperidine; or   EUR   ASAHINA, 1937
    CA A   JAP
    CA A + U A + AT   NOR   DAHL, 1952

P. cetrarioides Del. – Th
Ql. D. imbricaric A   EUR   ZOPF, 1907
    imbricaric A   NOR   DAHL, 1952
    imbricaric A; or imbricaric A + perlatolic JAP   ASAHINA, 1937
      or perlatolic A
    perlatolic A; or O A; or collatolic A   CULBERSON, 1964
Ch. T. morphologically indistinguishable Ch. strains   CULBERSON, 1964
    MP D, therefore species level   SHIBATA, 1965

P. furfuracea (L.) Ach. – Th
Ql. D. physodic A; or O A   JAP   ASAHINA, 1937
    physodic A + AT   N/AF   HALE, 1956
    O A + AT   GBR
    LE A + AT   USA
    physodic A + AT   NOR   DAHL, 1952
Ch. T. Ch. strains   HALE, 1956

P. isidiata (Anzi) Gyeln. – Th
Ql. D. ST A; or norST A; or SL A; or FPC A   USA   HALE, 1956
Ch. T. D in area

P. stenophylla (Ach.) Heug. – Th
Ql. D. SL A; or FPC A   HALE, 1956

P, tinctorum Despr.–Th
Ch. T. Ch. strains   NEELEKANTAN et al., 1954

10*   147

Parmeliopsis ambigua (Wulff) Nyl. – Th
Ql. D. U A; or AT/*hyperoptera* (Ach.) Vain.   CULBERSON, 1961

USNEACEAE

Ramalina carpathica Koerb. – Th
Ql. D. ramalinic A; or evernic A/var. *teplicskaensis*   BYSTREK–POPIOLEK, 1967
Gyeln.
Ch. T. 2 Ch. varieties; no D in geographical distri-
bution

R. farinacea (L.) Ach. – Th
Ql. D. PC A; or norST A/var. *subfarinacea* Nyl.;   CULBERSON, 1966
or norST A + SL A/var. *reagens* B. de
Lesd.; or hypoPC A
SL A/var. *salazinica* Hawksw.   HAWKSWORTH, 1968
Ch. T. *R. hypoprotocetrarica* Culb. sp. nov. and   CULBERSON
the other taxa at species level

R. scopulorum (Retz.) Ach. – Th
Ql. D. ST A   EUR   ASAHINA, 1937
SL A   JAP

R. siliquosa (Huds.) A. C. SM. – Th
Ql. D. PC A + A/var. *cuspidata* (Ach.) Magn.   JAP   ASAHINA, 1937
PC A + U A/var. *cuspidata*   FRA   CULBERSON, 1965
SL A + U A/var. *cuspidata*   JAP, SWE
norST A + U A   GBR, FRA
norST A + ST A + U A   GBR, FRA,
SWE, PORT
hypoPC A + U A   GBR, FRA,
PORT
U A   GBR, FRA
Ch. T. 6 distinct Ch. races   CULBERSON, 1965

Thamnolia vermicularis (Sw.) Schaer. – Th
Ql. D. thamolic A   ASAHINA, 1937
SQ A + béomycetic A/*subvermicularis*
Asah.
Ch. T. D at infraspecific level   RIEDL, 1962

Usnea comosa (Ach.) Röhl. – Th
Ql. D. U A + SQ A; or U A + thamnolic A; or   FUJITA, 1965b
U A + SL A; or U A + norST A
Ch. T. Ch. strains

U. confusa Asah. – Th
Ql. D. U A + SL A; or U A+PC A   FUJITA, 1965b
Ch. T. Ch. strains

U. dasypoga (Ach.) Röhl. – Th
Ql. D. U A + SL A   JAP   SCHINLER, 1957
U A + usnaric A + Tc A + barbatolic A   EUR

U. kushiroensis Asah. – Th
Ql. D. U A + norSTA + SL A; or U A +   Fujita, 1965b
    ST A + norST A
Ch. T. Ch. strains

U. longissima Asah. – Th
Ql. D. U A + B A + barbatolic A; or U A + B A;   Fujita, 1965b
    or U A + evernic A; or U A + diffrac-
    taic A; or U A + SL A; or U A + FPC
    A + (AT)
Ch. T. Ch. strains

U. montis-fuji Motyka – Th
Ql. D. U A + SL A; or AT + U A + SL A   Fujita, 1965b
Ch. T. Ch. strains

U. orientalis Mot. – Th
Ql. D. ST A; or SL A   Dhar et al., 1959
    ST A; or SL A; or psoronic A   Nair–Subramanian, 1962
Ch. T. morphologically indistinguishable 3 Ch. strains   Nair–Subramanian

U. roseola Vain. – Th
Ql. D. U A + B A; or U A + diffractaic A + un-   Fujita, 1965b
    known rosaceous substance
Ch. T. Ch. strains

U. rubescens Stirt. – Th
Ql. D. U A + nor St A + SL A; or U A + ST A   Fujita, 1965b
Ch. T. Ch. strains

U. rubicunda Stirt. – Th
Ql. D. U A + nor ST A + SL A; or U A + ST A   Fujita, 1965b
Ch. T. Ch. Strains

2.1.2. PHLOROGLUCINS

ASPLENIACEAE

Asplenium rhizophyllum L. – Sp
Ql. D. in number of phenolics (phloroglucins ?)   Smith–Levin, 1963

ASPIDIACEAE

Dryopteris assimilis Walk. – Rh
Ql. D. des ASP + para ASP   CAN   Hegnauer, 1961
    ASP + base X   EUR
    desASP+flavASP/var. *alpina* Moore
    MC: phloropyron 35% + flavASP 40%;   Widén, 1967b
    or desASP 32%; or paraASP 40%;
    or ASP 30%
Ch. T. DEP on origin area, and on genetic factors   Widén
    chemotypes

D. carthusiana (Vill.) H. P. Fuchs – Rh

Ql. D. ASP + flavASP; or ASP + base X   NED   HEGNAUER, 1961
       ASPol (paraASP?) Pst. or Abs.   GER-NED WIEFFERING et al., 1965
       MC: albASP; or flavASP Ac ASP   DEN-USA WIDÉN–SORSA, 1966
                                             FIN

Ch. T. IDP of MP D; Chemotypes, 'paraaspidin   WIDÉN, 1967
       type'

D. cristata (L.) A. Gray – Th

Ql. D. ASP Pst. or Abs.   NED   FIKENSCHER–HEGNAUER,
       ASPol + desASP   NED   1963
       albASP + paraASP + desASP + flavASP   FIN   WIDÉN–SORSA, 1966

D. dilatata (Hoffm.) A. Gray – Th

Qn. D. in phloroglucin-content   USSR   TOMINGAS, 1958
       0·28–5·03 % phloroglucins   USSR   JAUNSILA, 1961
       1·14   FIN   WIDÉN, 1967

Ql. D. ASP/albASP at different rate   BAL   MAIZITE, 1942
       ASP; or aspidinin   USSR   JAUNSILA, 1961
       various accessory phloroglucids   NED   HEGNAUER, 1961
       ASP + albASP + (paraASP?)   FIN   SCHANTZ, 1962
       ASP + paraASP   FIN   WIDÉN

Ch. T. simultaneous Ch. differentiation and MP   HEGNAUER
       VAR

D. fragrans (L.) Schott. – Rh

Ql. D. *MC:* albASP + unknown phloroglucid Pst.   FIN   SCHANTZ–WIDÉN, 1967
       or Abs./var. *remotiuscula* Kom.   CAN

Ch. T. DEP on area of origin

D. maderensis Alston – Rh

Ql. D. ASP acetylASP; or desASP + albASP   CAN   HEGNAUER, 1961
       MC: base X   CAN   WIEFFERING et al., 1965

D. villarii (Bell.) Woynar – Rh

Ql. D. paraASP Pst., ASP Abs.,   SWI   FIKENSCHER–HEGNAUER,
       paraASP Abs., ASP Pst./ssp. *pallida* Christ.; ITA   1963
       or paraASP Pst. + ASP in Tr.   SAD

2.1.3 RANUNCULINS

HELLEBORACEAE

Helleborus corsicus Willd. – Wp

Qn. D. 4·66 %; or 8·75 % ranunculin content   RUIJGROK, 1966

RANUNCULACEAE

Anemone vitifolia L. – Wp

Qn. D. 2·07 % ranunculin content of fresh plant   RUIJGROK, 1966
       0·07 % ranunculin/var. *alba-dura*

Clematis vitalba L. – Wp
Qn. D. 0·91 %; or 0·27 % ranunculin   RUIJGROK, 1966

Myosurus minimus L. – Wp
Qn. D. 0·23 %; or 0·46 % ranunculin   RUIJGROK, 1966

Ranunculus aconitifolius L. – Wp
Ql. D. 0·12 % ranunculin; or Abs.   RUIJGROK, 1966

R. aquatilis L. – Wp
Qn. D. 0·06%; or 0·21% ranunculin   RUIJGROK, 1966

R. auricomus L. – Wp
Qn. D. 1·27 %; or 0·41 % ranunculin; or protoane-   RUIJGROK, 1966
           monin Abs.

R. baudotii Godr. – Wp
Qn. D. 0·14%; or 0·54% ranunculin   RUIJGROK, 1966

R. cincinnatus Sibth. – Wp
Qn. D. 0·04%; or 0·13% ranunculin   RUIJGROK, 1966

R. ficaria L. – Wp
Ql. D. ranunculin Pst. or Abs.   RUIJGROK, 1966
Ch. T. possibility of genetic differentiation
           DEP on origin

R. lanuginosus L. – Wp
Qn. D. 0·77 %; or 0·11 % ranunculin   RUIJGROK, 1966

R. lingua L. – Wp
Qn. D. 2·27 %; or 1·19 % ranunculin   RUIJGROK, 1966

R. sardous Cr. – Wp
Qn. D. 2·38 %; or 0·45 % ranunculin   RUIJGROK, 1966

2.2. QUINONES

SPHAERIOIDACEAE

Phoma terrestris Hansen – My
Ql. D. phomazarin Pst.   KŐGL–SPARENBERG, 1940
           phomazarin Abs.   WRIGHT–SCHOFIELD, 1960

CAESALPINIACEAE

Cassia tora L. – Sd
Ql. D. rubrofuzarin; or chrysophanol + obtusi-   RANGASWAMI, 1962
           folin/*C. obtusifolia* L.

MYRSINACEAE

Ardisia crenata Sims – Fr
Ql. D. 3-alkyl-2-hydroxy-5 methoxy benzoquinone   OGAWA–NATORI, 1968
       Pst., or Abs./f. *taquetii* (Lew) Ohwi

A. quinquegona Blume – Ba
Ql. D. rapanone Pst.;   KAWAMURA, 1937
      or Abs.   OGAWA–NATORI, 1968

Myrsine seguinii Léveil. – Rt
Ql. D. rapanone + embelin Pst.; or Abs.   OGAWA–NATORI, 1968
Ch. T. DEP on origin

POLYGONACEAE

Rheum palmatum L. – Rt + Rh
Qn. D. in anthraquinone-content   SCHRATZ–VETHACKE, 1958
Ql. D. as *MC:* rhein, or chrysophanic A; as accessory
       components: emodin or aloe-emodin
Ch. T. CORR Abs. between Ch. and MP CHAR;   WALLACH, 1941
      inheritance of Ch. CHAR;   Os, 1957
      infraspecific Ch. sections   SCHRATZ, 1959

Rumex confertus L. – Rt
Ql. D. chrysophanol + emodin   CICIN, 1962
      chrysophanol alone   BAGRII, 1963

R. conglomeratus Murr. – Rt
Ql. D. emodin   KLEIN, 1932;
                               TSUKIDA, 1957
      chrysophanol   CZETSCH–LINDERWALD,
                               1943

R. crispus L. – Rt
Ql. D. physcion + emodin   KLEIN, 1932
      physcion + chrysophanol + emodin + oxy-   CZETSCH–LINDERWALD,
      methylanthraquinone   1943

LILIACEAE

Aloë ferox Mill. – Lf/J
Ql. D. aloin alone; or aloin + aloinoside A + B   MC CARTHY–RHEEDE
                               OUDTSHOORN, 1966
Ch. T. D in original area   RHEEDE OUDTSHOORN–
                               GERRITSMA, 1965

A. marlothii Berg. – Lf/J
Ql. D. aloin; or homonataloin   MC CARTHY–RHEEDE
Ch. T. D in area of origin; two Ch. races   OUDTSHOORN, 1966

3. PHENYLPROPANE DERIVATIVES AND FLAVONOIDS

3.1.1. SIMPLE PHENOLICS AND PHENYLPROPANE COMPOUNDS

LYCOPODIACEAE

Lycopodium annotinum L. – Wp
Ql. D. p-hydroxy benzoic A Pst /var. *acrifolium* Fern.
     vanillic A more, p-hydroxy benzoic A
     Abs./var. *pungens* Desv.

TOWERS–MASS, 1965

L. clavatum L. – Wp
Ql. D. vanillic A
     syringic A Pst. or Abs.

ACHMATOWITZ et al., 1958
TOWERS–MASS, 1965

L. sabinaefolium Willd. – Wp
Ql. D. syringic A Pst. or Abs.

TOWERS–MAASS, 1965

MONIMIACEAE

Doryphora sassafras Endl. – Lf/E–O
Ql. D. safrole 65 %; or safrole 30 % + methyl-
     eugenol 26 %
Ch. T. PHYS varieties

PENFOLD, 1922

MORS et al., 1959

LAURACEAE

Cinnamomum bodinieri Léveil. – Ba/E–O
Ql. D. safrole; or various other components

TSAI HUAN–JUAN et al., 1965

Ch. T. Ch. races, chemotypes

HEGNAUER, 1965

C. cecidodaphne Meissn. – Ba/E–O
Ql. D. methyleugenol; or methyleugenol 45 % +
     safrole 20 %; or safrole + elemicin +
     myristicin
Ch. T. as "var. *A, B*", and "type"

BIRCH, 1963

C. culilawan Blume – Ba/E–O
Ql. D. safrole 70–80 %; or safrole 35–53 % + me-
     thyleugenol 41–50 %; or eugenol 80–100 %
Ch. T. CORR Abs. between Ch. and MP CHAR;
     D in area of origin; as "type",
     and "var. *A or B*"

SPOON–SPRUIT, 1956

C. glanduliferum Meissn. – Wd/E–O
Ql. D. safrole as *MC* + myristicine + elemicine

  safrole 25 % + methyleugenol 45 %; or
  methyleugenol alone
Ch. T. as "type", and "var. *A* or *B*"

GILDEMEISTER–
  HOFFMANN, 1959
BIRCH, 1963

BIRCH, 1963

C. kiamis Nees – Ba/E–O
Ql. D. cinnamic aldehyde 45–62 % + eugenol 10 %
  or cinnamic aldehyde alone
Ch. T. as "var. *A* or *B*"

BIRCH, 1963

C. loureirii Nees – Wd/E–O
Ql. D. cinnamic aldehyde as *MC* + eugenol little

  eugenol; or cinnamic aldehyde
Ch. T. as "type", and "var. *A* or *B*"

GILDEMEISTER–
  HOFFMANN, 1959
BIRCH, 1963
BIRCH, 1963

C. pedunculatum (Nees) Presl – Lf/E–O
Ql. D. safrole 60 % + eugenol 3 %; or eugenol +
  methyleugenol
Ch. T. as "var. *A* or *B*"

BIRCH, 1963

C. sintok Bl. – Ba/E–O
Ql. D. eugenol 77 %, or 13 %

  eugenol; or methyleugenol 60 % + safrole
  40 %; or safrole
Ch. T. as "var. *B* or *A*" and "type"

GILDEMEISTER–
  HOFFMANN, 1959
BIRCH, 1963

BIRCH, 1963

C. tamala Nees et Eberm. – Lf/E–O
Ql. D. eugenol; or cinnamic aldehyde; or safrole
Ch. T. as "var. *A* or *B*"

BIRCH, 1963

C. zeylanicum Bl. – Ba/E–O
Ql. D. cinnamic aldehyde 65–76 %   CEY
  cinnamic aldehyde 32 % + safrol   SEY
  cinnamic aldehyde + eugenol 65–95 %
Ch. T. as "var. *C* or *A* or *B*"

GILDEMEISTER–
  HOFFMANN, 1959
BIRCH, 1963
BIRCH, 1963

Ocotea pretiosa (Nees) Mez – Wd/E–O
Ql. D. safrole 90–93 %
  safrole 3–6 % + methyleugenol 45–78 %
  safrole 40 % + methyleugenol 20 %; cam-
    phor Pst. or Abs.
  safrol 46–58 % + camphor 15–45 %; or
    safrol 11 % + methyleugenol
Ch. T. PHYS varieties; inheritance of Ch. CHAR
  possibility of introgression

GUENTHER, 1956
MORS et al., 1959
GOTTLIEB–MAGALHAES,
  1960
MOLLAN, 1961

MORS et al., 1959
GOTTLIEB et al., 1962

154

PIPERACEAE

Piper betle L. – Lf/E–O
Ql. D. allylbrenzcatechine + chavicol + chavibe-
      tol (the three 82 %)   UEDA–SASAKI, 1951
      eugenol 41 %; allylbrenzcatechine Abs.   NIGAM–PUROHIT, 1962

MYRTACEAE

Backhousia myrtifolia Hook. f. et Harv. – Lf/E–O
Ql. D. elemicin; or isoelemicin; or eugenolmethyl-   PENFOLD et al., 1953
      ether; or isoeugenolmethylether + isoele-
      micin
Ch. T. as "type" and "form *A* or *B* or *C*"   PENFOLD et al., 1953
      Ch. forms   McKERN, 1965

Melaleuca bracteata Muell. – Lf/E–O
Ql. D. methyleugenol 90–95 %   INDO   HULSSEN–MEIJER, 1940
      methylisoeugenol; or elemicin   AUL   PENFOLD et al., 1950
      methyleugenol 75–82 % + eugenol   GILDEMEISTER–HOFFMANN,
Ch. T. PHYS forms   1961

Syzygium aromaticum (L.) Merr. et Perry – Fl/E–O
Ql. D. eugenol; or eugenin; or eugenone   MEIJER, 1946

RUTACEAE

Zieria smithii Andr. – Lf/E–O
Ql. D. safrole + zierone; or methyleugenol 80 %   PENFOLD, 1950
Ch. T. area D of Ch. varieties; as "type" and "var. *A*"

LAMIACEAE / LABIATAE

Ocimum sanctum L. – Wp/E–O
Ql. D. methylchavicol 60 %   PHIL   BACON, 1910
      chavibetol 23 % + cineol 15 %   IND   ANONYMOUS, 1937
      eugenol 71 %; or aldehydes 68 %   IND   TAYAL–DUTT, 1938

Thymus drucei Ronn. – Wp/E–O
Ql. D. phenols much/ssp. *praecox*; or little/ssp.   HEGNAUER, 1948
      alpigenus
Ch. T. chemotypes   HEGNAUER, 1965

DIPTEROCARPACEAE

Shorea robusta Gaertn. – OR
Ql. D. homobrenzcatechin + dimethoxypropyl-   NIGAM–DUTT, 1946
      benzol 16 %
      p-cymol + naphthalines; alkoxyls Abs.   PANNIKAR–BHATTAHAR-
                                    RYYA, 1961

ERICACEAE

Arctostaphylos uva-ursi (L.) Spreng. – Lf
Ql. D. methylarbutine 30 % (in % of arbutine- SWI   ROSENTHALER, 1929
      content; or Abs.   NOR
Ch. T. DEP on areal D; chemotypes   HEGNAUER, 1965

3.1.2. COUMARINS AND STILBENES

PINACEAE

Pinus radiata D. Don – Ba
Ql. D. pinosylvin Pst.; or Abs./var. *insignis* Dougl.   ERDTMAN, 1963

LAURACEAE

Aniba firmula (Nees et Hart.) Mez. – Wd
Ql. D. 4-methoxyparacotoin + 5·6-dihydrokawain;   MORS et al., 1962
      or 4-methoxyphenylcoumaline + anibin
      /*A. fragrans* Ducke
Ch. T. areal D; two separated taxa at species level

FABACEAE

Derris scandens Benth. – Rt
Ql. D. warangalone; or chandalone   OLLIS, 1968

MYRTACEAE

Eucalyptus clavigera A. Cunn. – Lf
Ql. D. stilbenes Pst. or Abs.   HILLIS, 1966

E. dalrympleana Maiden – Lf
Ql. D. stilbenes Pst. or Abs.   HILLIS, 1966
Ch. T. Ch. D of stilbenes Pst.   BILLEK, 1964

E. glaucescens Maiden – Lf
Ql. D. stilbenes Pst. or Abs.   HILLIS, 1966
Ch. T. Ch. D of stilbenes Pst.   BILLEK, 7964

E. kondininensis Maiden – Lf
Ql. D. stilbenes Pst. or Abs.   HILLIS, 1966

E. longicornis F. Muell. – Lf
Ql. D. stilbenes Pst. or Abs.   HILLIS, 1966
Ch. T. Ch. D of stilbenes Pst.   BILLEK, 1964

E. melliodora A. Cunn. – Lf
Ql. D. stilbenes Pst. or Abs.   HILLIS, 1966

E. papuana F. Muell. – Lf
Ql. D. stilbenes Pst. or Abs.   HILLIS, 1966
Ch. T. Ch. D of stilbenes Pst.   BILLEK, 1964

E. rugosa R. Br. – Lf
Ql. D. stilbenes Pst. or Abs.   HILLIS, 1966

E. salmonophloia F. Muell. – Lf
Ql. D. stilbenes Pst. or Abs.   HILLIS, 1966
Ch. T. Ch. D of stilbenes Pst.   BILLEK, 1964

E. sideroxylon A. Cunn. – Lf
Ql. D. stilbene-glucosides Pst. or Abs. (Tr.)   HILLIS–HASEGAWA, 1962
    rhapontin; or piceid; or astringin as *MC* or   HILLIS–ISOI, 1965
    in combination (various predominance)
Ch. T. PHYS forms   HILLIS–HASEGAWA
    IDP of ecological, but DEP on areal factors;   HILLIS–ISOI
    CORR Abs. between Ch. and MP CHAR;
    Ch. varieties

E. smithii R. T. Baker – Lf
Ql. D. stilbenes Pst. or Abs.   HILLIS, 1966

RUTACEAE

Phebalium drummondii Benth. – Wp
Ql. D. imperatorin oxide racemic;   CLOW et al., 1966
    or (–) antipode

Ptelea trifoliata L. – Lf
Ql. D. isopimpinellin + phellopterin; or   WERNY–SCHEUER, 1963
    byakangelicin

APIACEAE / UMBELLIFERAE

Ammi majus L. – Fr
Ql. D. xanthotoxin 60 % + imperatorin   EGY   TROJÁNEK et al., 1961
    xanthotoxin 20 % + isopimpinellin 66 %   CSR
    xanthotoxin 5 % + isopimpinellin 46 %   USSR   NIKONOV, 1965
    + marmesin 40 %/imperatorin Abs.
    – Wp
    bergaptene; or isopimpinellin; or coumarins CSR   BLAZEK–STARY, 1965
    Abs.
Ch. T. IND VAR of Ch. CHAR   BLAZEK–STARY, 1965

Angelica archangelica L. – Rt
Ql. D. archangelicin + archangin Pst./ssp. *norve-*   BAERHEIM–SVENDSEN,
    gica (Upr.) Nordn.; or Abs. unknown   1954
    coumarin Pst./ssp. *litoralis* (Fr.) Thell.
    umbelliprenin + imperatorin + bergaptene   FUJITA, 1963
    + xanthotoxol + xanthotoxin

Angelica archangelica (continued)
        – Fr
     osthenol + archangelicin   JAP   FUJITA, 1963
     archangelin + prangolarin/var. *himalaica*   IND   CHATTERJEE–GUPTA, 1964
Ch. T. var. *himalaica* may be an IDP species   FUJITA, 1966

A. dahurica Benth. et Hook. – Rt
Ql. D. byak-angelicol; or isoimperatorin + oxy-   FUJITA, 1963
     peucedanin hydrate/var. *pai-chi* Kimura,
     Hata et Yen

A. saxicola Makino – Fr
Ql. D. angelicin; or angelicin + calcicolin + oro-   FUJITA, 1963
     selol/var. *yoshinagae* Makino

A. silvestris L. – Sd
Ql. D. oxypeucedanin; or isoimperatorin + oxy-   FUJITA, 1965c
     peucedanin hydrate

Laser trilobum (L.) Borkh. – Rt
Ql. D. silerin   BUL   IVANOV–TOMOVA, 1957
     oxypeucedanin + prangenin + sesquiter-   USSR   PIGULIEVSKY et al., 1965
     penelactons

Pastinaca sativa L. – Fr
Ql. D. pastinacin Pst. or Abs.; xanthotoxol Pst. or   MAKSIUTINA–KOLESNIKOV,
     Abs.; predominance of xanthotoxin or iso-   1962
     pimpinellin
     bergaptene 34 % + imperatorin 18 % +   BEYRICH, 1965
     xanthotoxin 18 %

RUBIACEAE

Galium mollugo L. – Wp
Ql. D. 6-methoxy-7-coumarin Pst. or Abs.   KOHLMÜNZER, 1964

GUTTIFERAE / HYPERICACEAE

Calophyllum inophyllum L. – Sd
Ql. D. calophyllic Ac;   V-N   DIETRICH et al., 1953
    or calophyllic A + inophyllolid + calo-   MAD   POLONSKY, 1957
     phyllolid
     calophyllolid + calophyllic A + inophyllic A   IND   MITRA, 1957
Ch. T. possibility of Ch. races   HEGNAUER, 1965

3.1.3. AMIDIC ACRIDS

SOLANACEAE

Capsicum annuum L. – Fr
Qn. D. 0·02–0·15 % capsaicine or 0·7–0·9 % capsai-   BENEDEK, 1958
     cine content
     capsaicine Pst. or Abs./convar. *grossum*   JUHÁSZ–TYIHÁK, 1967

Ch. T. inheritance of capsaicine level   BENEDEK, 1958
       negative CORR with sugar content   CEREVITINOV, 1949

C. baccatum L. – Fr
Qn. D. 0·18 %–1·69 % VAR of capsaicine con-   SCHRATZ–RANGOONWALA,
       tent/var. *pendulum* (Willd.) Esh.   1965
Ql. D. 2 or 3 different capsaicines   JUHÁSZ–TYIHÁK, 1967

C. frutescens L. – Fr
Qn. D. in capsaicine-content   SCHRATZ–RANGOONWALA,
                          1965
Ql. D. capsaicine Pst. or Abs.   JUHÁSZ–TYIHÁK, 1967

C. pubescens Ruiz et Pavon – Fr
Qn. D. in capsaicine content   SCHRATZ–RANGOONWALA,
                          1965

3.2. FLAVONOIDS

MNIACEAE

Mnium affine Bland. – Th
Ch. T. chemovars   ALSTON, 1968

POLYPODIACEAE

Pityrogramma triangularis Kaulf. – Exudate of glan-
       dular cells
Ql. D. flavonoid aglycons; or ceroptene pigment   SMITH, 1968
Ch. T. morphologically similar plants

PINACEAE

Picea abies (L.) Karst. – Lf/PS
Ql. D. 2 types of fluorescence with blue (chloroge-   BÖRTITZ, 1963
       nic A?) or yellow (flavonglycosides?)
       spot

Pinus nigra Arn. – Wd
Ql. D. pinobanksin Pst./var. *austriaca* Bad.; or   ERDTMAN et al., 1966
       Abs./var. *poiretiana* Sch.

P. strobus L. – Wd
Ql. D. pinocembrin Pst. or Abs.   SEIKEL et al., 1965
Ch. T. IDP of geographical D; IND Ch. VAR

Pseudotsuga menziesii (Mirb.) Franco – Ba
Ql. D. in flavone-constituents (taxifolin?)   TÉTÉNYI, 1963
Ch. T. IDP of MP varieties, of height on tree, of age

TAXODIACEAE

Cunninghamia lanceolata (Lamb.) Hook. – Lf
Ql. D. sotetsuflavone Pst. or Abs./var. *konishii* Fuj.   FUJITA, 1962b
Ch. T. *C. konishii* at the level of variety

CUPRESSACEAE

Chamaecyparis obtusa (S. et Z.) Endl. – Lf
Ql. D. sotetsuflavone Pst. or Abs.; when Abs. then   BAKER–OLLIS, 1962
      taxifolin Pst./var. *breviranea* Mast.; or
      Abs./var. *filisoides* Mast.
Ch. T. two separated species   ERDTMAN, 1959

MAGNOLIACEAE

Magnolia grandiflora L. – Lf
Ql. D. *MC:* quercetin; or kaempferol   KUBITZKI–REZNIK, 1966

Liriodendron tulipifera L. – Lf
Ql. D. rhamnetin Pst. or Abs.   KUBITZKI–REZNIK, 1966

WINTERACEAE

Drymys brasiliensis Miers – Lf
Ql. D. apigenin Pst. or Abs.   KUBITZKI–REZNIK, 1966

D. confertifolia Phil. – Lf
Ql. D. dihydroquercetin + apigenin Pst. or Abs.   KUBITZKI–REZNIK, 1966

D. granadensis L. f. – Lf
Ql. D. *MC:* dihydroquercetin; or only Pst.   KUBITZKI–REZNIK, 1966

D. lanceolata (Poir.) Baill. – Lf
Ql. D. *MC:* apigenin + luteolin Pst.; or apigenin   KUBITZKI–REZNIK, 1966
      Pst. – luteolin Abs.

D. piperita Hook. f. – Lf
Ql. D. *MC:* quercetin/var. *celebica* Warb.; or quer- KUBITZKI–REZNIK, 1966
      cetin + dihydroquercetin; or dihydroquer-
      cetin + apigenin; or dihydroquercetin +
      luteolin; or luteolin

D. winteri Forst. – Lf
Ql. D. *MC:* dihydroquercetin Pst. or Abs.   KUBITZKI–REZNIK, 1966

Pseudowintera axillaris (Forst.) Dandy – Lf
Ql. D. *MC:* quercetin; or apigenin; or kaempferol;   KUBITZKI–REZNIK, 1966
      or quercetin + apigenin; or kaempferol +
      apigenin

EUPOMATIACEAE

Eupomatia laurina R. Br. – Lf
Ql. D. quercetin Pst. or Abs.   KUBITZKI–REZNIK, 1966

MONIMIACEAE

Laurelia novae-zealandiae A. Cunn. — Lf
Ql. D. leucoanthocyanins Pst.   BATE–SMITH–METCALFE,
                                                                     1957
  leucoanthocyanins Abs.   CAIN et al., 1961

EUPTELEACEAE

Euptelea polyandra S. et Z. – Lf
Ql. D. *MC:* quercetin; or kaempferol   KUBITZKI–REZNIK, 1966

LARDIZABALACEAE

Akebia trifoliata (Thunb.) Koidz. – Lf
Ql. D. *MC:* quercetin; or kaempferol   KUBITZKI–REZNIK, 1966

MENISPERMACEAE

Cissampelos pareira L. – Lf
Ql. D. *MC:* quercetin + luteolin; or kaempferol   KUBITZKI–REZNIK, 1966

Menispermum canadense L. – Lf
Ql. D. luteolin + apigenin Pst.; or Abs.   KUBITZKI–REZNIK, 1966

HAMAMELIDACEAE

Hamamelis japonica Sieb. et Zucc. – Lf
Ql. D. leucoanthocyanins 1·5 % + myricetin Tr. +   JAY, 1968
      quercetin 0·2 $^o/_{oo}$; or leucoanthocyanins
      0·7 %, myricetin-quercetin Abs./var. *rosea*

ROSACEAE

Geum urbanum L. – Wp
Ql. D. leucoanthocyanins Abs.   BATE–SMITH–METCALFE,
                                                                     1957
  leucoanthocyanins Pst./var. *strictum* Hook.   CAIN et al., 1961

Malus zumi Rehd. – Lf
Ql. D. phloridzin alone; or phloridzin + sieboldin;   WILLIAMS, 1966
      or sieboldin more than phloridzin

11   161

Pyrus betulifolia Bge. – Lf
Ql. D. apigenin + luteolin Pst. or Abs.   CHALLICE–WILLIAMS, 1968

P. calleryana Decne – Lf
Ql. D. quercetin + chrysoeriol; or only chryso-   CHALLICE–WILLIAMS, 1968
        eriol; or only quercetin/var. *faurei*
        (Schneid.) Rehd.

P. pashia D. Don.
Ql. D. luteolin + apigenin; or apigenin; or flavon-   CHALLICE–WILLIAMS, 1968
        glycosides Abs.

P. phaeocarpa Rehd. – Lf
Ql. D. luteolin Pst. – catechin Abs.; or luteolin Abs.   CHALLICE–WILLIAMS, 1968
        – catechin Pst./var. *globosa* Rehd.

GROSSULARIACEAE

Carpodetus serratus J. R. et G. Forst. – Lf
Ql. D. leucodelphinidin Pst.   BATE–SMITH–METCALFE,
                                          1957
      leucoanthocyanidins Abs.   CAIN et al., 1961

MIMOSACEAE

Acacia dealbata Link. – Lf
Ql. D. mearnsitrin Pst. or Abs.   ZEIJLEMAKER–MACKENZIE,
                                          1965–66

A. mearnsii De Wild. – Lf
Ql. D. mearnsitrin Pst. or Abs.   ZEIJLEMAKER–MACKENZIE,
Ch. T. quantitative D occur; inheritance controlled   1965–66
        by a single dominant gene

FABACEAE / PAPILIONACEAE

Baptisia leucophaea Nutt. – Sh
Ql. D. phenolic compounds Pst. or Abs.   BREHM–ALSTON, 1964
Ch. T. no close CORR with MP entities, but geo-
        graphical CORR; 2 chemotaxonomic races

Lathyrus luteus (L.) Peterm. – Lf
Ql. D. quercetin Pst.; or Abs./var. *laevigatus* Beck   BRUNSBERG, 1965
        caffeic A Pst.; or Abs./var. *transsylvanicus*
        Beck
Ch. T. IDP of chromosome number; var. *transsyl-*
        vanicus as separate species

L. sphaericus Retz. – Lf
Ql. D. cyanidin Pst.; or Abs. unknown flavonoid Pst.   DEN   BRUNSBERG, 1965

162

Ch. T. DEP on geographical distribution; on MP S/EUR
      CHAR; IDP of chromosome number;
      3 biochemical groups

Lotus corniculatus L. – Lf
Ql. D. unknown phenol + sinapic A Pst. or Abs.   HARNEY–GRANT, 1964

L. pedunculatus Cav. – Lf
Ql. D. quercetin + sinapic A Pst. or Abs.   HARNEY–GRANT, 1964

Pongamia glabra Vent – Rt Ba
Ql. D. kanugin + desmethoxykanugin   IND   MITTAL–SESHADRI, 1956
      karanjin + pongapin + gamatin + pinna-   AUL   PAVANARAM–ROW, 1956
      tin/*P. pinnata*

Pterocarpus indicus Wild. – Wd
Ql. D. pterocarpin + homopterocarpin   PHIL   BROOKS, 1910
      angolensin   IND   GUPTA–SESHADRI, 1956
      angolensin 93 % + pterocarpin 6 %   AUL   COOKE–RAE, 1964
      homopterocarpin 96% + formononetin 4%;   BHRARA et al., 1964
      or homopterocarpin 96 % + pterocarpin
Ch. T. D of compounds represent different stages   COOKE–RAE, 1964
      of evolution

Trifolium israeliticum Zahary et Katzn. – Lf
Ql. D. *MC:* biochanin A; or only in Tr. – genistein   FRANCIS et al., 1966
Ch. T. intervarietal VAR of isoflavone content

T. lappaceum L. – Lf
Ql. D. *MC:* genistein; or formononetin + biocha-   FRANCIS et al., 1966
      nin A
Ch. T. intervarietal VAR of isoflavone content

T. pilulare Boiss. – Lf
Ql. D. *MC:* genistein; or formononetin   FRANCIS et al., 1966
Ch. T. intervarietal VAR of isoflavone content

T. subterraneum L. – Lf
Ql. D. biochanin A; or genistein + kaempferol; or   FRANCIS et al., 1966
      only kaempferol; or genistein + daidzein
      /mutants of cv. 'Geraldton'
      MC: genistein + formononetin/ssp. *yanni-*   GRE   WONG–FRANCIS, 1968
      nicum; genistein; flavonols Abs./ssp. *bra-*   AUL
      chycalycinum   N/EUR
      biochanin A/ssp. *subterraneum*, flavones +
      chalcones Abs.
      biochanin A + quercetin/Red Lf mutant
      formononetin/cv. 'Geraldton'
      formononetin + biochanin A;
Ch. T. DEP on variety D and on area of origin

11*

MYRTACEAE

Eucalyptus angophoroides R. T. Bak. – Lf
Ql. D. *MC:* myricetin + astringin; or ellagic A +   HILLIS, 1966
    rhapontin

E. apodophylla Blakely et Jacobs. – Lf
Ql. D. *MC:* ellagic A; or ellagic A + unknown   HILLIS, 1966
    compound

E. caliginosa Blakely et McKie – Lf
Ql. D. myricetin; or unknown compound   HILLIS, 1967
Ch. T. not due to undetected hybridism

E. camaldulensis Dehnh. – Lf
Ql. D. ratio of ellagic A relative to quercetin 5 : 5;   HILLIS, 1966
    or 5 : 2
    VAR in relative amounts of polyphenol   HILLIS–BANKS, 1968
    compounds
Ch. T. IDP of environment   HILLIS, 1966
    CORR of MP and Ch. CHAR; 6 phytoche-   HILLIS–BANKS, 1968
    mical provenances

E. confertiflora Kipp – Lf
Ql. D. *MC:* myricetin; or ellagic A   HILLIS, 1966
Ch. T. not due to undetected hybridism

E. cornuta Labill. – Lf
Ql. D. *MC:* ellagic A; or ellagic A + quercetin   HILLIS, 1967

E. dalrympleana Maiden – Lf
Ql. D. astringin + rhapontin; or kaempferol/ssp.   HILLIS, 1966
    heptantha

E. eugenioides Sieb. – Lf
Ql. D. renantherin Pst.; or Abs.   HILLIS, 1967
Ch. T. not due to undetected hybridism

E. fibrosa F. Muell. – Lf
Ql. D. myricetin Pst./ssp. *nubila*; or Abs.   HILLIS, 1967

E. glaucescens Maiden – Lf
Ql. D. astringin + rhapontin; or delphinidin +   HILLIS, 1966
    cyanidin; or astringin + quercetin

E. kondininensis Maiden – Lf
Ql. D. rhapontin; or chlorogenic A   HILLIS, 1966

E. leucoxylon F. Muell. – Lf
Ql. D. *MC:* quercetin; or ellagic A + gallic A; or HILLIS, 1966, 1967
    ellagic A + quercetin

E. melliodora A. Cunn. – Lf
Ql. D. *MC:* quercetin; or ellagic A   HILLIS, 1967

E. obliqua L'Hérit. – Lf
Ql. D. leucodelphinidins Pst. or Abs.   HILLIS, 1966

E. odorata Behr. – Lf
Ql. D. leucodelphinidin Pst. or Abs.   HILLIS, 1966

E. oleosa F. Muell. – Lf
Ql. D. *MC:* ellagic A; or engelitin   HILLIS, 1967
Ch. T. Ch. variety

E. ovata Labill. – Lf
Ql. D. myricetin Pst. or Abs.   HILLIS, 1966

E. papuana F. Muell. – Lf
Ql. D. *MC:* myricetin; or myricetin + ellagic A;   HILLIS, 1966
      or myricetin + pelargonidin; or quercetin

E. phaeotricha Blakely – Lf
Ql. D. *MC:* delphinidin + ellagic A; or only ella-   HILLIS, 1966
      gic A

E. risdonii Hook. f. – Lf
Ql. D. *MC:* delphinidin; or quercetin   HILLIS, 1966

E. rugosa R. Br. – Lf
Ql. D. *MC:* quercetin; or ellagic A + astringin   HILLIS, 1966

E. salmonophloia F. Muell. – Lf
Ql. D. *MC:* aromadendrin; or astringin; or rhapontin   HILLIS, 1966

E. sideroxylon (Benth.) A. Cunn. – Lf
Ql. D. *MC:* leucocyanidin + ellagic A; or quer-   HILLIS, 1967
      cetin + ellagic A; or quercetin + ellagic
      A + gallic A

E. sieberi F. Muell. – Lf
Ql. D. *MC:* myricetin; or ellagic A   HILLIS, 1966

E. smithii R. T. Baker – Lf
Ql. D. astringin Pst. or Abs.   HILLIS, 1966

E. tereticornis Sm. – Lf
Ql. D. *MC:* myricetin Pst. or Abs.   HILLIS, 1966, 1967
Ch. T. not due to undetected hybridism

E. watsoniana F. Muell. – Lf
Ql. D. *MC:* myricetin; or gallic A   HILLIS, 1966

Psidium guaiava L. – St + Ba
Ql. D. leucoanthocyanins + ellagic A diglycosides   SESHADRI–VASHISTA, 1963
      myricetin + ellagic A + leucoanthocyanins   NAIR–SUBRAMANIAN, 1964
      in small amounts
Ch. T. VAR in Ch. components   NAIR–SUBRAMANIAN, 1964

165

RUTACEAE

Evodia micrococca F. Muell. – Lf
Ql. D. pinoresional dimethyl ether; or sesamin/var.   CAMERON–SUTHERLAND,
      pubescens   1961

Melicope ternata Forst. – St + Ba
Ql. D. meliternin + meliternatin + ternatin   CAIN et al., 1961
      meliternin + narangin + xanthoxyle-   CAMBIE, 1960
      tin; or meliternatin as *MC*/var. *man-*
      tellii Buch.
Ch. T. infraspecific Ch. VAR   FUJITA, 1961

SIMAROUBACEAE

Harrisonia perforata (Blanco) Merr. – Lf
Ql. D. quercetin + myricetin + cyanidin Pst. or Abs.   NOOTEBOOM, 1966

MELIACEAE

Dysoxylum spectabilis Hook. f. – St + Ba + Wd
Ql. D. leucoanthocyanins Pst.   CAIN et al., 1961
      leucoanthocyanins Abs.   CAMBIE, 1959

CORYNOCARPACEAE

Corynocarpus laevigatus J. R. et G. Forst. – Lf
Ql. D. leucocyanidin Pst.   BATE-SMITH–METCALFE,
                                    1957
      leucocyanidin Abs.   CAIN et al., 1961

APIACEAE / UMBELLIFERAE

Daucus carota L. – Rt
Ql. D. carotene + carotenoids Pst.; or Abs., but   RANGESWAMI, 1962
      syanidin diglucoside Pst. (cv.)   IND
Ch. T. two distinct species

RUBIACEAE

Galium mollugo L. – Wp
Ql. D. hesperidin Pst. or Abs.   AUS   KLEIN, 1921
      hesperidin Abs., but asperuloside + chloro- POL   KOHLMÜNZER, 1964
      genic A Pst.
Ch. T. IDP of origin, of area; of MP CHAR; Ch.   KLEIN, 1921
      races

LAMIACEAE/LABIATAE

Teucrium chamaedrys L. – Wp
Ql. D. scutellarin Pst.

    scutellarin Abs.

Ch. T. chemotypes

MOLISCH–GOLDSCHMIEDT, 1901
HŐRHAMMER–WAGNER, 1962
HEGNAUER, 1965

MALVACEAE

Hoheria sexstylosa Col. – Wp
Ql. D. leucocyanidin Pst.

    leucoanthocyanins Abs.

BATE-SMITH–METCALFE, 1957
CAIN et ál., 1961

FUMARIACEAE

Dicentra formosa Walp. – Lf + Fl
Ql. D. kaempferol + quercetin Pst. or
    Abs./ssp. *oregana*

FAHSELT–OWNBEY, 1968

THEACEAE

Camellia sinensis L. – Lf
Ql. D. in flavonoids Pst. or Abs., and in rate of it
Ch. T. CORR between flavonoid Pst. and Ca-oxalate
    crystals bearing-cell frequency

ROBERTS et al., 1958
WIGHT–BARUA, 1954

HYPERICACEAE

Hypericum perforatum L. – Lf
Ql. D. quercetin Pst.   CSR/Slovaky LEIFERTOVÁ, 1966
    or Abs.   CSR/Moravi

ERICACEAE

Lyonia ovalifolia S. et Z. – Lf
Ql. D. astilbin + quercitrin; or quercitrin alone,   E/JAP   YASUE et al., 1965
    astilbin Abs.   W/JAP

Pieris japonica (Thunb.) Don – Lf
Ql. D. asebotin; or phloridzin; or both
Ch. T. IDP of MP CHAR; chemotypes

MURAKAMI–FUKUDA, 1965
HEGNAUER, 1965

ASTERACEAE/COMPOSITAE

Helichrysum bracteatum (Vent) Willd. – Fl
Ql. D. quercetin + apigenin + antochlor Pst.; or
    in combinations; or Abs.

RIMMLER et al., 1963

Hymenoxys scaposa (DC.) Parker – Fl
Ql. D. wide VAR from flavonol-7-glycosides to   Seeligmann–Alston,
flavonol-3-glycosides   1967
Ch. T. DEP on area of origin; IDP of MP D
H. scaposa and *H. acaulis* (Pursh) Parker
a single taxon – not representing biochemical parallelisms

Solidago virgaurea L. – Lf
Ql. D. quercitrin   BUL   Fuchs–Ilieva, 1949
rutin + astragalin; or chlorogenic A + ast-   DEN   Björkman–Holmgren,
ragalin   1958, 1960
rutin + quercitrin   POL   Sckrzypczakova, 1961,
1962

rutin + astragalin + chlorogenic A + iso-   COLL   Tétényi, 1962
chlorogenic A; all, or in combinations or
Abs.
Ch. T. DEP on origin; D in enzyme-activity   Björkman–Holmgren
IDP of origin; clinal type of VAR;   Tétényi, 1962
OG changes; chemodemes

Thelesperma simplicifolium A. Gray – Lf
Ql. D. in flavonoid components (antochlors)   Melchert, 1966
Ch. T. IDP of MP CHAR; DEP on ploidity level
and on geographical source; chemodemes

POLYGONACEAE

Fagopyrum esculentum Moench – Wp
Qn. D. in rutin-content   FRA   Paris, 1949
3·6–4·7 % glycosides-content   HUN   Gubányi, 1956
8–53 mg rutin (pro 100 Sd)   USSR   Yermakov, 1960
Ch. T. IDP of MP CHAR; Ch. races   Os, 1957

F. tataricum (L.) Gaertn. – Wp
Qn. D. 3·4–5·6 glycosides content   HUN   Gubányi, 1956
in rutin-content   NED   Os, 1957
Ch. T. OG changes   Paris, 1949

Polygonum hydropiper L. – Wp
Ql. D. rhamnasin   POL   Krynske, 1935
persicarin/var. *vulgare* Meisn.   JAP   Kawaguchi–Kim, 1937
persicarin-7-methylaether   JAP   Tatsuta, 1955
rutin + one quercetinglycoside   GER   Valentin–Wagner, 1953
rhamnasin + rhamnasinbisulphate   GER   Hőrhammer–Hänsel,
1953, 1954
quercitrin + hyperin   GER   Hőrhammer–Rao, 1954
Ch. T. originated from mutation of the Japanese   Hőrhammer–Hänsel,
form   1954
Ch. races   Hegnauer, 1957

168

P. persicaria L. – Wp
Ql. D. hyperin; or hyperin + avicularin; or hype-
    rin + quercitrin; or hyperin + avicularin
    + quercitrin
Ch. T. stable forms with area D

HÄNSEL–HŐRHAMMER,
1954

Rumex acetosa L.
Ql. D. hyperin; or hyperin + rutin

HŐRHAMMER–HÄNSEL,
1954

    hyperin + rutin + quercitrin

HŐRHAMMER–VOLZ,   1955

JUGLANDACEAE

Juglans regia L. – Lf
Ql. D. hyperin + quercetin-3-galactoside + two
    kaempferols

HERRMANN, 1955

    kaempferol-3-arabinosid/var. *sinensis* DC.
    quercetin + kaempferol + cyanidin + caf-
    feic A

NAKAOKI–MORITA, 1958
BATE–SMITH, 1962

LILIACEAE

Allium douglasii Hook. – Lf
Ch. T. 4 morphogeographic races characterized
    by distinct flavonoid-like components

MINGRONE–OWNBEY, 1968

Smilax glyciphylla Smith – Lf
Ql. D. glyciphyllin Pst.
    glyciphyllin Abs.
    dihydrochalcones Pst. or Abs.; mangiferin
    Pst., when dihydrochalcones Abs.
Ch. T. mutation in chemism and MP VAR; Ch. forms

RENNIE, 1886
WILLIAMS, 1959
WILLIAMS, 1964

WILLIAMS, 1964

GRAMINEAE

Agropyron intermedium (Host) Beauv. – Fl
Ql. D. in number of flavonoid compounds Pst.
    (13–24)
Ch. T. DEP on ploidity level

LORENZ et al., 1964

LEMNACEAE

Lemna perpusilla Torrey – Wp
Ql. D. in apigenin-7-glycoside content

McCLURE–ALSTON, 1966

4. ALKALOIDS

4.1. PROTOALKALOIDS; ANOMALIC ORGANIZED PEPTIDES

CLAVICIPITACEAE/HYPOCREACEAE (sensu lato)

Claviceps paspali Stev. et Hall – My
Ql. D. lysergic A derivatives + hydroxyethylamide   ITA   ARCAMONE et al., 1961
     lysergic A amide; or methylcarbinol amide   AUL   GRÖGER–TYLER, 1964
     MA: ergotamine   KOBEL et al., 1964
Ch. T. Ch. races   KOBEL et al., 1964

C. purpurea (Fr.) Tul. – Sc
Qn. D. 0·01–1·0 % continuous VAR   HUN   BÉKÉSY, 1943
     0·01–0·8 % continuous or discontinuous   GER   ROCHELMAYER, 1949
     VAR   USA
     0·01–0·6 % discontinuous VAR   FIN   SILBER–BISCHOFF, 1954
     0·1–0·3 % normal distribution   CSR   KOVACIC et al., 1956
     only Tr.   PR   MOTHES, 1960
     exempt of alkaloid   SIB   OSTROVSKI–BANKOVSKAIA,
       CAU   1961
Ql. D. ergotamine; or   C/EUR   STOLL, 1942
     ergotoxine   SPA+USSR
     ergotaminine   N-Z   HASSALL, 1944
     ergotamine + ergometrine   N-Z   GESSNER, 1953
     ergotamine + ergometrine + ergotoxine   USA   SVOBODA et al., 1954
     ergotamine   FIN   PENTTILA, 1955
     ergometrine 80 %   KAH   GRÖGER, 1961
     ergocristine 58 %; or ergotamine 63 %   USSR   OSTROVSKI et al., 1964
     ergocryptine 80 %   S/AM   SZENDEY et al., 1961
     lysergic A derivatives   E/AS   MOTHES, 1960
     isolysergic-alkaloids   COLL   VOIGT, 1958
     clavinic alkaloids 9–97 %   COLL   VOIGT, 1962
Ch. T. inheritance of Ch. CHAR   BÉKÉSY, 1943
     genetically fixed 5 races   KYBAL–BREJCHA, 1955
     Ch. strains with wide VAR   MOTHES, 1960
     CORR Abs. between Sc colour and Ch.   GARAY–ÁDÁM, 1955
     CHAR
     IDP of ecological influence   SILBER–BISCHOFF, 1954

AGARICACEAE

Amanita phalloides (Fr.) Kummer – Sp
Ql. D. phalloidine + amanitines   EUR   WIELAND–WIELAND, 1959
     α-amanitine Pst., toxins Abs.   USA   ISAACS–TYLER, 1963
Ch. T. DEP on strain D   WIELAND–WIELAND, 1955

Inocybe xanthomelas Bours et Kükin – Sp
Ql. D. muscarine Pst. alkaloids Abs.   TYLER–STUNTZ, 1963
      alkaloids Pst. muscarine Abs./var. *nigrescens*   MALONE et al., 1962
      Atk.

EQUISETACEAE

Equisetum arvense L. – Wp

Ql. D. nicotine + metoxypiridine	CAN	MANSKE, 1942
palustrine	SWI	KARRER et al., 1949
nicotine; palustrine Abs.	GER	PHILLIPSON–MELVILLE, 1960
alkaloids Pst.	COLL	AURICH et al., 1965

EPHEDRACEAE

Ephedra distachya L. — Tw

On. D. 0.65 − 1.7+ alkaloids	USSR	HAMMERMANN et al., 1957
alkaloids Abs.	USSR	SOKOLOV, 1952
Ql. D. ephedrine alone	CSR	BAUER et al., 1957
pseudoephedrine alone	USSR	SPEHR, 1890
ephedrine 71–66 %; or 4–28 %	USSR	MASSAGETOV, 1938

E. gerardiana Wall. – Tw

Qn. D. 0·3–2·6 % alkaloid content	IND	GHOSE–KRISHNA, 1930
1·6 % alkaloids	JAP	KAWATANI, 1959
0·4–2 % alkaloid content	IND	QAZILBASH, 1948
Th. T. 0·1 % ephedrine		CHOPRA–KRISHNA, 1931
ephedrine 56–68 %	IND	SINGH, 1950

E. intermedia Schrenk et C. A. Mey. – Tw

Qn. D. 1·1–1·8 % alkaloid content	IND	READ–FENG, 1928
0·1 % alkaloid content	KAS	ANONYMOUS, 1929
0·5–2·2 % alkaloid content	USSR	MASSAGETOV, 1938
Ql. D. *MA:* pseudoephedrine	USSR	MASSAGETOV, 1938
pseudoephedrine alone	IND	QAZILBASH, 1960
ephedrine 4–45 %	IND	GHOSE–KRISHNA, 1930
ephedrine 30–40 %	IND	READ–FENG, 1928
ephedrine 59 %	IND	CHOPRA–DUTT, 1929–30

E. nebrodensis (Tineo) Stapf – Tw

Qn. D. 0·39 % alkaloid content	ITA	CAVELLO–CAPONE, 1950
1·46 % alkaloid content	USSR	SOKOLOV, 1952
2·8 % alkaloid content	IND	BAL, 1953
Ql. D. ephedrine (only Tr.)	MAR	NARBONNE, 1940
ephedrine 26 % + pseudoephedrine 35 %	ITA	CAVELLO–CAPONE, 1950
ephedrine 65 %	USSR	SOKOLOV, 1952

CONVULVULACEAE

Ipomoea violacea L. – Sd
Ql. D. lysergic and isolysergic A amide at different   GENEST, 1965
      rate with clavinic alkaloids

4.2. ALKALOIDS PROPER

LYCOPODIACEAE

Lycopodium annotinum L. – Wp
Ql. D. obscurine + annotine; or acrifoline/var.   CAN   Manske–Marion, 1942
     acrifolium Fern.   1943
     acrifoline Pst. or Abs.   GER   Bertho–Stoll, 1952
     obscurine + acrifoline   POL   Achmatowitz–Rode-
                                           wald, 1955
Ch. T. Ch. races   Hegnauer, 1957
     chemically differentiated two species   Manske–Marion, 1947
     only variety level is suggested   Alston-Turner, 1963

L. clavatum L. – Wp
Ql. D. clavatine + clavatoxine Pst.   POL   Achmatowitz–Uzieblo,
                                         1938
     clavatine-clavatoxine Abs.   CAN   Marion–Manske, 1944
     clavolonine + lycodine + lopholine JAM   Burrell–Taylor, 1960
Ch. T. Ch. races   Hegnauer, 1957

L. saururus Lam. – Wp
Ql. D. pillijanine   Arata–Canzoneri, 1892
                                       Dominguez, 1932
     saururine + sauroxine   Deulofeu–Langhe, 1942

HIMANTANDRACEAE

Galbulimima belgraveana (F. Muell.) Sprg. – Ba
Qn. D. 0·5 % alkaloid-content, or only Tr.   Binns et al., 1965
Ql. D. MA: himgaline + himbadine; or himbacine Q-L
     + himandridine   N-G

MONIMIACEAE

Daphnandra micrantha Benth. – Ba
Ql. D. micranthine; or micranthine + daphnand-   Bick et al., 1953
     rine; micranthine + daphnoline; or mic-
     ranthine + daphnoline + daphnandrine
Ch. T. DEP on areal D

HERNANDIACEAE

Gyrocarpus americanus Jacq. – Ba
Ql. D. phaeanthine + magnocurarine   AUL   McKenzie–Price, 1953
     both + o-desmethylphaeanthine   IND   Ramachandra–
                                           Anjaneyulu, 1962

LAURACEAE

Cryptocarya bowiei (Hook.) Druce – Ba
Ql. D. cryptoaustoline; or cryptowoline   Ewing et al., 1953
Ch. T. DEP on area D

Ocotea rodiaei (Schomb.) Mez – Ba
Ql. D. sepeerine + ocotine

    norrodiasine + dirosine + octeamine +
    ocotanine + demerarine + ocodemerine

GRUNDON–McGRAVEY,
1960
HEARST, 1964

MENISPERMACEAE

Cissampelos pareira L. – Rt
Ql. D. hayatine + hayatinine; or hayatine +   KAS
    l-curine
    l-curine   IND
    d-isochondrodendrine + hayatine   MAD

BHATTACHARRYYA et al.,
1956
KUPCHAN et al., 1960
BOISSIER et al., 1965

BERBERIDACEAE

Berberis asiatica Roxb. – Ba
Ql. D. berberine + oxyacanthine
    berberine + palmatine; oxyacanthine Abs.

CHOPRA et al., 1928
CHATTERJEE et al., 1954

B. laurina Thunb. – Rt
Ql. D. berberine + hydrastine
    berberine/hydrastine Abs.; or various alka-
    loids Pst. (4–8), but berberine Abs.
    berberastine

COSTA–SILVA, 1933
LIBERALLI–SHAROVSKY,
1957–58
NIJLAND, 1962

B. thunbergii DC. – Rt
Ql. D. magnoflorine + isotetrandrine

    Pst. or Abs./var. *maximoviczii* Regel

TOMITA–CANG–HSIUNG,
1960
NIJLAND, 1962

Nandina domestica Thunb. – St + Tw
Ql. D. nandinine + nantenine + menisporine; or
    nantenine/var. *leucocarpa* Makino; or
    protopine/f. *shina-nanten* hort.

TOMITA–SUGAMOTO, 1961

RANUNCULACEAE

Thalictrum dasycarpum Fisch. et Lall. – Rh
Ql. D. magnoflorine + berberine/var. *hypoglau-*
    cum Rydb.
    magnoflorine + thalicarpine
    berberine + magnoflorine
    thalicarpine

HOGG–BEAL, 1963

KUPCHAN et al., 1963
BORKOWSKI et al., 1963
TOSHIAKI et al., 1965

T. foliolosum DC. – Rh
Ql. D. berberine + magnoflorine
    berberine + palmatine; magnoflorine Abs.
    magnoflorine Pst.

VASHISTA–SIDDIQUI, 1941
CHATTERJEE et al., 1952
GOPINATH et al., 1959

T. minus L. – Rh
Ql. D. thalicmine + thalicmidine   USSR   YUNUSOV–PROGRESSOV, 1950

       magnoflorine + thalictuberine + thalicrine   JAP   FUJITA–TOMIMATSU, 1959
       /var. *hypoleucum* S. et Z.
       berberine + magnoflorine   POL   BORKOWSKI et al., 1963
       berberine + magnoflorine/var. *adianti-*   PATEL et al., 1965
         folium hort.
Ch. T. morphologically indistinguishable races *A*   PATEL et al., 1965
       and *B*, D in pharmacological activity

ROSACEAE

Sanguisorba minor Scop. – Sh
Ql. D. alkaloids Pst.; or Abs./ssp. *muricata* (Spach)   AURICH et al., 1965, 1966
      Briqu.

CRASSULACEAE

Sedum acre L. – Wp
Qn. D. 230 mg/kg alkaloids   GER   FRANCK–HARTMANN, 1960
       Tr. → 200 mg/kg alkaloid VAR   HUN   PRISZTER–TÉTÉNYI, 1963
Ql. D. sedamine   USSR   KOLESNIKOV–SVARCMAN, 1939

       sedamine + nicotine   CAN   MARION, 1945
       sedridine   NED   BEYERMANN–MÜLLER, 1955

       sedamine + sedridine; nicotine Abs.   GER   FRANCK–HARTMANN, 1960
       sedamine; or sedridine/var. *almádii* Priszter;
       or sedinine as *MA*, and/or in combination   COLL   PRISZTER–TÉTÉNYI
Ch. T. PHYS varieties   BERGANE–NORDAL, 1958
      IDP of some MP CHAR, DEP on area D;   PRISZTER–TÉTÉNYI
      chemovars, chemosubspecies   TÉTÉNYI, 1963
      OG changes in composition of alkaloids   TÉTÉNYI–VÁGÚJFALVI, 1962

CAESALPINIACEAE

Crotalaria anagyroides H. B. et K. – Sd
Ql. D. 1-methylene pyrrolisidine 98 %   AUL   CULVENOR–SMITH, 1959
       senecionine + 1-methylene pyrrolisidine   IND   SETHI–ATAL, 1964

C. retusa L. – Sd
Ql. D. monocrotaline; or monocrotaline-N-oxide   CULVENOR–SMITH, 1957

C. spectabilis Roth – Sd
Ql. D. monocrotaline   USA   ADAMS–ROGERS, 1939
       monocrotaline + spectabiline   AUL   CULVENOR–SMITH, 1957
Ch. T. USA plants growing in AUL without specta-   HILLIS, 1966
      biline

FABACEAE/PAPILIONACEAE

Baptisia leucophaea Nutt. – Wp
Ql. D. wide VAR of alkaloids Pst. or Abs.   BREHM–ALSTON, 1964

Cytisus monspessulanus L. – Lf + St
Ql. D. cytisine much + N-methylcytisine   AUL   WHITE, 1943
          monspessulanine 36 % + lupanine 18 % +   SWI   GILL–STEINEGGER, 1964
          methylcytisine 18 % + cytisine 9 %

C. nigricans L. – Lf + St
Ql. D. calycotomine 100 %   AUL   WHITE, 1943
          sparteine 59 % + calycotomine 41 %   SWI   GILL–STEINEGGER, 1964

C. supinus L. – Lf + St
Ql. D. lupanine; or sparteine; or lupanine + spar-   BUL   AVRAMOVA, 1962
          teine
          lupanine 63 % + anagyrine 16 % + spar-   POL   GILL–STEINEGGER
          teine in Tr.; or lupanine 57 % + sparteine SWI
          25 %, anagyrine Abs.

Galega officinalis L. – Wp
Qn. D. 800; or 600; or 350 mg % galegine   SCHÄFER–STEIN, 1967
Ql. D. galegine   GER   WEHMER, 1931
          peganine + chinasolon-4; galegine Abs.   USSR   LINIUCHEV–BANKOVSKI,
                                                          1959
          galegine + anagyrine   GER   REUTER, 1961
          peganine + galegine   PUFAHL–SCHREIBER, 1964
          galegine little or exempt   SCHRÖCK, 1941
          galegine + hydroxygalegine + peganine   SCHÄFER–STEIN, 1967
Ch. T. breeding possibility and inheritance of gale-   SCHRÖCK, 1941
          gineless CHAR
          IDP of OG (flowering) changes   SCHÄFER–STEIN, 1967

Genista aetnensis DC. – Lf + St
Ql. D. sparteine   GER   JARETZKY–AXER, 1934
          retamine + sparteine Tr.; or sparteine   N-Z   WHITE, 1946
          retamine   USSR   BANKOVSKI et al., 1959
          sparteine 49 % + retamine 25 %   ITA   STEINEGGER et al., 1963

G. hispanica L. – Lf + St
Ql. D. sparteine 38 % + retamine 31 %; or spar-   SPA   GILL–STEINEGGER, 1964
          teine 35 % + retamine 20 %/var. *villosa*
          Wilk.
          alkaloids Abs.   N-Z   WHITE, 1944

G. pumila (Deb. et Rev.) Vierh. – Lf + St
Ql. D. retamine 32 % + sparteine 22 % + lupanine   BERNASCONI et al., 1965
          16 % + cytisine 9 %; or sparteine 22 % +
          cytisine 15% + lupanine 12% + retamine
          11 %/var. *mugronenis* (Vierh.) Heyw.

175

Spartium junceum L. – Wp
Qn. D. in alkaloid-content   SPA   RIBAS–SEOANE, 1953
Ql. D. sparteine   WEHMER, 1931
     cytisine   N-Z   WHITE, 1943
     alkaloids Abs.   BRA   RIBAS–SEOANE, 1953

Thermopsis fabacea DC. – Fl
Ql. D. cytisine + methylcytisine   RABININ–ILINA, 1955
     cytisine + anagyrine + sparteine + lupa-   BALCAROWNA, 1963
     nine
     cytisine + pachycarpine + thermopsine   DAUKSA–DENISOVA, 1966
         – Wp
     lupanine 50 % + sparteine 21 % + methyl-   BALCAR–SKRZYDLEWSKA
     cytisine 21 %; or lupanine 42 % + ther-   and BORKOWSKI, 1966
     mopsine 28 % + methylcytisine 8 %

Th. caroliniana Curt. – Wp
Ql. D. lupanine 90 %; or lupanine 38 % + anagy-   BALCAR–SKRZYDLEWSKA
     rine 38 % + cytisine 23 %   and BORKOWSKI, 1966

Ulex europaeus L. – Sh
Ql. D. anagyrine   CLEMO–RAPER, 1935
     alkaloids Abs.   N-Z   WHITE, 1943
         – Fr
     cytisine   WHITE, 1943
     anagyrine   RIBAS–BASANTA, 1952
Ch. T. different alkaloid localization   WHITE, 1943

RUTACEAE

Flindersia dissosperma Domin – Lf + Ba
Ql. D. alkaloidal composition differs from sample   BINNS et al., 1957
     to sample; *MA:* maculine; or dictamnine;
     or flindersiamine

F. maculosa F. Muell. – Lf + Ba
Ql. D. *MA:* maculine; or dictamnine; or maculosi-   BINNS et al., 1957
     dine; or kokusaginine; or flindersiamine;
     or maculosine
Ch. T. alkaloidal composition differs from sample to
     sample

SAPINDACEAE

Dodonaea viscosa Jacq. – Lf
Ql. D. alkaloids Pst.   WEBB, 1949
     alkaloids Abs.   CAIN et al., 1961

CELASTRACEAE

Catha edulis Forsk. – Lf + St
Ql. D. cathine + cathinine + cathidine   STOCKMANN, 1912

d-nor-isoephedrine   WINTERFELD–
                                            BERNSMANN, 1960
d-nor-pseudoephedrine (cathine)   GORDON et al., 1961

APIACEAE / UMBELLIFERAE

Prangos pabularia Lindl. – Wp
Qn. D. 0,1 % or 0·01 % alkaloid content   KOROLEVA, 1948
Ch. T. D in area and in flowering time of the
        "sweet" and of the "bitter" subspecies

LOGANIACEAE

Gelsemium elegans Benth. – Rt + Wp
Ql. D. koumidine + koumine   BOIT, 1961
        MA: koumine + koumicine + koumidine; CHI   CHU-CSIN LIN et al., 1961
        sempervirine-koumidine Abs.
        sempervirine + koumine; koumidine Abs. V-N   JANOT et al., 1953

Strychnos colubrina L. – Wp
Ql. D. strychnine; or strychnine + brucine   INDO   BOORSMA, 1902
        strychnine + brucine   IND   GEIGER, 1901

S. henningsii Gilg – Ba
Ql. D. strychnine + brucine   KLEMPERER–WARREN,
                                                        1955
        MA: diaboline + henningsoline + henning-   GROSSERT et al., 1965
        samine + rindline

S. ignatii Berg. – Sd
Ql. D. strychnine + brucine   PHIL   FLÜCKIGER, 1886
        strychnine alone/var. *tieute* Lesch.   INDO   BISSET, 1957
        more brucine, then strychnine/var. *ovalifolia* MAL   CALDERBANK, 1957
        Wall.

S. nux-vomica L. – Sd
Ql. D. brucine + strychnine;   IND   BISSET, 1966
        or very little alkaloid; or Abs.   BUR
Ch. T. no more than varieties or forms   LEENHOUTS, 1962

APOCYNACEAE

Aspidosperma australe Muell.-Arg. – Ba
Ql. D. aspidospermine   ORAZI, 1946
        olivacine + guatambuine   ONDETTI–DEULOFEU, 1959
Ch. T. possibility of Ch. races   SCHMUTZ, 1961

A. cuspa (HBK) S. F. Blake – Ba
Ql. D. aspidospermine Pst.   PECKOLT, 1929
        aspidospermine Abs.   SCHMUTZ, 1961

12   177

A. nigricans Handro – Ba
Ql. D. uleine + dihydrouleine Pst.; or Abs.   ARNDT et al., 1967

A. pyricollum Muell.-Arg. – Ba(Rt + St)
Ql. D. aspidospermine   KLEIN, 1932
    uleine + olivacine/*A. olivaceum* Muell.-Arg.   SCHMUTZ–HUNZIKER,
                                                         1958
    olivacine + guatambuine/*A. longepetiolatum*   MARINI–BETTOLO, 1959
      Hassl.
    uleine   GILBERT et al., 1960
    uleine + apparicine + dasycarpidone   ARNDT et al., 1967
Ch. T. ISP Ch. varieties or separated species   SCHMUTZ, 1961

A. quebracho-blanca Schlecht. – Ba
Ql. D. yohimbine   WEHMER, 1931
    yohimbine Abs.   LEPRESTRE, 1927
    yohimbine + aspidospermine   MARINI–BETTOLO, 1959
    querbrachacidine + yohimboic A   TUNMANN–RACHER, 1960
    aspidospermine/var. *pendula* Speg.   DOMINGUEZ, J. 1932
    yohimbine + aspidospermine + quebracha-   BIEMANN et al., 1963
      mine + quebrachine

Catharanthus roseus G. Don. – Wp
Qn. D. in alkaloid level   PARIS, 1965
Ql. D. in number of alkaloids Pst.   PRISTA, 1964
Ch. T. DEP on origin   PARIS, 1965
                                                         PRISTA, 1964

Rauvolfia canescens L. – Rt
Ql. D. deserpidine Pst.   IND   SCHLITTLER et al., 1952
    deserpidine Abs.   CAM   WOODWARD–SMITH, 1962

R. ligustrina Roem. et Schult. – Rt
Qn. D. alkaloid in Tr.   TRI   ANDERSON et al., 1961
    0·44 % alkaloid-content
Ql. D. reserpine   BRA   FERNANDEZ, 1958
    reserpine + reserpinine/var. *indecora*   MÜLLER, 1957
      Woods
    reserpine + deserpidine/var. *ternifolia* H. B.   KORZUN et al., 1957
      et K.
Ch. T. possibility of Ch. varieties   ANDERSON et al., 1961

R. serpentina (L.) Benth. – Rt
Qn. D. 1·35–2·66 % total alkaloids   DHAR, 1965
Ql. D. ajmaline + serpentine   SIDDIQUI–SIDDIQUI, 1931
    ajmaline + serpentinine   SIDDIQUI, 1939
    alkaloids at various rate   HOLT–COSTELLO, 1954
    rauvolfinine; or ajmaline + rauvolfinine; or   CHATTERJEE et al., 1956
      ajmaline, serpentine, rauvolfinine Abs.
Ch. T. DEP on area D   CHATTERJEE et al., 1956
    Ch. races   STEINEGGER, 1957

R. vomitoria Afz. – Rt
Qn. D. 0·2 % alkaloid-content; or 3·0 % alkaloid- SEN   WOODWARD–SMITH, 1962
    content   CON

178

Ql. D. ajmaline + sarpagine   CON   PARIS, 1943
       ajmaline + alstonine   CON   SCHLITTLER et al., 1952
       reserpine + raumitorine   GUI   GOUTAREL et al., 1954
       rescinnamine   GUI   KIDD, 1955
       rescinnamine + ajmaline + rauvomitine   GUI   HAACK et al., 1955
       rescinnamine + reserpine + reserpiline   KORZUN et al., 1957
       seredine + raumitorine + sarpagine   GUI   POISSON, 1959
       or reserpine + rauvomitine; or reserpine +   I-C
          ajmaline   CON
       reserpine + ajmaline   ANG   VALE, 1963
       raumitorine + rauverine   GUI   POISSON et al., 1964
Ch. T. Ch. varieties   DILLEMANN, 1959

Vinca major L. – Wp
Ql. D. reserpinine + majdine   BRA   JANOT–LE MEN, 1954
       reserpine   POL   BORKOWSKI et al., 1964
       reserpinine + carapaunabine   CSR   KAUL–TROJÁNEK, 1966
         /var. *pubescens* Urv.
Ch. T. expression of doubt of being one species   KAUL–TROJÁNEK, 1966

V. minor L. – Wp
Qn. D. 0·6–2·8 % alkaloid-content   HUN   SZÁSZ–MÁRK, 1962
       1·1–3·3 % alkaloid-content   HUN   SÁRKÁNY, 1962
       1·3 % alkaloid-content   USSR   LAPUNOVA–BORISIUK,
                                         1961
Ql. D. vincamine   USSR   ZABOLOTNAJA, 1950
       isovincamine; or vincamine   COLL   KOSTKA–PIJEWSKA, 1961
       vincamine: isovincamine at different rate   COLL   NECZYPOR, 1965
Ch. T. area and ecological factors influence   MÁTHÉ–SZABÓ, 1963

Voacanga thouarsii Roem. et Sch. – St. Ba
Ql. D. dregamine/var. *dregei* Pichon; or voaka-   PUISIEUX et al., 1965
         mine/var. *obtusa* Pichon

RUBIACEAE

Cinchona calisaya Wedd. – Ba
Ql. D. quinidine Pst.   INDO   MOENS, 1882
       quinidine Abs.   PERU   ZHUKOVSKI, 1950

C. ledgeriana Moench – Ba
Ql. D. cinchonidine; or quinidine; or both Abs.   INDO   MOENS, 1882
       cinchonidine Abs.   USA   BONNISTEEL, 1940
Ch. T. some minor MP D at varietas level;   MOENS, 1882
         inheritance of Ch. CHAR   BÉZANGER–BEAUQUESNE,
                                         1958

C. micrantha Ruiz et Pav. – Ba
Ql. D. cinchonine 99 %; or cinchonine 70 % +   ZHUKOVSKI, 1950
         cinchonidine 30 %

C. officinalis L. – Ba
Ql. D. in number and level of alkaloids   EQU   CAMP, 1946
     MA: quinine; or cinchonine; or cinchonidine   PERU   ZHUKOVSKY, 1950
     quinine 80 %   EWERS–CALDWELL, 1959
Ch. T. biochemical clines   CAMP, 1946
     D genetically determined   EWERS–CALDWELL, 1959
     possibility of ISP Ch. systematics   MANSFELD, 1959

C. pubescens Vahl – Ba
Ch. T. possibility of ISP Ch. and PHYS races   MANSFELD, 1959

Crucianella angustifolia L. – Sh
Ql. D. alkaloids Pst.; or Abs.   AURICH et al., 1966

Mitragyna parvifolia (Roxb.) Korth. – Lf
Ql. D. rotundifoline + isorotundifoline + rhyn-   IND   SHELLARD et al., 1967
     chophylline + isorhynchophylline;   Kerala
     or akuammigine + pteropodine + isopte-   IND
     ropodine + speciophylline   Mahestra
     mitraphylline   60 %-isomitraphylline   40 %   IND/Bihar SHELLARD–ALAM, 1968
     mitraphylline + isomitraphylline + specio-   IND
     phylline + uncarine F + pteropodine   Lucknow
     isoajmalicin 40 % + mitraphylline 40 %   IND
     + isomitraphylline 20 %   Dehra Dun
     pteropodine   30 % + mitraphylline 20 %   IND
     + isomitraphylline 20 % + isopteropo-   Uttar
     dine 10 % + speciophylline 10 %   Pradesh
     rhynchophylline + isorhynchophylline +   CEY
     pteropodine + isopteropodine
     isorhyinchophylline 50% + rhynchophylline   CEY
     20 % + hirsutine 18 % + dihydrocory-
     nantheine 2 %
     isorhynchophilline 60 % + rhynchophylline   CBA
     40 %
     isorhynchophylline   25 % + isopteropodine   BUR
     25 % + pteropodinex   17 % + rhyncho-
     phylline 15 % + akuammine 11 %
Ch. T. possibility of existing Ch. races

M. speciosa Korth. – Lf
Ql. D. rotundifoline + isorotundifoline + specio-   MAL   BECKETT et al., 1965
     foline;   or   mitraphylline + isomitraphyl-   THAI
     line + speciophylline + rhynchophylline
     + isorhynchophylline

SOLANACEAE

Atropa bella-donna L. – Rt and/or Sh
Qn. D. maximum of alkaloid-content in   ROWSON, 1945;
     var. *bella-donna*   SAN–MARTIN, 1953
     var. *intermedia* Pater   MATVEEV, 1959
     var. *lutea* Doell   ARNY–MULFORD, 1917;
     PÁTER, 1923; etc.

Ql. D. hyoscyamine + hyoscine; or hyoscine	BUL	Küssner, 1939
hyoscyamine + cuscohygrine at various rate	COLL	Phokas–Steinegger, 1956
hyoscyamine-less, hyoscine little	COLL	Tétényi, 1965
Ch. T. IDP of flower colour		Sievers, 1913
IDP of fruit shape and size		Pascher, 1959
DEP on origin-area		Deltscheff, 1957
OG changes in alkaloid-level		Elzenga–Bruyn, 1956
inheritance Abs. of quantitative D		Elzenga, 1958
inheritance of Ch. qualitative D; Ch. taxa		Tétényi, 1965

Browallia viscosa H. B. et K. – Sh + R

Ql. D. alkaloids Pst. or Abs.		Aurich et al., 1966, 1967

Datura arborea L. – Wp

Qn. D. 0·02 % alkaloid-content	PERU	Aguero, 1943
0·287 % alkaloid	CLU	Barriga–Villalba et al., 1943
0·15 % alkaloid	PERU	Montesinos, 1949
only Tr. of alkaloids	URU	Suarez, 1952
0·217 % alkaloids	IND	Shah–Sadji, 1966

D. ferox L. – Wp

Qn. D. 0·13–0·44 % alkaloid-content	USSR	Gerasimenko, 1961
Ql. D. hyoscyamine	USSR	Libizov, 1939
hyoscyamine	AUL	Barnard–Finnemore, 1945
hyoscine + meteloidine	RHD	Evans–Partridge, 1948
Ch. T. OG changes		Verzár–Sárkány, 1961

D. metel L. – Wp

Ql. D. hyoscyamine + meteloidine; or hyoscine + hyoscyamine/var. *rubra* (Bernh.) Dan.; or hyoscine/var. *fastuosa* (Bernh.) Dan.	COLL	Verzár–Sárkány, 1961
hyoscyamine alone – Rt	USSR	Libizov, 1939
hyoscyamine 62 % + hyoscine 15 %; or hyoscyamine 40 % + hyoscine 28 %/var. *fastuosa*	IND	Shah–Khanna, 1965
Ch. T. Ch. forms		Libizov, 1939
OG changes		Hegnauer, 1954

D. sanguinea R. et P. – Sh

Ql. D. atropine	POR	Villalba et al., 1945
MA: hyoscine; hyoscyamine Pst.		Drey–Foster, 1953
hyoscine more, or at the same level as hyoscyamine		Evans et al., 1965

D. stramonium L. – Wp

Qn. D. IDP of variety of CHAR		Schratz, 1960a
Ql. D. hyoscine 9–34 %		Lien Song-Go–Hegnauer, 1955
hyoscyamine: hyoscine, at various rate		Avery et al., 1959
meteloidine Pst. or Abs.		Verzár–Sárkány, 1961
MA: hyoscine (cyto-races 'Poinsettia' and 'Globe')		Stary, 1960, 1963

Ch. T. DLP on OG and ecological factors   EVANS–PARTRIDGE, 1953
        cytological differentiated taxa   STARY, 1960
        the causes of OG changes   COSSON et al., 1966

Duboisia hopwoodii F. Muell. – Lf
Ql. D. nicotine; or nornicotine   AUL   BARNARD, 1952
Ch. T. DEP on area-origin; inheritance of Ch.
        CHAR

D. leichhardtii F. Muell. – Lf
Ql. D. *MA:* hyoscyamine; or hyoscine   BARNARD, 1952
        norhyoscyamine   HILLIS et al., 1954
Ch. T. DEP on area D; inheritance of Ch. CHAR   BARNARD, 1952

D. myoporoides R. Br. – Lf
Ql. D. hyoscine; or hyoscyamine; or hyoscine +   BARNARD, 1952
          hyoscyamine; or tropane bases + nicotine
          nicotine + nornicotine + hyoscine   BARRAU, 1957
          anabasine + isopelletierine   SCHRÖTER, 1965
Ch. T. DEP on area; localization of Ch. CHAR   BARNARD, 1952
        inheritance of Ch. CHAR   HILLS et al., 1954
        OG Ch. differentiation   MORTIMER–WILKINSON,
                                                           1957

Physalis ixocarpa Brot. – Sh
Ql. D. alkaloids Pst. or Abs.   AURICH et al., 1965, 1966

Solanum aculeatissimum Jacq. – Sh
Ql. D. alkaloids Pst. or Abs.   AURICH et al., 1965, 1967

S. atropurpureum Schrank – Sh
Ql. D. alkaloids Pst. or Abs.   AURICH et al., 1966, 1967

Withania somnifera Dun. – Wp
Ql. D. nicotine Pst.;   MAJUMDAR, 1955
        or nicotine Abs.   ROTHER et al., 1961
        alkaloid components the same, but **D** in *MA*   KHAFAGY et al., 1962

GERANIACEAE

Geranium sanguineum L. – Sh
Ql. D. 2 alkaloids in Tr./var. *prostratum* (Cav.) Pers.   COLL   AURICH et al., 1965
        or Abs.

OXALIDACEAE

Oxalis corniculata L. – Wp
Ql. D. alkaloids Pst.   N-Z   CAIN et al., 1961
        alkaloids Abs.   AUL   WEBB, 1949

ERYTHROXYLACEAE

Erythroxylum coca Lam. – Lf

Ql. D. cocaine 52 % + cinnamylcocaine 23 %   PERU   BÉZANGER–BEAUQUESNE,
                                                                      1958

  MA: cocaine   PERU   PEREIRA, 1957–58
  MA: cocaine;   INDO   EWERS–CALDWELL, 1959
  or cocaine 8 % + cinnamylcocaine 51 %   BOL
  cocaine + tropacocaine/var. *novogranatense*   HEGNAUER–FIKENSCHER,
    Morris; cocaine + cuscohygrine; or   1960
    cocaine + cynnamylcocaine/var. *spruceca-*
    num Burck

Ch. T. some minor MP D   EWERS–CALDWELL, 1959
  DEP on areal D; OG changes; Ch. races   HEGNAUER–FIKENSCHER,
                                                                     1960

EUPHORBIACEAE

Croton flavens L. – Wp

Ql. D. norsinoacutine/as crystalline compound/+   STUART–CHAMBEPS, 1967
    flavinantine/serrate leaf margin variety
  norsinoacutine/amorphous solid/+ salutaridine   CHAMBERS et al., 1966
    /C. *balsamifera* Jacq.
  norsinoacutine+sinoacutine+flavinantine   CHAMBERS–STUART, 1968

Ch. T. Ch. inhomogeneity of the species, the entire   CHAMBERS–STUART
    leaf margin variety has the ability to
    perform N-methylations; IDP of area

C. sparsiflorus Morong – Lf

Ql. D. sparsiflorine/amorphous powder   SAHA, 1959
  sparsiflorine/as crystal   CHATTERJEE et al., 1965
  crotsparine + pronuciferine   BHAKUNI–DHAR, 1967

Phyllanthus discoideus Muell.-Arg. – R. Ba

Ql. D. allosecurinine + phyllanthine + phyllanti-   CON   PARELLO–MUNAVALLI,
    dine   1965
  allosecurinine   NIG   BEVAN et al., 1964
  phyllanthine   I-C   PARELLO, 1963

Securinega suffruticosa (Pall.) Rehd. – Lf

Ql. D. securinine + suffruticodine + suffruticonine   USSR   MURAVEVA–KUZUVKOV,
                                                                     1963
  securine + allosecurinine + dihydrosecuri-   JAP   SAITO et al., 1963
    nine
  allosecurine   IND   CHATTERJEE et al., 1964
  securinine; or securinine + virosecurinine   JAP   HORII et al., 1964
    /var. *amami*
  allosecurinine; or securinine + dihydro-   SAITO et al., 1964
    securinine/var. *amami*

Ch. T. DEP on areal D; and on sex of plants   HEGNAUER, 1966

S. virosa (Willd.) Pax et Hoffm. – R. Ba

Ql. D. hordenine   PARIS et al., 1955
  hordenine + virosecurinine + norsecurinine   JAP   NAKANO at al., 1963
  norsecurinine 99 % + dihydronorsecurine   TAI   SAITO et al., 1965

PAPAVERACEAE

Argemone platyceras Link et Otto – Wp
Ql. D. protopine + allocryptopine   Boit–Flentje, 1960
        platycerine; or no-phenolic bases   Slavik–Slavikova, 1963

A. pleiacantha Greene – Wp
Ql. D. berberine 60 % + allocryptopine 10 %; or   Stermitz, 1968
        berberine 45 % + allocryptopine 30 %/ssp.
            ambigua Ownb.;
        or berberine 30 % + cryptopine 25 %/ssp.
            ambigua;
        or berberine 10 % + bisnorargemonine 45%;
        or bisnorargemonine 20 % + protopine 55 %
        /ssp. *ambigua*;
        or bisnorargemonine 15 % + munitagine
        75 %/ssp. *pinnatisecta* Ownb.

A. sanguinea Greene – Wp
Ql. D. berberine 94 % (purple Fl.); or   Stermitz, 1968
        berberine 68 % + allocryptopine 22 %
        (white Fl)

A. squarrosa Greene – Wp
Ql. D. allocryptopine as *MA*, if not the only   Soine–Willette, 1960
        muramine 80 % + berberine 20 %; or   Stermitz, 1967
        berberine 80 % + muramine 20 %
Ch. T. related to a genetic nonhomogeneity   Stermitz

Chelidonium majus L. – Rt
Qn. D. 0·7–2·5 % alkaloid-content   Slavik et al., 1965

Eschscholtzia californica Cham. – Wp
Ql. D. allocryptopine   Battandier, 1895
        chelerythrine + sanguinarine   Slavik–Slavikova, 1954
        allocryptopine + berberine   Gertig, 1964

Glaucium flavum Crantz – Wp
Ql. D. aurotensine   CAN   Manske, 1939
        glaucine   GER   Fischer, 1901
        corydine + norcorydine; or chelidonine +   CSR   Slavik–Slavikova, 1955,
            norchelidonine   1959
        glaucine   POL   Gertig et al., 1966

Papaver argemone L. – Wp
Ql. D. rhoeadin + protopine + rhoeagenine   Santavy et al., 1960
        rhoeadin Abs., but 14 alkaloids   Slavik–Appelt, 1965

P. bracteatum Lindl. – Wp + Rt or LX
Ql. D. isothebaine + oripavine + bracteine   USSR   Kiseliov–Konovalova,
                                                          1948
        thebaine 98 %   COLL   Neubauer–Mothes, 1963
        isothebaine + bractamine   GER   Heydenreich–Pfeifer,
                                                          1965

184

bractamine + orientalinone + salutaridine	HEYDENREICH–PFEIFER, 1966
thebaine + alpinigenine; or thebaine	BŐHM, 1966
Ch. T. latex D as Ch. races	SCHRATZ, 1960b
Ch. races	NEUBAUER–MOTHES, 1963
OG changes; Fl colour CORR with number of alkaloids and with thebaine presence morphologically indistinguishable Ch. types	BŐHM, 1966

P. dubium L. – Wp/LX

Ql. D. in number and Rf of alkaloids	ASAHINA et al., 1957
aporheine; or berberine/var. *lecoquii* (Lamotte) Fedde	SLAVIK, 1958
aporheidine + aporheine	BOIT–FLENTJE, 1960
rhoeagenine/var. *lecoquii*	PREININGER et al., 1962
rhoeadine + protopine	SANTAVY, 1963
berberine + allocryptopine/var. *lecoquii;* berberine + allocryptopine/ssp. *albiflorum* (Boiss.) Dost.	SLAVIK, 1964
Ch. T. Ch. D at species level	SLAVIK, 1964

P. fugax Poir. – Wp

Ql. D. mecambrine + armepavine + floripavine	YUNUSOV, 1961
pronuciferine + armepavine little	KÜHN–PFEIFER, 1965

P. glaucum Boiss. et Hausskn. – Wp

Ql. D. *MA:* rhoeadine	SANTAVY et al., 1960
glaucamine + glaupavine + coptysine	BOIT–FLENTJE, 1960
glaudine + glaucamine + papaverrubine B	PFEIFER–MANN, 1965
glaupavine + glaucamine + coptysine + glaudine; rhoeadine Abs.	SLAVIK–APPELT, 1965
Ch. T. Ch. races	PFEIFER–MANN, 1965

P. lateritium C. Koch – LX

Ch. T. D in composition; Ch. races	SCHRATZ, 1960b

P. nudicaule L. – Wp

Ql. D. nudaurine/var. *aurantiacum* Loisel; or amuronine + amuroline + muramine /var. *amurense* hort.; or amurine + muramine + protopine/var. *croceum* Ledeb.	BOIT–FLENTJE, 1959
MA: muramine/ssp. *rubro-aurantiacum* Fedde and ssp. *xanthopetalum* (Trautv.) Fedde	MATUROVÁ–PREININGER, 1962
protopine Pst. or Abs./ssp. *xanthopetalum;* or rhoeadine + protopine/var. *leiocarpum* Turz.	MATUROVA et al., 1966
coptysine + sanguinarine	HAKIM et al., 1961
Ch. T. LX D as Ch. races	SCHRATZ, 1960b

P. orientale L. – Wp

Ql. D. thebaine + isothebaine	GER	KLEE, 1914
thebaine + oripavine	USSR	KONOVALOVA et al., 1935
isothebaine + glaucidine	USA	FULTON, 1944

P. orientale (continued)

thebaine + isothebaine; or isothebaine alone	COLL	DAWSON–JAMES, 1956
D in number and Rf of alkaloids	JAP	ASAHINA et al., 1957
isothebaine + thebaine; or thebaine alone; or isothebaine + laudanine + (protopine, or narcotine); or isothebaine and thebaine Abs.	COLL	NEUBAUER–MOTHES, 1961
Ch. T. OG changes		KLEE, 1914
Ch. races		KLEINSCHMIDT, 1961
Ch. race as "type" and "variation"		NEUBAUER–MOTHES, 1961

P. pavonium Fisch. et Mey. – Rt

Ql. D. roemeridine + α-allocryptopine	USSR	PLATONOVA et al., 1956
rhoeadine + unknown alkaloid	CSR	SANTAVY et al., 1960
protopine + allocryptopine + roemeridine; rhoeadine Abs.		SLAVIK–APPELT, 1965

P. persicum Lindl. – Wp

Ql. D. coptysine 80 %	SLAVIK, 1960
mecambrine + armepavine; or mecambrine alone	KÜHN–PFEIFER, 1965

P. rhoeas L. – Wp

Ql. D. rhoeadine + morphine + papaverine	USSR	SOKOLOV, 1952
rhoeadine + 3 unknown alkaloids	GER	AWE–WINKLER, 1957
rhoeadine + protopine + coptisine Tr.	CSR	SLAVIK, 1959
rhoeadine + thebaine/*P. strigosum*	CSR	SANTAVY et al., 1960
rhoeadine, thebaine Abs./*P. strigosum* Schur	CSR	SLAVIK–APPELT, 1965
Ch. T. LX D as Ch. races		SCHRATZ–EGELS, 1958

P. somniferum L. – Fr

Ql. D. in morphine content: 1–10 ‰	USSR	MATVEEV, 1959
0·5–7 ‰	COLL	ZOSCHKE, 1962
in codeine content: 0–46 γ	COLL	TÉTÉNYI–LŐRINCZ, 1964
in thebaine content: 0–32 γ		
in papaverine cont.: 0–50 γ		
Ql. D. morphine 50–88 %		KÜSSNER, 1940
codeine 19–22 %, or 0·3–0·8 % (of morphine)		SARAEVA, 1952
narcotine 3–57 % (of morphine)		PFEIFER, 1956
MA: morphine; or codeine; or narcotoline;		MOTHES, 1958, 1961
		PFEIFER–HEYDENREICH, 1961
or narceine		NEUBAUER–MOTHES, 1961
MA: morphine; or thebaine; or codeine; or papaverine; or in combinations		TÉTÉNYI–LŐRINCZ, 1964
Ch. T. inheritance of Ch. CHAR; Ch. races		MOTHES, 1958
DEP on geographical and ecological factors		ILINSKAYA–YOSIFOVA, 1956
localization intraindividual		NIKONOV, 1965
DEP on Fr form, Sd colour		DETERMANN, 1940
IDP of MP CHAR		SÁRKÁNY et al., 1959
IDP of Fl and Sd colour		TÉTÉNYI-LŐRINC, 1964
OG changes, and differentiation; chemoconvar.		VÁGÚJFALVI–TÉTÉNYI, 1965

LOBELIACEAE

Lobelia inflata L. – Wp
Qn. D. 122–1049 mg % alkaloid-content   BRANDT, 1951
Qh. T. CORR Abs. between Ch. and MP CHAR

ASTERACEAE / COMPOSITAE

Anthemis tinctoria L. – Sh
Ql. D. alkaloids Pst.; or Abs./var. *pallida* DC.   AURICH et al., 1967

Gnaphalium luteo-album L. – Wp
Ql. D. alkaloid Pst.   WEBB, 1949
alkaloid Abs.   CAIN et al., 1961

Nardosmia laevigata (Willd.) DC. – Rh
Ql. D. platyphylline + renardine + senecionine   MASSAGETOV–KUZUVKOV,
1953
platyphylline + seneciphylline   GLIZIN–SENOV, 1965

Senecio platyphyllus DC. – Rh
Ql. D. platyphylline + seneciphylline + heliotri-   KONOVALOVA, 1951
dane
sarracine   BANKOVSKAYA–BANKOVSKI,
1959
Ch. T. 2 direction in breeding for Ch. CHAR   MATVEEV, 1959

S. riddellii Torr. et Gray – Wp
Ql. D. riddelliine; or retrorsine +   ADAMS–GOVINDACHARI,
riddelliine/var. *parksii* Cory   1949

Siegesbeckia orientalis L. – Wp
Ql. D. alkaloid Pst.   WEBB, 1949
alkaloid Abs.   CAIN et al., 1961

Vittadinia triloba DC. – W
Ql. D. alkaloid Pst.   WEBB, 1949
alkaloid Abs.   CAIN et al., 1961

NYCTAGINACEAE

Heimerliodendron brunonianum (Endl.) Skottsb. – Wp
Ql. D. alkaloid Pst.   CAIN et al., 1961
alkaloid Abs.   WEBB, 1952

CARYOPHYLLACEAE

Gypsophila paniculata L. – Lf
Ql. D. alkaloids Pst.; or Abs.   AURICH et al., 1965, 1967

187

Melandrium album (Mill.) Garcke – Sh
Ql. D. alkaloids Pst.; or Abs.   AURICH et al., 1965, 1967

CHENOPODIACEAE

Anabasis aphylla L. – Wp
Qn. D. 0·5–5 %; or 5–14 % alkaloid-content   MASSAGETOV, 1947
Ql. D. anabasine 88–95 %; or 2–22 %
    additional unknown alkaloid (cotton   MOTHES, 1962
    deterioring)
Ch. T. CORR Abs. between Ch. and MP CHAR   MASSAGETOV, 1947
    OG changes   KLISHCHEV, 1961

Beta vulgaris L. – St + Rt
Ql. D. betacyanines in various number   REZNIK, 1955
    betaxanthines in various number and level   PIATRELLI et al., 1965
    betacyanic glycosides in various number and TYIHÁK, 1964
    level

Girgensohnia oppositifolia (Pall.) Fenzl – Wp
Qn. D. 1 % alkaloid-content; or only in Tr.   SOKOLOV, 1957
Ql. D. girgensonine; or methylpiperideine   JANASHEVSKI–STEPANOV,
                                                 1946

Salsola kali L. – Wp
Qn. D. 0·2 % salsoline   BORKOWSKI et al., 1959
    alkaloid only in Tr.   BERNÁTH–OGNIANOV, 1962

S. paletzkiana Litw. – Wp
Ql. D. alkaloid Pst. (0·2 %); or Abs.   SOKOLOV, 1952

S. richteri Kar. – Wp
Ql. D. salsoline 90 %; or salsolidine 60 %; or alka- SOKOLOV, 1952
    loids Abs.
Ch. T. OG changes   SOKOLOV, 1959

AMARANTHACEAE

Alternanthera denticulata R. Br. – Wp
Ql. D. alkaloid Pst.   WEBB, 1952
    alkaloid Abs.   CAIN et al., 1961

AMARYLLIDACEAE

Amaryllis bella-donna L. – Bu
Ql. D. ambelline + lycorine + caranine   SAR   MASON et al., 1955
    or all 3 + bellamarine   USA
    all 4 + amaryllidine   NED   BOIT–EHMKE, 1956
    belladine   FRA   WARNHOFF, 1957
    amaryllidine + lycorine + caranine + am-   BOIT–DÖPKE, 1959
      belline + galanthamine + lycorenine/var.
      purpurea

188

Leucojum aestivum L. – Rh + Lf
Qn. D. 0·01 %, or 0·13 % alkaloid content   USSR   Utkin, 1959
Ql. D. galanthamine + lycorine + isotacettine; or   USSR   Proskurnina, 1957
    galanthamine 24 % + lycorine 18 %, iso-   GER   Boit et al., 1957
    tacettine Abs.
    galanthamine Pst. or Abs.   BUL   Stojanov–Savtchev, 1964

Ch. T. 2 chemotypes, without MP D   Stojanov–Savtchev

Pancratium maritimum L. – Bu
Ql. D. lycorine   FRA   Dumérac, 1954
    lycorine + tacettine + haemanthidine   USSR   Proskurnina, 1955
    lycorine 8 % + tacettine 43 %   NED   Boit–Ehmke, 1956
    tacettine Pst. or Abs.   MED   Sandberg–Agurell, 1959

Ch. T. inheritance of Ch. CHAR; Ch. races IDP
    of ecological factors; DEP on origin   Sandberg–Michel, 1963

GRAMINEAE

Lolium perenne L. – Wp
Qn. D. 0·3–100 mg % alkaloids   Grimett–Melville, 1941
    11–27, or 72–173 mg % alkaloids   Clare–Morice, 1945
Ql. D. perloline in wide VAR: 1·5–50 %   Reifer–Bathurst, 1943

Phalaris arundinacea L. – Lf
Ql. D. hordenine + methoxy–methyltriptamine   Wilkinson, 1958
    gramine + dimethyltriptamine at   Culvenor et al., 1964
    various proportions
Ch. T. DEP on palatable or unpalatable   Culvenor et al.
    strains

5. ISORHODANIDOGENES

LIMNANTHACEAE

Limnanthes douglasii R. Br. – Sd
Ql. D. glucolimnanthine

ETTLINGER–LUNDEEN, 1956

unknown isorhodanidogene differing from glucolimnanthin/var. *nivea* C. T. Mason

MILLER et al., 1964

EUPHORBIACEAE

Putranjiva roxburghii Wall. – Sd
Ql. D. glucocochlearin 69 % + glucoputranjivin 28 % + phenyl-isothiocyanate 3 %

PUNTAMBEKAR, 1950

glucoputranjivin 82 % + glucochlearin 16 % + 2-methylbutyl-isothiocyanate 2 %

KJAER–FRIAS, 1962

CAPPARIDACEAE

Crataeva roxburghii R. Br. – Ba
Ql. D. glucotropeolin   IND

CHAKRAVARTI, 1951

glucocapparin   DEN

KJAER–THOMSEN, 1962

BRASSICACEAE/CRUCIFERAE

Arabis hirsuta (L.) Scop. – Sd
Ql. D. glucohirsutin alone; or as *MC;* or at the same level as 5 other isorhodanidogenes

KJAER–HANSEN, 1958

A. holboelli Hornem. – Sd
Ql. D. one secondary isorhodanidogene more or less

KJAER–HANSEN, 1958

Brassica juncea (L.) Czern. et Coss. – Sd
Ql. D. 0·4–0·5, or 1–1·2 % isothiocyanate

KUCHUMOVA, 1959

0·7, or 0·9–1·1 % isothiocyanate

DUBLIANSKAYA, 1958

Ql. D. sinigrin

HOFMANN, 1888

sinigrin + gluconapin 50 %

ANONYMOUS, 1910

gluconapin (crotonylisothiocyanate)

PEACH–TRACEY, 1955

sinigrin; or sinigrin + gluconapin

DELAVEAU, 1957, 1959

sinigrin; or gluconapin

HEMINGWAY et al., 1961

Ch. T. CORR with CHAR of varietas

DELAVEAU, 1959

DEP on original area	HEMINGWAY et al., 1961
inheritance of Ch. CHAR	DUBLIANSKAIA–MARCHENKO, 1963
2 Ch. differentiated geographical taxa	VAUGHAN et al., 1963

B. napus L. – Sd
Qn. D. 0·26–0·54 % isothiocyanates/cv. of var.   TRZEBNY, 1967
    oleifera DC.
    in glucobrassicin and neoglucobrassicin con-   ELLERSTRŐM–JOSEFFSON,
    tent   1967
Ch. T. CORR between plants and their progenies;
    VAR in rhodanid content genetically
    determined

B. nigra (L.) Koch – Sd

Qn. D. great varietal D	DEN	JENSEN et al., 1953
0·9–1·4 % sinigrin-content	USSR	VOSKRESENSKAIA, 1958
0·3–1·7 % sinigrin-content	COLL	TÉTÉNYI, 1963
Ql. D. in number, Rf and level of isorhodanidogene-components presents	COLL	TÉTÉNYI, 1963
Ch. T. inheritance of Ch. CHAR of quantitative D chemoconcultas	COLL	TÉTÉNYI, 1963

B. oleracea L. – Wp
Qn. D. in rhodanidogenic glucosides between varie-   JOSEFSSON, 1966
    ties/var. *acephala* DC.
    132–164 mg % thiocyanate in dry matter;   JOHNSTON–JONES, 1966
    or 86–90 mg% ; or only 46 %/var. *ace-*
    phala DC. (kale)
Ch. T. three exclusive groups of varieties
    IDP of polyploidy level

B. rapa L. – Sd
Qn. D. 0·3–0·5 %, or 0·7–1·5 % isothiocyanates   WETTER, 1955, 1957
    0·5–0·85 % isothiocyanates (cv.-s of var.   TRZEBNY, 1967
    oleifera DC.)
    great VAR in isothiocyanates-contents   APPELQUIST, 1962
Ch. T. CORR with MP forms   APPELQUIST, 1962

Capsella bursa-pastoris L. – Wp
Qn. D. great VAR of strains: very picking (sinigrin)   KJAER, 1962
    or harmless

Iberis sempervirens L. – Sd
Ql. D. glucoiberin; or glucoibervirin (cv.)   GMELIN, 1966

LILIACEAE

Allium falcifolium H. et A. – Bu + Lf
Ql. D. allylsulfide radical 12·8 % (pink Fl); or only   SAGHIR et al., 1966
    0·7 % (white Fl)

191

CONCLUSIONS

Surveying the literature on the occurrences of infraspecific chemical taxa and taking into account also our own experimental results, we are able to report on the polychemism and the chemical taxa of 106 plant families and about 750 species of medicinal plants. Besides the otherwise chemically differentiated algae (from *Chlorophyta* to *Rhodophyta*), infraspecific chemical differences can be found in the plant kingdom in all phyla, in the majority of classes and in all the branches of *Angiospermae* (cf. Table IV).

All that has been said above, considering the relatively short history of research in this field as well, proves that infraspecific chemical taxa are generally universal. Moreover, they can be found ubiquitously, from the primitive species to those of the highest organization. The existence of infraspecific chemical taxa is not an isolated occurrence of individual character but rather a general aspect of the phylogeny of the plant kingdom thus far studied only to a small extent. We hope, however, that in the near future research will extend all families and genera demonstrating species not yet treated so far from this point of view. Screening for further active principles of medicinal plant species will certainly lead to a better and wider knowledge of this field.

We can see from the data reviewed in this book that polychemism very often occurs without any morphological differences. This is true even though we have applied the name of a morphologically determined taxon below the rank of species, indicating only that the chemical and morphological relations of the differentiated species have not yet been clarified. But we have to resume that besides the morphological differentiation accepted so far as a fundamental criterion, or even to a fuller extent, the rule of differentiation in the chemism, metabolism prevails. This rule is more fundamental and more closely connected with both physiology and practical life itself than the earlier accepted morphological, anatomical or cytological differences, and at the same time it also shows the other, the primary aspect of the living. We must follow this line — the differentiated and sometimes clearly integrated patterns of vital function — if we want to arrive at a deeper notion of phylogeny.

Since morphological properties are fortuitous because they are not in close correlation with chemism, the chemical ones are more suitable for taxonomic purposes. On the basis of our present knowledge, this must be taken into account in classification, systematization, mainly within the species itself.

TABLE IV

TAXA WITH INFRASPECIFIC CHEMICAL DIFFERENTIATION

PHYLA	FAMILIAE
MYCOPHYTA	*Aspergillaceae, Clavicipitaceae, Agaricaceae, Sphaerioidaceae,*
LICHENOPHYTA	*Rocellaceae, Peltigeraceae, Stictaceae, Cladoniaceae, Lecanoraceae, Parmeliaceae, Usneaceae*
BRYOPHYTA	*Grimaldiaceae, Mniaceae*
PTERIDOPHYTA	*Lycopodiaceae, Equisetaceae, Polypodiaceae, Aspleniaceae, Aspidiaceae*
GYMNOSPERMATOPHYTA	*Pinaceae, Taxodiaceae, Podocarpaceae, Cupressaceae, Ephedraceae*
ANGIOSPERMATOPHYTA*	*Magnoliaceae, Himantandraceae, Winteraceae, Eupomatiaceae, Monimiaceae, Hernandiaceae, Lauraceae, Myristicaceae, Eupteleaceae, Lardizabalaceae, Menispermaceae, Berberidaceae, Ranunculaceae, Helleboraceae, Aristolochiaceae, Piperaceae, Hamamelidaceae, Rosaceae, Grossulariaceae, Crassulaceae, Mimosaceae, Caesalpiniaceae, Fabaceae, Myrtaceae, Rutaceae, Burseraceae, Simaroubaceae, Meliaceae, Sapindaceae, Corynocarpaceae, Celastraceae, Apiaceae, Valerianaceae, Dipsacaceae*
	Loganiaceae, Apocynaceae, Asclepiadaceae, Rubiaceae, Polemoniaceae, Convolvulaceae, Verbenaceae, Lamiaceae, Solanaceae, Scrophulariaceae, Myoporaceae, Malvaceae, Limnanthaceae, Geraniaceae, Oxalidaceae, Erythroxylaceae, Zygophyllaceae, Euphorbiaceae, Buxaceae
	Papaveraceae, Fumariaceae, Capparidaceae, Brassicaceae, Cucurbitaceae, Dipterocarpaceae, Theaceae, Hypericaceae, Ericaceae, Lobeliaceae, Asteraceae,
	Nyctaginaceae, Caryophyllaceae, Chenopodiaceae, Amaranthaceae, Myrsinaceae, Polygonaceae, Moraceae, Cannabiaceae, Betulaceae, Juglandaceae
	Liliaceae, Amaryllidaceae, Agavaceae, Dioscoreaeaec, Cyperaceae, Gramineae, Zingiberaceae
	Araceae, Lemnaceae

*Based on Soó's (1967) Die modernen Systeme der Angiospermen.

PLANT GENERA INDEX*

Abies [3] 95
Acacia [2] 162
Achillea 33 [13] 56, 74, 121—122
Acocanthera [1] 132
Aconitum [2] 139
Acorus [1] 37, 131
Agastache [1] 109
Agauria [1] 136
Agave [9] 28, 137—138
Agropyron [1] 169
Akebia [1] 161
Allium [2] 169, 191
Alnus [2] 136
Aloë [2] 152
Alpinia [2] 130—131
Alternanthera [1] 136, 188
Althaea 56
Amanita [1] 170
Amaryllis [1] 188
Ambrosia [9] 125—126
Ammi [1] 23, 157
Anabasis [1] 33, 35, 188
Andropogon see Cymbopogon
Anemone [1] 150
Anethum 27 [1] 106
Angelica [4] 56, 157—158
Aniba [2] 100, 156
Anthemis [1] 187
Antiaris [1] 136
Anzia [2] 146
Arabis [2] 190
Arachis 42
Arctostaphylos [1] 156
Ardisia [2] 152
Argemone [4] 184
Artemisia [24] 56, 122—124 126—127
Asahinea [1] 146
Asarum [1] 101
Asiasarum [2] 101

Aspergillus [1] 144
Aspidosperma [5] 177—178
Asplenium [1] 149
Atropa [1] 28, 32, 56, 180

Backhousia [3] 101, 155
Baeckaea [1] 101
Baptisia [1] 18, 37, 45, 162, 175
Berberis [3] 173
Beta [1] 188
Blepharocalyx [1] 101
Boronia [3] 104—105
Bothriochloa [5] 129
Bowiea [1] 137
Brassica [5] 53, 56, 59, 74, 190—191
Browallia [2] 133, 181
Bursera [1] 106
Buxus [1] 143

Calophyllum [1] 158
Calythrix [1] 101
Camellia [1] 167
Cannabis [1] 56, 74, 129
Capsella [1] 191
Capsicum [4] 56, 158—159
Carex [1] 139
Carpodetus [1] 162
Carum [1] 27, 28, 56, 106
Cassia [1] 151
Catha [1] 176
Catharanthus [1] 178
Celosia [1] 136
Cerbera [2] 132
Cestrum [2] 133
Cetraria [3] 146
Chamaecyparis [1] 99, 160
Chelidonium [1] 184
Chenopodium [5] 128
Chrysanthemum [3] 23, 56, 124—125, 127

Cinchona [5] 10, 50, 72, 73—74, 179—180
Cinnamomum [13] 59, 73, 74, 100, 153—154
Cissampelos [1] 161, 173
Cistus 56
Citrullus [2] 135—136
Citrus [6] 105
Cladonia [7] 195
Claviceps [2] 22, 43, 54, 110
Clematis [1] 151
Cnicus [1] 127
Cocculus 23
Coriandrum [1] 20, 27, 56, 107
Corynocarpus [1] 166
Crataegus 35
Crataera [1] 190
Crithmum [1] 107
Crotalaria [3] 174
Croton [2] 183
Crucianella [1] 180
Cryptocarya [1] 172
Cucumis [1] 136
Cucurbita [1] 136
Cuminum [1] 107
Cunninghamia [1] 98, 160
Cymbopogon [5] 10, 56, 180
Cyperus [1] 129
Cytisus [3] 49, 175

Dacrydium [3] 98—99
Daphnandra [1] 172
Datura [5] 25, 28, 56, 69, 181
Daucus [1] 107, 166
Derris [1] 156
Dicentra [1] 167
Dictamnus 21
Digitalis [4] 22, 37, 56, 65 71, 134

*Figures given in square brackets refer to the number of the species treated in this book.

194

REFERENCES* TO THE SPECIAL PART

Abbayes, des H., Chadefaud, M., Ferré de, Y., et al. (1963) *Botanique*. Masson et Cie. Paris
Abisch, E. and Reichstein, T. (1960) *Helv. Chim. Acta* **43**, 1844
Abraham, A., Kirson, I., Glotter, E. and Lavie, D. (1968) *Phytochem.* **7**, 957
Achmatowicz, O. and Rodewald, W. (1955) *Roczn. Chem.* **29**, 509
Achmatowicz, O. and Uzieblo, W. (1938) *Roczn. Chem.* **18**, 88
Achmatowicz, O., Werner, O. and Zamojska, F. (1958) *Roczn. Chem.* **32**, 1127
Adams, R. and Govindachari, T. R. (1949) *J. Am. Chem. Soc.* **71**, 956
Adams, R. and Rogers, E. F. (1939) *J. Am. Chem. Soc.* **61**, 2815
Aebi, A. and Djerassi, C. (1959) *Helv. Chim. Acta* **42**, 1785
Aellen, P. (1960) Chenopodiaceae. In: Hegi, *Illustrierte Flora von Mitteleuropa*. vol. III. 2. 569. Hanser Vlg. München
Aguero, C. N. (1943) *Bol. Mus. Hist. Nat.* Prado **7**, 228
Ahmed, Z. F., Rizk, A. M. and Hamonda, F. M. (1964) *Lloydia* **27**, 115
Ahti, T. (1966) *Ann. Bot. Fenn.* **3**, 380
Aitken, P. W. (1928) *J. Indian Chem. Soc.* **47** T. 223
Aitken, P. W. (1929) *J. Indian Chem. Soc.* **48** T, 346
Alkemeyer, M. and Sander, H. (1961) *Tagungsber. Dtsch. Akad. Wiss.* Berlin, No. 27, 23
Alston, R. (1968) in: *Recent advances in phytochemistry* vol. **1**, 305
Alston, R. E. and Turner, B. L. (1963) *Biochemical Systematics*. Prentice Hall. Ind. Englewood Cliffs, N. J.
Anderson, E. (1950) *Ceiba* **1**, 50
Anderson, J. E., Evans, W. C. and Trease, C. W. (1961) *J. Pharm. Pharmacol.* **13**, 224
Anderweg, J. M. and de Bruyn, J. W. (1959) *Euphytica* **8**, 13
Anonymous (1910) *Ber. Roure–Bertrand*. Avril, 65
Anonymous (1910) *Schimmel Ber.* **112**, 135
Anonymous (1929) *Pharm. J.* **122**, 531
Anonymous (1937) *Bull. Imp. Inst.* **35**, 304
Anonymous (1961) *Miltitzer Berichte* **40**, 105, 108
Anonymous (1962) *Ann. Rep. of Pyrethrum Res. Sect. Rep. Board Kenya for 1962*
Anzaldo, F. E., Maranon, J. and Ancheta, S. F. (1957) *Philipp. J. Sci.* **86**, 233
Aplin, R. T. and Cambie, R. C. (1964) *N. Z. J. Sci.* **7**, 258
Aplin, R. T., Cambie, R. C., and Rutledge, P. S. (1963) *Phytochem.* **2**, 205
Appelquist, L. A. (1962) *Acta Chem. Scand.* **16**, 1284
(Arasimovich, V. V.) Арасимович, В. В. (1937) *Изв. АН СССР, сер. биол.* (Rec. Acad. Sci. USSR, Ser. Biol.) 1835
Arata, P. N. and Canzoneri, F. (1892) *Gaz. Chim. Ital.* **22**, 146
(Arbuzov, B. A.) Арбузов, Б. А. (1932) *Хим. Ж. Сер. Б.* (Chem. J. Ser. B) **5**, 788
(Arbuzov, B. A., Abramov, V. and Valitova, F.) Арбузов, Б. А., Абрамов, В., Валитова, Ф. (1932) *Ж. Общ. Хим.* (J. Gen. Chem.) **2**, 376
(Arbuzov, B. A., Krestinski, V., Liverovski, N. and Malberg, V.) Арбузов, Б. А., Крестинский, В., Ливеровский, Н., Мальберг, В. (1931) *Ж. Практ. Хим.* (J. Pract. Chem.) **129**, 97
Arcamone, F., Chain, E. B., Ferrett, A., et al. (1961) *Proc. Roy. Soc. Ser. B.* **155**, 26

*Bibliography given here comprises only the material published till December 1968.

Arndt, R. R., Brown, S. R., Ling, N. C., Roller, P., Djerassi, C., Ferreira, J. M., Gilbert, F. B., Miranda, E. C. and Flores, S. E. (1967) *Phytochem.* **6,** 1953

Arny, L. W. and Mulford, N. (1917) *J. Heredity* No. 3

Asahina, Y. (1937) *Bot. Mag. (Tokyo)* **51,** 759

Asahina, Y. (1964) *J. Jap. Bot.* **39,** 165, 205

Asahina, H., Kawatani, T., Ohno, M. and Fujita, S. (1957) *Bull. Narcot.* **9,** 20

Asahina, H. and Mizumachi, S. (1957) *Bull. Nat. Hyg. Lab.* **75,** 117

Asahina, Y. and Shibata, S. (1954) *Chemistry of Lichen substances.* Jap. Soc. Ueno, Tokyo

Attaway, A. A., Pieringer, A. P. and Barabas, L. J. (1966) *Phytochem.* **5,** 141

Augustin, B., Jávorka, S., Giovannini, R. and Rom, P. (1948) *Magyar gyógynövények* (Medicinal Plants in Hungary). Ministry of Agriculture, Budapest

Aurich, O., Danert, S., Pufahl, K., Romeike, A. et al. (1966) *Kulturpflanze* **14,** 447

Aurich, O. Danert, S., Romeike, A., Rönsch, H. et al. (1967) *Kulturpflanze* **15,** 205

Aurich, O., Osske, G., Pufahl, K., Romeike, A. and Rönsch, H. (1965) *Kulturpflanze* **13,** 622

Avery, A., Satina, S. and Rietsema, J. (1959) in: *The Genus Datura* (by Blakeslee, A. F.) Ronald Press, New York

(Avramova, B.) Аврамова, Б. (1962) *Фармация (София)* (Pharmacy) Sophia **12,** 14

Awe, W. and Winkler, W. (1957) *Arch. Pharm.* **290,** 367

Bacon, R. F. (1910) *Philipp. J. Sci.* **5,** 251

Baerheim-Svendsen, A. (1954) *Zur Chemie Norwegischen Umbelliferen.* J. Grundt Tanum Forlag, Oslo

(Bagrii, O. K.) Багрий, О. К. (1963) *Фармацевт. Ж.* (Pharmac. J.) **18,** 25

Baker, R. T. and Smith, H. G. (1902—1920) *A research on the Eucalyptus in regard to their essential oils.* Ed. 1, 2, Sydney

Baker, R. T. and Smith, H. G. (1922) *J. Roy. Soc.* N. S. W. **56,** 115

Baker, W. and Ollis, W. D. (1962) Byflavonyls. In: *Recent development in the Chemistry of natural phenolic compounds.* By W. D. Ollis, New York

Bal, S. N. (1953) *Ind. J. Pharm.* **15,** 91

Balansard, J. and Delphaut, J. (1945) *Médicine Tropic.* **5,** 170

Balcarovna, E. (1963) *Biul. Inst. Rosl. Leczn.* **9,** 1

Balcar-Skrzydlewska, E. and Borkowski, B. (1966) Abhdlgen Dtsch. Ak. Wiss. Berlin, 3. Intern. Symp. No 3, 265

Bally, D. R. O., Thudim, F., Mohr, K., Schindler, O. and Reichstein, T. (1958) *Helv. Chim. Acta* **41,** 446

Banes, D., Houk, A. E. M. and Wolff, J. (1958) *J. Am. Pharm. Ass.* **47,** 625

(Bankovskaya, A. N. and Bankovski, A. I.) Банковская, А. Н., Банковский, А. И. (1959) *Тр. ВИЛАР* (Works of St. Inst. Medicinal and Aromatic Plants) **11,** 46

(Bankovski, A. I., Frolova, V. I. and Zherlesnova, J. S.) Банковский, А. И., Фролова, В.И., Жерлеснова, Й. С. (1959) *Мед. Промышл.* (Med. Industr.) **11,** (12) 23

Bannister, M. H., Breverton, H. V. and McDonald, I. R. C. (1959) *Svensk Pappers Tidning* **62,** 567

Bannister, M. H., Williams, A. C., McDonald, I. R. C. and Forde, M. B. (1962) *N. Z. J. Sci.* **5,** 486

Baquar, S. R. and Reese, G. (1965) *Pharmazie* **20,** 214

Barcelo, C. M. (1949) *Timol. Afinidad* **26,** 63

Barnard, C. (1952) *Econ. Bot.* **6,** 3

Barnard, C. and Finnemore, K. (1945) *J. Counc. Sci. Ind. Res. Austr.* **18,** 277

Barrau, J. (1957) *J. Agr. Trop. Bot. Appl.* **4,** 453

Barraud, M. (1950) *Schimmel Berichte* 111

Barriga-Villalba, A. M., Medina, M. R. and Albarraica, L. (1945) *An. Soc. Biol. Bogota* 189

Barton, D. H. R., De Mayo, P. and Orr, J. C. (1956) *J. Chem. Soc.* 4160

Baslas, K. K. (1955) *J. Ind. Chem. Soc.* **32,** 228

Baslas, K. K. (1968) *Ess. Oil. Rec.* **59,** 103

Bate-Smith, E. C. and Metcalfe, C. R. (1957) *J. Linn. Soc.* **55,** 669

Battandier, J. A. (1895) *C. Rend. Ac. Sci. France* **120,** 1276
Bauer, S., Masler L. and Országh, S. (1957) *Chem. Abstr.* **51,** 8374
Bauer, S., Országh, S. and Bauerova, O. (1960) *Planta Med.* **8,** 145
Beath, G. B. (1933) *J. Indian Chem. Soc.* **52,** 338
Beckett, A. H., Shellard, E. J. and Tackie, A. N. (1965) *Planta Med.* **13,** 241
Bejnarowitz, E. A. and Kirch, E. R. (1963) *J. Pharm. Sci.* **52,** 988
Békésy, M. (1943) *MTA Math. Term. Tud. Ért.* (Rec. of Mathematics and Natural Sciences of Hung. Acad. Sci.) **62,** 137
Békésy, M. and Garay, A. (1960) Az anyarozs. Claviceps purpurea (Fr.) Tul. *Magyarország Kultúrflórája* (Cult. Flora of Hungary) vol. I, 10. Akadémiai Kiadó, Budapest
Benedek, L. (1958) Délalf. Mg. Kis. Int. Jelentése (Report of the Exp. Agr. Inst. South-Hungarian Plain) 258
(Berezovskaya, T. P.) Березовская, Т. П. (1962) *Сб. Тр. Повыящ. XX. Фармацевт. Фак.* (Coll. of works devoted to XX. Pharmac. Fac.)
Bergane, K. and Nordal, A. (1958) *Medd. Norsk. Farmac. Selsk.* **20,** 70
Bernasconi, R., Gill, S. and Steinegger, E. (1965) *Pharm. Acta Helv.* **40,** 275
Bernáth, G. and Ognyanov, I. (1962) *Acta Chim. Hung.* **32,** 467
Bertho, A. and Stoll, A. (1952) *Chem. Ber.* **85,** 663
Berthold, R., Wehrli, W. and Reichstein, T. (1965) *Helv. Chim. Acta* **48,** 1634
Bertram, J. and Walbaum, H. (1897) *Arch. Pharmaz.* **235,** 176
Bewan, C. W. L. et al. (1964) *Chem. and Ind.* **838,** 2054
Beyermann, H. C. and Muller, Y.M.F. (1955) *Rec. Trav. Chim.* 1568
Beyrich, T. (1965) *Planta Med.* **13,** 439
Bézanger-Beauquesne, L. (1958) *Bull. Soc. Bot. France* **105,** 266
Bhakuni, D. S. and Dhar, M. M. (1957) *Experientia* **24,** 10
Bhargava, P. P. and Haksar, C. N. (1962) *Ind. Oil. Soap J.* **27,** 147
Bhattacharryya, S. C. (1956) *J. Indian Chem. Soc.* **33,** 579
Bhattacharryya, S. C. and Sharma-Dhar, R. (1956) *J. Sci. Ind. Res.* **15B,** 363
Bhrara, S. C., Jain, A. C., Seshadri, T. R. (1954) *Current Sci.* **33,** 303
Bianchi. E. (1960) *Rass. Chim.* **12**(5), 42
Bianchi, E., Culvenor, C. C. J. and Loder, J. W. (1968) *Austral. J. Chem.* **21,** 1109
Bick, I. R. C., Taylor, W. I. and Todd, A. R. (1953) *J. Chem. Soc.* 695
Bienmann, K., Spiteller, G. and Friedmann, M. (1963) *J. Am. Chem. Soc.* **85,** 631
Billek, G. (1964) *Fortschritte Chem. Org. Naturstoffe* **22,** 115
Binns, S. V., Halpern, F., Hughes, R. K. and Ritchie, E. (1957) *Austral. J. Chem.* **10,** 480
Binns, S. V., Dunstan, P. J., Guise, G. B., Holder, G. H., Mollis, A. F., McCredil, R. S., Pinkey, J. T., Frager, R. H., Rasmussen, H., Ritchie, E. and Taylor, W. E. (1965) *Aus. J. Chem.* **18,** 569
Birch, A. J. (1963) Biosynthetic Pathways. In: *Chemical Plant Taxonomy.* Ed. T. Swain. Academic Press, London and New York, 141
Birrell, K. S. (1932) *J. Soc. Chem. Ind.* **51** T, 397
Bisset, N. G. (1957) *Ann. Bogor* **2,** 193, 211, 219
Bisset, N. G. (1966) *Lloydia* **29,** 1
Bite, P. (1960) Private communication
Bite, P., Jókay, L. and Pongrácz-Sterk, L. (1962) *Acta Chim. Ac. Sci. Hung.* **34,** 363
Björkmann, O. and Holmgren, P. (1958) *Physiol. Pl.* **11,** 154
Björkmann, O. and Holmgren, P. (1960) *Physiol. Pl.* **13,** 582
Blackie, W. J. (1929) *J. Soc. Chem. Ind.* **48** T, 357
Blazek, Z. and Stary, F. (1961) *Pharmacie* **16,** 477
Blazek, Z. and Stary, F. (1965) *XXV. Congr. Int. FIP (Prague) Res. Trav.* 84
Blight, M. M. and McDonald, I. R. C. (1963) *N. Z. J. Sci.* **6,** 229
Blight, M. M. and McDonald, I. R. C. (1964) *N. Z. J. Bot.* **2,** 44
Blight, M. M. and McDonald, I. R. C. (1965) *N. Z. J. Sci.* **7,** 212
Bognár, R. and Makleit, S. (1961) *Tagungsber. Dtsch. Akad. Wiss.* Berlin, No. 27, 87

Bognár, R. and Makleit, S. (1962) *Magy. Kém. Lapja* **68,** 432

Bognár, R. and Makleit, S. (1965) *Pharmazie* **20,** 39

Bogonina, Z. S., Gogol, O. N. and Koubrak, M. N. (1965) *III. Congr. Int. E−O,* Sophia, 183

Böhm, H. (1966) *Biochemische-Genetische Untersuchungen in d. Gattung Papaver.* Dissert. Univ. Halle-Wittenberg

Boissier, J. R., Combes, G., Pernet, R. and Dumont, C. (1965) *Lloydia* **28,** 191

Boit, H. G. (1961) *Ergebnisse d. Alkaloid-Chemie bis 1960.* Akademie Verlag, Berlin

Boit, H. G. and Döpke, W. (1959) *Chem. Ber.* **92,** 2578

Boit, H. G., Döpke, W. and Stender, W. (1957) *Chem. Ber.* **90,** 2203

Boit, H. G. and Ehmke, H. (1956) *Chem. Ber.* **89,** 2044

Boit, H. G. and Flentje, H. (1959) *Naturwiss.* **46,** 594

Boit, H. G. and Flentje, H. (1960) *Naturwiss.* **47,** 180, 323

Boiteau, O. and Ratsimamanga, A. R. (1957) *Fitoterapia* **28,** 738

Boll, P. M. and Andersen, B. (1962) *Planta Med.* **10,** 421

Bonaccorsi, K. (1936) *Riv. Ital. Ess. Profum.* **18,** 21

Bonnisteel, W. M. (1940) *J. Am. Pharm. Assoc.* **29,** 404

Boorsma, W. G. (1902) *Meded. Lds. Plt. Tuinb.* Batavia. **52,** 1

Borkowski, B., Batkiewicz, E. and Prost, K. (1964) *Diss. Pharm.* **16,** 171

Borkowski, B., Frencel, I. and Michalewska, M. (1963) *Acta Pol. Pharm.* **22,** 431

Borkowski, B., Grabarczyk, H. and Biernaczyk, H. (1959) *Diss. Pharm.* **11,** 39

Borkowski, B., Kozlowski, J. and Krzysztofikowa, B. (1961) *Biul. Inst. Rosl. Leczn.* **7,** 14

Borkowski, B., Drost K., and Pasichova, B. (1959) *Acta Pol. Pharm.* **16,** 57

Borsutzki, H. (1955) *Arch. Pharm.* **288,** 336

Börtitz, S. (1963) *Flora* **153,** 320

Bowyer, R. C. and Jefferies, P. R. (1962) *Austral. J. Chem.* **15,** 145

(Bradishchev, I. I. and Cherches, Kh. A.) Брадищев, И. И., Черчес, Х. А. (1959) *Сборник научн. работ. Акад. Наук. Белорус ССР Инст. Физ. Орг. Хим.* (Coll. Sci. Works of Acad. Sci. Belorous. SSR. Inst. Phys. Org. Chem.) No. 7, 96

Brandt, C. (1951) *Beitrag zur Kenntnis der chemischen Eigenschaften einigen Lobelia-Arten im Zusammenhang mit Selektionierungsversuchen.* Promotionsarbeit, Zürich, No. 1915

Brandt, R., Kaufmann, W. and Reichstein, T. (1966) *Helv. Chim. Acta* **49,** 1844

Bredemann, G., Schwanitz, F. and Sengbush, R. (1956) *Bull. Narcot.* **8,** 31

Brehm, B. G. (1966) *Brittonia* **18,** 194

Brehm, B. G. and Alston, R. E. (1964) *Am. J. Bot.* **51,** 644

Briasco-Murray, M. J. (1952) *J. Appl. Chem.* **2,** 187

Brieskorn, C. H. and Fuchs, A. (1962) *Dtsch. Ap. Ztg.* **102,** 1268

Briggs, L. H. (1946) *J. Roy. Soc. N–S. W.* **80,** 151

Briggs, L. H. and Cambie, R. C. (1950) *J. Chem. Soc.* 1422

Briggs, L. H. and Cawley, R. W. (1948) *J. Chem. Soc.* 1888

Briggs, L. H. and Loe, J. A. (1950) *J. Chem. Soc.* 958

(Brink, N. P.) Бринк, Н. П. (1956) *Пряные растения* (Aromatic Plants) Сельхозгиз Москва. Ed. Sel'hozgiz, Moscow

Brooks, B. T. (1910) *Philippine J. Sci.* **5,** 439

Brown, J. M. and Koch, de W. T. (1959) *S-Afr. Ind. Chem.* **13,** 189

Brunsberg, K. (1965) *Bot. Notiser* **118,** 377

Bruylants, G. (1878) *Ber. Dtsch. Chem. Ges.* **11,** 449

Burnell, R. H. and Taylor, D. R. (1960) *Chem. and Ind.* 1239

Burns-Runge, C. (1948) *Pharmazie* **3,** 262, 315

Butler, J. M. and Holloway, J. T. (1939) *J. Soc. Chem. Ind.* **58.** 223

Bystrek J. and Popiolek Z. (1967) *Acta Soc. Bot. Pol.* **36,** 545

Cai Sjan-Juan, Chei Jang-Ting and Din Ching-Kai (1964) *Acta Pharm. Sin.* **11,** 808

Cai Sjan-Juan, Ou Ci-Cheng and Din Ching-Kai (1965) *Acta Pharm. Sin.* **12,** 30

Cain, B. F., Scanell, S. and Cambie, R. C. (1961) *N.Z. J. Sci.* **4,** 3, 604, 707

Calcandi, V., Calcandi, I. and Lungeanu, I. (1965) *Pharmazie* **20,** 43

REFERENCES

Calderbank, K. E. (1957) *Proc. 9th Pacif. Sci. Congr.* Bangkok **5,** 62

Cambie, R. C. (1959) *J. Chem. Soc.* 468

Cambie, R. C. (1960) *J. Chem. Soc.* 2376

Cameron, C. W. and Sutherland, M. D. (1961) *Austral. J. Chem.* **14,** 135

Cameron, J. W. and Scora, R. W. (1968) *Taxon* **17,** 128

Camp, W. H. (1946) *Amer. J. Bot.* **33,** 134

Camus, E. G. and Camus, A. (1910) *Roure-Bertrand Fils.* **3,** 23

Camus, E. G. and Camus, A. (1920) *Roure-Bertrand Fils.* Avril 18

Canham, P. A. S. and Warren, F. L. (1951) *Chem. Abstr.* **45,** 4063

Cannon, J. R. and Corbett, N. H. (1962) *Austral. J. Chem.* **15,** 168

Carboni, S. (1941) *Ricerce Sci. Progr. Techn. Econ. Naz.* **11,** 472

Cavello, M. and Capone, A. (1950) *Il Farmaco* **5,** 684

(Cerevitinov, F. V.) Церевитинов, Ф. В. (1949) *Химия свежих плодов и овощей.* Торгиздат Москва (Chemistry of fresh fruits and vegetables). Torgizdat. Moscow

Cerny, V. and Lábler, L. (1959) *Collect. Chem.* **24,** 3468

(Chagovec, R. K. and Borisiuk, Yu. G.) Чаговец, Р. К., Борисьюк, Ю. Г. (1957) *Украйн. Хим. Ж.* (Ukrain. Chem. J.) **23,** 82

Chakravarti, R. N. (1951) *Indian Med. Gaz.* **86,** 182

Chakravarti, R. N. and Bhattacharryya, S. C. (1954) *Ind. Pharm.* 218

Chakravarti, R. N. and Bhattacharryya, S. C. (1955) *Perf. Ess. Oil Rec.* **46,** 356

Challice, J. S. and Williams, A. H. (1968) *Phytochem.* **7,** 1781

Chambers, C., Haynes, L. J. and Stuart, K. L. (1966) *Chem. Commun.* **31,** 449

Chambers, C. and Stuart, K. L. (1968) *Chem. Commun.* **33,** 328

Chao Hua-Wu et al. (1958) *Chem. Abstr.* **52,** 19019

Chapon, S. and David, S. (1953) *Bull. Soc. Chim. (France),* 333

Chatterjee, A. (1953) *Fortschr. d. Chemie org. Naturstoffe* **10,** 390

Chatterjee, A., Banerjee, A., Barua, A. K. and Gupta, A. K. (1954) *J. Indian Chem. Soc.* **31,** 83

Chatterjee, A. and Bose, S. (1954) *J. Indian Chem. Soc.* **31,** 17

Chatterjee, A., Das, B., Dutta, C. P. and Mukherjee, K. S. (1965) *Tetrahedron Letters* 67

Chatterjee, A. and Gupta, S. S. (1964) *Tetrahedron Letters* 1961

Chatterjee, A., Majumdar, P. L., Mukherjee, R., Saha, S. K. and Talapatra, S. K. (1965) *Tetrahedron Letters* 1539

Chatterjee, A. Mukherjee R., Das, B. and Chosal, S. (1964) *J. Indian Chem. Soc.* **41,** 163

Chatterjee, A., Pakrashi, S. C. and Wena, C. (1956) *Fortschr. d. Chemie org. Naturstoffe* **13,** 346

Chatterjee, R., Guha, M. P. and Chatterjee, A. (1952) *J. Indian Chem. Soc.* **29,** 371

Chaudhary, S. S., Singh, G. and Handa, K. I. (1958) *Indian J. Pharm.* **20,** 70

Chiang Hsi-Chang (1958) *Perf. Ess. Oil Rec.* **49,** 14

(Chistova, Z. G.) Чистова, З. Г. (1958) In: *Chemical composition of wormwood.* Goriayev et al. 1962

Chládek, M., Kosova, V. and Hruby, K. (1958) *Pharmazie* **13,** 712

Chopra, I. C. and Dutt, A. (1929 —30) *Ind. J. Med. Res.* **17,** 647

Chopra, I. C., Ghosh, K. and Ratnagiriswaran, F. (1928) *Ind. Res.* **17A,** 8

Chopra, I. C. Handa, K. L., and Abrol, B. K. (1958) *J. Sci. Ind. Res.* **17A,** 8

Chopra, I. C., Nigam, S. S. and Handa, K. L. (1963) *Parf. Kozmet.* **44,** 123

Chopra, I. C., Vashist, V. N. and Handa, K. L. (1964) *Ind. Oil Soap J.* **30,** 41

Chopra, R. N., Krishna, S., and Ghose, T. P. (1931–32) *Ind. J. Med. Res.* **19,** 177

Choudry, I. I., Singh, G. and Handa, K. L. (1959) *Ind. J. Pharm.* **21,** 38

Chou-Yun, Dagan, H. and Vej-Juan (1965) *Acta Pharm. Sin.* **12,** 392

Chowdhry, G. R., Sharma, V. N. and Kaul, K. N. (1958) *J. Sci. Res. Ind.* **17B,** 473

Chu-Chin Lin, Jen-Yung Lu, Tsu-Ching Chu and Chi-Hao Weng (1961) *Hua Hsueh Hsueh Pao* **27,** 47

(Cicin, N. V.) Цицин, Н. В. (1962) *Атлас лекарственных растений СССР* (Atlas of the medicinal plants of USSR). Moscow, Medgiz.

Clare, E. M. and Morice, J. M. (1945) *N. Z. J. Sci. Techn.* **27B,** 36

Clemo, R. G. and Raper, R. (1935) *J. Chem. Soc.* 10

Clow, P. W., Duffield, A. M. and Jefferies, P. R. (1966) *Austral. J. Chem.* **19,** 483

Cocker, W., Lipman, C., McMurry, T. B. and Wheeler, B. M. (1958) *J. Sci. Food. Agr.* **9,** 828

Cooke, R. G. and Rae, J. D. (1964) *Austral. J. Chem.* **17,** 379

Corbett, R. E. and Wong, L. C. K. (1955) *J. Sci. Food. Agr.* **6,** 739

Cosson, L., Chouard, P. and Paris, R. (1966) *Lloydia* **29,** 19

Costa, A. J. F. (1945) Subsidios para o estudo plantas aromat. *Essencios Thymus (Coimbra)*

Costa, A. and Silva, da D. (1933) *Rev. Soc. Bras. Chim.* **4,** 199

Costa, F. and Vale, de C. J. (1959) *Perf. Ess. Oil Rec.* **50,** 291

Costa, F., Vale, de C. J. and Vale, de M. A. M. (1959) *Perf. Ess. Oil Rec.* **50,** 487

Covello, M. and Ciampa, G. (1960) *J. Chromatogr.* **3,** 591

Culberson, C. F. (1965) *Phytochem.* **4,** 951

Culberson, W. L. (1961) *Brittonia* **13,** 381

Culberson, W. L. (1961) *Rev. Bryol. et Lichen.* **29,** 321

Culberson, W. L. (1964) Science **143,** 255

Culberson, W. L. (1966) *Rev. Bryologique* **34,** 841

Culberson, W. L. and Culberson, C. F. (1956) *Am. J. Bot.* **43,** 678

Culberson, W. L. and Culberson, C. F. (1965) *Brittonia* **17,** 182

Culvenor, C. C. J. and Smith, L. W. (1957) *Austral. J. Chem.* **10,** 464,

Culvenor, C. C. J. and Smith, L. W. (1959) *Austral. J. Chem.* **12,** 255

Culvenor, C. C. J., Bon, R. D. and Smith, L. W. (1964) *Austral. J. Chem.* **17,** 1301

Curtis, R. F. Hassall, C. H. and Jones, D. W. (1959) *Chem. and Ind.* 1283

Czabajska, W., Duchnowska, A., Pavelczyk, E. and Wrocinska, V. (1959) *Biul. Inst. Rosl. Leczn.* **5,** 252

Czetsch-Linderwald, H. (1943) *Dtsch-Heilpflanzen* **9,** 16

Dahl, E. (1952) *Rev. Bryol. et Lichen.* **21,** 119

Dakshinamurti, K. (1953) *Ind. Pharm.* **8,** 257

Dandiya, F. C., Baxter, R. M., Walker, G. C. and Cullumbine, H. (1959) *J. Pharm. Pharmacol.* **11,** 163

(Dauksa, A. D. and Denisova, E. K.) Даукса, А. Д. и Денисова, Е. К. (1966) *Раст. Ресурс.* (Resources of plant origin) **2,** 50

Davenport, J. B., Jones, T. G. H. and Sutherland, D. M. (1949) *The Ess. Oil of Queensland Flora* 23. Univ. Queensland Papers **1,** 36, 1

Davila, C. A. and Panizo, F. M. (1958) *Anal. Real Soc. Espan. fis. y quim.* Madrid. **54B,** 697

Dawson, R. F. and James, C. (1956) *Lloydia* **19,** 59

Delaveau, P. (1957) *Bull. Soc. Bot. (France)* **104,** 148

Delaveau, P. (1959) *C. R. Soc. Biol.* **153,** 579

Delépine, M. (1910) *C. R. Acad. Sci.* **150,** 1061

Deltscheff, G. (1957) *Pharmazie* **12,** 686

Dersch, G. and Sander, H. (1962) *Pharm. Ztg.* **107,** 1540

Determann, W. (1940) *Z. Pflanzenzücht.* **23,** 371

Deulofeu, V. and Delanghe, J. (1942) *J. Am. Chem. Soc.* **64,** 968

Dhalla, N. S., Sastry, M. S. and Malhotra, C. L. (1961) *J. Pharm. Sci.* **50,** 876

Dhar, R. (1965) *Proc. Ind. Ac. Sci. Ser. B.* **62,** 242

Dhingra, D. R., Gupta, G. N. and Mehrota, J. N. (1951) *Ind. Soap J.* **17,** 43

Dietrich, M. P., Lederer, E. and Polonsky, J. (1953) *Bull. Soc. Chim. (France),* 546

Dillemann, G. (1959) *Ann. Pharm. (France)* **17,** 214

Dillemann, G. (1960) *Planta Med.* **8,** 263

Dominguez, J. A. (1932) *Rev. Farm.* Buenos Aires **73,** 82

Dominguez, N. (1932) *Rev. Centre Est. Farm. Bioquim.* **20,** 534

Dominguez, E. and Romo, J. (1963) *Tetrahedron* **19,** 1415

(Domoreva, T. V., Lapunova, A. A., Ryabinin, A. A. and Saltykova, I. A.) Доморьева, Т. В., Лапунова, А. А., Рябинин, А. А., Салтыкова, И. А. (1961) *Ж. Общ. Хим.* (J. Gen. Chem.) **31,** 2434

Drey, B. E. A. and Foster, G. E. (1953) *J. Pharm. Pharmacol.* **5,** 839

Dubenchiek, A. S., (1955) *Perf. Ess. Oil. Rec.* **46,** 298

(Dublianskaya, N. F.) Дубльянская, Н. Ф. (1958) *Краткий отчет ВНИИМЕМК за 1957* (Short Rec. of St. Sci. Res. Inst. Oil and Essential Oil Cult. for 1957) 96

(Dublianskaya, N. F. and Marchenko, L. N.) Дубльянская, Н. Ф., Марченко, Л. Н. (1963) *Селекц. Семеновод.* (Breeding and Seedgrowing) **28,** 71

Dulou, R. and Pétard, P. (1947) *Ann. Pharm. (France)* **5,** 534

Dumérac, M. L. (1954) *C. R. Acad. Sci.* **239,** 300

Dupont, G. (1937) *Bull. Inst. Pin* **3,** 134

Dupont, G. and Barraud, M. (1925) *Proc. Verb. Soc. Sci.* Bordeaux 6

Dusinszky, G. and Tyllova, M. (1962) *Chem. Zvesti.* **16,** 701

Dusinszky, G. and Tyllova, M. (1963) *Chem. Abstr.* **58,** 8233

Dutt, S. (1939) *Proc. Ind. Acad. Sci.* **9A,** 72

Dutt, S. (1940) *Ind. Soap J.* **6,** 248

Dutt, S. (1958) *Ind. Soap J.* **23,** 201

Dutt, S. (1960) *Ind. Perfum.* **4,** 17

Dutta, T. and Basu, U. P. (1962) *J. Sci. Industr. Res.,* India, **21B,** 239

Egels, W. (1959) *Planta Med.* **7,** 92

El-Hamidi, A. and Richter, G. (1965) *Lloydia* **28,** 252

Ellerström, S. and Joseffson, E. (1967) *Zeitschr. f. Pflanzenzücht* **58,** 128

Elzenga, G. (1958) *Stud. Kning. Plant Veredel.* Wageningen. 780

Elzenga, G. and De Bruyn, J. W. (1956) *Euphytica* **5,** 259

Emboden, W. A. and Lewis, M. (1967) *Brittonia* **19,** 152

Erdtman, H. (1959) *Proc. 4th Intern. Congr. Biochem.* vol. II, 1 Pergamon Press, London

Erdtman, H. (1963) *Pure and appl. Chem.* **6,** 679

Estrada, H. (1959) *Bol. Inst. Quim. Univ.* Nao Auton. Mex. **11,** 15

Ettlinger, M. G. and Hodgkins, J. E. (1955) *J. Am. Chem. Soc.* **77,** 1851

Ettlinger, M. G. and Lundeen, A. J. (1956) *J. Am. Soc. Chem.* **78,** 1952

Evans, W. C., Major, V. A. and Than, P. M. (1965) *Planta Med.* **13,** 353

Evans, W. C. and Partridge, M. W. (1948) *Quart. J. Pharm. Pharm.* **21,** 126

Evans, W. C. and Partridge, M. W. (1953) *J. Pharm. Pharm.* **5,** 772

Ewers, N. and Caldwell, D. (1959) *The chemistry of drugs.* Ed. Benn., London 197

Ewing J., Hughes, G. K., Ritchie, E. and Taylor, W. C. (1953) *Austral. J. Chem.* **6,** 58

Fahselt, D., and Ownbey, M. (1968) *Am. J. Bot.* **55,** 335

Farmilo, C. G. (1955) *Analyse de la résine de cannabis . . .* U.N. Council. Econ. Soc. E/CN. 7/304, 1

Fauconnet, L. (1960) *Pharm. Acta Helv.* **35,** 121

Faugeras, G. (1965) Personal communication

Faugeras, G. and Dillemann, G. (1960) *Ann. Pharm. France* **18,** 466

Faugeras, G. and Paris, R. (1960) *Ann. Pharm. France* **18,** 474

(Favorskaya, M. A.) Фаворская, М. А. (1935) *Ж. Общ. Хим.* (J. Gen. Chem.) **5,** 1804

Felklova, M. (1958) *Ceskosl. Farm.* **7,** 433

Fernandez, A. (1958) *Univ. Nat. de Colombia* 9

Fesneau, A. (1950) *Ind. Parfume* **5,** 132

Fester, G. A. (1950) *Rev. Fac. Quim. Ind. Agr.* **19,** 1

Fester, G. A., Martinuzzi, E. A., Retamar, J. A. and Ricciardi, A. I. A. (1955) *Rev. Fac. Ing. Quim.* **24,** 37

Fester, G. A., Martinuzzi, E. A., Retamar, J. A. and Ricciardi, A. I. A. (1958) *Bol. Acad. Nac. Cience* Cordoba **40,** 189

Fester, G. A., Martinuzzi, E. A., Retamar, J. A. and Ricciardi, A. I. A. (1960) *Rev. Fac. Ing. Quim.* **29,** 21

Fester, G. A., Martinuzzi, E. A. and Ricciardi, A. I. A. (1951) *Rev. Fac. Ing. Quim.* Santa Fé **20,** 47

Fester, G. A., Retamar, J. A., Ricciardi, A. I. A. and Cassano, A. (1961) *Rev. Fac. Ing. Quim.* **30,** 5, 11

Fester, G. A., Retamar, J. A., Ricciardi, A. I. A and Fonseca, L. R. (1959) *Rev. Fac. Ing. Quim.* **28**, 9, 19

Fikenscher, L. and Hegnauer, R. (1963) *Planta Med.* **11**, 348

Fischer, R. (1901) *Arch. Pharm.* **239**, 426

Fischer, G. S. (1963) *Chem. and Ind.* 1761

Flake, N., Rudloff, von E., and Turner, B. L. (1968) (In press)

Flück, H. (1960) *Planta Med.* **8**, 297

Flückiger, F. A. (1886) *Arch. Pharm.* **227**, 145

Flury, E., Weiss, E. K. and Reichstein, T. (1965) *Helv. Chim. Acta* **48**, 1113

(Fodorov, A. A.) Фодоров, А. А. (1961) *Бот. Ж.* (Bot. J.) **46**, 1385

Fontán-Candela, J. L. (1954) *An. Real. Soc. Espan. Fis. Quim.* **50B**, 441

Forde, M. B. and Blight, M. M. (1964) *N. Z. J. Bot.* **2**, 44

Francesconi, L. and Sernagiotto, E. (1913) *Atti Reale Acad. Nat. Lincei*, Roma **22**, 231, 312, 382

Francis, C. M., Millington, A. J. and Bailey, E. T. (1967) *Austral. J. Agr. Res.* **18**, 47

Franck, B. and Hartmann, W. (1960) II. Kongr. Biochem. *Alkaloide* Jena

Franck, B. and Hartmann, W. (1963) Abhdlg. Dtsch. Akad. No. 4, *Biochem. Phys. Alkaloide*, 111

Freise, F. W. (1938) *Pharm. Zentralhalle* **79**, 49

Fried, J., Numerot, F. P. and Loy, N. A. (1952) *J. Am. Chem. Soc.* **74**, 3041

Fried, J., White, L. and Wintersteiner, O. (1950) *J. Am. Chem. Soc.* **72**, 4621

Fuchs, L. (1952) *Sci. Pharm.* **20**, 1

Fuchs, L. and Ilijev, V. (1949) *Sci. Pharm.* **17**, 128

Fujita, Y. (1937) *Chem. Soc. (Japan)* **58**, 1182

Fujita, Y. (1943) *J. Chem. Soc. (Japan)* **64**, 1226

Fujita, Y. (1951) *Bot. Mag.* Tokyo **64**, 165

Fujita, Y. (1955) *Rep. Govern. Ind. Res. Inst.* Osaka **296**, 306

Fujita, Y. (1960) *Acta Phytotax. Geobot.* **18**, 183

Fujita, Y. (1961) *J. Jap. Bot.* **36**, 332

Fujita, Y. (1962a) *Acta Phytotax. Geobot.* **20**, 132

Fujita, Y. (1962b) *J. Jap. Bot.* **37**, 145

Fujita, Y. (1963) *J. Jap. Bot.* **38**, 244, 359

Fujita, Y. (1965a) *Bot. Mag.* Tokyo **78**, 212

Fujita, Y. (1965b) *Rep. Govern. Ind. Res. Inst.* Osaka **306**, 34

Fujita, Y. (1965c) *Biol. Sci.* Tokyo **17**, 126

Fujita, Y. (1966) *J. Jap. Bot.* **41**, 65

Fujita, Y., Tanaka, Y. and Iwamura, J. (1967) *Nippon Kagaku Zashi* **88**, 763

Fujita, Y. and Tomomatsu, (1959) *J. Pharm. Soc. Jap.* **79**, 1252

Fujita, Y. and Ueda, T. (1957) *J. Chem. Soc. Jap.* **78**

Fujita, Y., Ueda, T. and Fujita, S. (1964) *Nipp. Kagaku Zashi* **85**, 892

Fujita, Y., Ueda, T. and Mizohata, H. (1965) *Nipp. Kagaku Zashi* **86**, 1074

Fulton, C. C. (1944) *The opium poppy and other poppies.* U.S. Treas. publications. Printing Office, Washington

Gagnebin, F. (1964) *Rev. Hort. Suisse* **37**, 53

Garay, A. and Ádám, H. (1955) *Naturwiss.* **42**, 646

(Garbuzova, D. A.) Гарбузова, Д. А. (1964) *Вестник Сельхоз. Наук.* (Rec. Agricult. Sci.) (7), 40

Gardner, C. A. and Watson, E. M. (1947/48) *J. Roy. Soc. West Austral.* **34**, 73

Geiger, P. (1901) *Beiträge z. Kentniss d. Ipoh-Pfeilgifte.* Inaug.-Diss. Univ. Zürich

Geismann, T. A. and Matsueda, S. (1968) *Phytochem.* **7**, 1613

Geismann, T. A., Stewart, T. and Irwin, M. A. (1967) *Phytochem.* **6**, 90

Genest, K. (1965) *J. Chromatogr.* **19**, 531

(Gerasimenko, I. I.) Герасименко, И. И. (1961) *Бот. Ж.* (Bot. J.) **46**, 1202

Gertig, H. (1964) *Acta Polon. Pharm.* **22**, 127

Gertig, H., Kowalewski, Z. and Novaczyk, K. (1966) *Herba Pol.* **12,** 117

Gessner, O. (1953) *Gift- und Arzneipflanzen von Mitteleuropa.* Universitätsverlag, Heidelberg

Ghose, T. P. and Krishna, S. (1930) *Arch. Pharm.* **268,** 636

Gilbert, B., Antonaccio, L., Ascher, A. A. P. G. and Djerassi, C. (1960) *Experientia* **16,** 61

Gildemeister, E. and Hoffmann, F. (1958–1961) *Die ätherischen Öle,* vol. IV–VII. Akad. Verlag, Berlin

Gill, S. and Steinegger, E. (1964) *Pharm. Acta Helv.* **39,** 508, 556

Gisvold, O. (1958) *J. Amer. Pharm. Assoc.* **47,** 594

(Glizin, V. I. and Senoto, P.L.) Глизин, В. И., Сеното, П. Л. (1965) *Апт. Дело* (Pharm. Affairs) **14,** 29

Gmelin, R. (1966) *Planta Med.* **14,** Suppl. 119

Goldblatt, L. and Burgdahl, A. (1952) *Ind. Eng. Chem.* **44,** 1934

Gopinath, K. W., Gowindachari, T. R., Rajappa, S. and Ramada, C. V. (1959) *J. Sci. Ind. Res.* **18B,** 444

Gordon, A. A., Fairchild, D. M. and Jensen, M. (1961) *J. Med. Pharm. Chem.* **3,** 323

(Goriayev, M. I., Baziliczkaia, V. S. and Poliakov, P. P.) Горяев, М. И., Базилицкая, В. С., Польяков, П. П. (1962) *Химический состав полыней* (Chemical composition of wormwood). Acad. Kazakh. SSR, Alma-Ata

(Goriayev, M. I. and Gimaddinov, Zh.) Горяев, М. И., Гимаддинов, Ж. (1954) *Вестн. АН, Казах. ССР* (Rec. Acad. Sci. Kazakh. SSR) **12,** 68

(Goriayev, M. I. and Gimaddinov, Zh.) Горяев, М. И., Гимаддинов, Ж. (1964) *Докл. АН, СССР* (Rep. Acad. Sci. USSR) **156,** 1459

(Goriayev, M. I. and Ignatova, L. A.) Горяев, М. И., Игнатова, Л. А. (1959) *Изв. Ак. Наук Казах. ССР, Сер. Хим.* (Rec. Acad. Sci. Kazakh. SSR, Ser. Chem.) **15,** 90

(Goriayev, M. I. and Satdarova, E. I.) Горяев, М. И., Сатдарова, Е. И. (1959) *Тр. Инст. Хим. Наук* (Works of Inst. Chem. Sci.) **14,** 48

(Goriayev, M. I. and Shvakina, V. R.) Горяев, М. И., Швакина, В. Р. (1948) *Вестн. АН. Казак. ССР* (Rep. Acad. Sci. Kazakh. SSR) **5,** 28

Gottlieb, O. R., Fineberg, M. and Magalhaes, T. (1962) *Perf. Ess. Oil. Rec.* **53,** 299

Gottlieb, C. R. and Magalhaes, M. T. (1960) *Perf. Ess. Oil. Rec.* **51,** 243

Goulding, E. and Earl, J. C. (1914) *Proc. Chem. Soc.* **30,** 10

Goutarel, R., Le Hir, A., Poisson, J. and Janot, M. (1954) *Bull. Soc. Chim. France,* 1481

Gracza, L. and Szász, K. (1962) *Arch. Pharm.* **295,** 859

Grahle, A. (1952) *Z. Naturforschung* **7B,** 326

Granger, R., Passet, J. and Verdier, R. (1963) *France Parf.* 225

Granger, R., Passet, J. and Verdier, R. (1964) *C. R. Ac. Sci.* **258,** 5539

Gregg, O. H. and Gisvold, O. (1954) *J. Am. Pharm. Assoc. Sci.* **43,** 106

Greshoff, M. (1899) *Meded. Las Pl. Tuinb.* Batavia No. 25, 179

Grimett, B. E. R. and Melville, J. (1941) *Nature* **148,** 782

Grlic, L. and Andrec, A. (1961) *Experientia* **17,** 325

Gröger, D. (1957a) 1. Beiheft: *Biochemie der Kulturpflanze,* 226

Gröger, D. (1957b) *Abh. Dtsch. Akad. Wiss.* Berlin, No. **7,** 243

Gröger, D. (1961) *Angew. Chemie,* **73,** 74

Gröger, D. and Tyler, V. E. (1963) *Lloydia* **26,** 174

Grossert, J. S., Hugo, J. M., Klemperer, von M. E. and Warren, F. L. (1965) *J. Chem. Soc.* 2812, 2816

Grundon, M. F. and McGravey, J. E. B. (1960) *J. Chem. Soc.* 2739

Gubányi, E. (1956) *Annual Rep. Hung. Res. Inst. Medic. Plants,* 52

Guenther, E. (1938) *Drug Cosm. Ind.* **42,** 442

Guenther, E. (1952) *Econ. Bot.* **6,** 315

Guenther, E. (1953) *The essential oils.* vol. I—VI, Van Nostrand, New York, 2. Ed.

Guenther, E. (1956) *Ins. Parfumerie* **11,** 407

Guha, C. and Roy, A. N. (1942) *J. Ind. Inst. Sci.* **23A,** 209

Guillaumin, A. (1930) *Bull. Sci. Pharmacol.* **37,** 431

Guinier, M. (1961) *Bull. Soc. Bot.* France **108**, 37

Gupta, G. N., Ganeshchandra and Zaidi, S. T. H. (1955) *Proc. Ind. Sci. Congr.* 167

Gupta, G. N. and Gupta, J. C. (1958) *J. Proc. Oil Techn. Ass.* India, **12**, 119

Gupta, G. N. and Seshadri, T. R. (1956) *J. Sci. Ind. Res.* India, **15B**, 146

Gupta, R. C. and Muthana, M. S. (1954) *J. Ind. Sci.* **36A**, 76, 122

(Gurvich, N. L.) Гурвич, Н. Л. (1936) *Докл. АН, СССР* (Rep. Acad. Sci. USSR) **12**, 141

(Gurvich, N. L.) Гурвич, Н. Л. (1938) *Тр. Бот. Инст. Азерб. Фил. АН, ССР (Баку)* (Works Bot. Inst. Azerb. Fil. Acad. Sci. SSR, Baku) **3**, 199

(Gurvich, N. L.) Гурвич, Н. Л. (1940) *Тр. Бот. Инст. Азерб. Фил. АН, ССР (Баку)* (Works Bot. Inst. Azerb. Fil. Acad. Sci. SSR, Baku) **9**, 137

(Gurvich, N. L.) Гурвич, Н. Л. (1960) *Раст. Сырье* (Raw material of plant origin) **6**, 7–126

Gurvich, N. L. (1965) *III. Congr. Int. E – O* Sophia 133

(Gurvich, N. L. and Gadzhiev, I. Yu.) Гурвич, Н. Л., Гаджиев, И. Ю. (1938) *Тр. Бот. Инст. Аз. ФАН ССР (Баку)* (Works Bot. Inst. Azerb. Fil. Acad. Sci. SSR, Baku) **3**, 137

Haack, E., Popelak, A. and Spingler, H. (1955) *Naturwiss.* **42**, 627

Haagen-Smit, A. J. (1949) *Econ. Bot.* **3**, 71

Haagen-Smit, A. J., Redeman, C. T., Wang, H. and Mirov, N. T. (1950) *J. Amer. Pharm. Ass.* **39**, 260

Hagenström, V. and Schmersahl, K. (1954) *Planta Med.* **2**, 51

Hakim, S., Misovic, V. and Walker, J. (1961) *Nature* **188**, 198

Hale, M. E. (1956) *Am. J. Bot.* **43**, 456

Hale, M. E. (1963) *Brittonia* **15**, 126

(Hammermann, A. F., Monteverde, N. N. and Sokolov, V. S.) Гаммерманн, А. Ф., Монтеверде, Н. Н., Соколов, В. С. (1957) *Раст. Сырье СССР* (Raw material of plant origin, USSR) **2**, 425

Handa, K. I., Chopra, I. C. and Sceti, S. N. (1957) *J. Sci. Ind. Res.* **16A**, 1

Handa, K. L., Smith, D. M., Nigam, I. C. and Levi, L. (1964) *J. Pharm. Sci.* **53**, 1407

Hanover, J. W. (1966) *Heredity* **21**, 73

Hänsel, R. and Hörhammer, L. (1954) *Arch. Pharm.* **287**, 117

Harney, P. M. and Grant, W. F. (1964) *Am. J. Bot.* **51**, 621

Harrod, D. C. (1960) *J. Pharm. Pharmacol.* **12**, 245

Hassall, C. H. (1944) *N. Z. J. Sci. Techn.* **25B**, 169

Hawksworth, D. L. (1968) *Bot. Notiser* **121**, 318

Hearst, P. J. (1964) *J. Org. Chem.* **29**, 466

Hedge, B. J. and Rao, B. S. (1935) *J. Chem. Soc. Ind.* **54T**, 388

Heeger, E. F. (1947) *Pharmazie* **2**, 368

Heeger, E. F. (1956) *Handbuch der Arznei- und Gewürzpflanzenbaues.* Ed. Dtsch. Bauernverl. Berlin

Hegglin, A. (1957) *Untersuchungen über Selektionierung von Datura innoxia.* Promotionsarbeit Zürich. No. 2653

Hegi, H. R. and Flück, H. (1956) *Pharm. Acta Helv.* **31**, 428

Hegnauer, R. (1948) *Ber. Schweiz. Bot. Ges.* **58**, 391

Hegnauer, R. (1954) *Pharm. Acta Helv.* **29**, 203

Hegnauer, R. (1955) *Planta Med.* **3**, 17

Hegnauer, R. (1957) *Pharm. Weekbl.* **92**, 541

Hegnauer, R. (1961) *Pharm. Acta Helv.* **36**, 21

Hegnauer, R. *Chemotaxonomie der Pflanzen.* Birkhäuser Verlag Basel 1962–1966, vol. I–IV

Hegnauer, R. (1963) In: *Chemical Plant Taxonomy.* Ed. T. Swain, Academic Press, London and New York

Hegnauer, R. and Fikenscher, L. H. (1960) *Pharm. Acta Helv.* **35**, 43

Hegnauer, R. and De Jong, J. I. M. (1956) *Pharm. Acta Helv.* **31**, 367

Heitz, S. Lapin H., Sannié, C. and Barchewitz, P. (1954) *Bull. Soc. Chim. Biol.* **36**, 227

Held, G. and Vágújfalvi, D. (1965) *Bot. Közl.* (Bot. Rev.) **52**, 201

Helfenberger, H. and Reichstein, T. (1952) *Helv. Chim. Acta* **35**, 1503

Hellyer, P. O. (1957) *Austral. J. Chem.* **10**, 509

Hellyer, R. O., McKern, H. H. G. and Willis, J. L. (1955) *J. Proc. Roy. Soc. N. S. W.* **89,** 30

Hemingway, J. S., Schofield, H. J. and Vaughan, J. G. (1961) *Nature* **192,** 993

Henning, J. G. (1962) *Vloeistof-Vloeistof Verdeling als Onderzoes-methode van einige Rassen von Digitalis purpurea* Groningen N. V. Dijkstr's Drukk

Hennipmann, J. (1967) *Persoonia*, **4,** 427

Henricks, W. E. and Kremers, E. (1899) *Pharm. Arch.* **2,** 76

(Henry, T. A.) Генри, Т. А. (1956) *Химия растительных алкалоидов.* Научн. Техн. Изд. Москва (Chemistry of plant-alkaloids) Moscow

Herout, V. (1952) *Chem. Listy* **46,** 438

Herout, V. (1966) *IV. Int. Symp. IUPAC* Stockholm Abstr. Book, 168

Herrmann, K. (1955) *Arch. Pharm.* **268,** 362

Herty, C. H. (1908) *J. Am. Chem. Soc.* **30,** 863

Herz, W. (1966) Contribution to the *IV. Int. Symp. IUPAC* Stockholm

Herz, W. (1968) In: *Recent advances in Phytochemistry* vol. 1. 229

Herz, W. and Högenauer, G. (1961) *J. Org. Chem.* **26,** 5011

Herz, W. and Högenauer, G. (1962) *J. Org. Chem.* **27,** 905

Herz, W. and Inayama, S. (1964) *Tetrahedron* **20,** 341

Herz, W., Rohde, W. A., Rabindran, K., Tayaraman, P. and Visnathan, V. (1962) *J. Am. Chem. Soc.* **84,** 3857

Herz, W., Romo de Vivar, A. and Lakshmikantham, M. V. (1965) *J. Org. Chem.* **30,** 118

Heydenreich, K. and Ffeifer, S. (1965) *Pharmazie* **20,** 521

Heydenreich, K. and Ffeifer, S. (1966) *Pharmazie* **21,** 121

Hillis, W. E. (1966) *Phytochem.* **5,** 541

Hillis, W. E. (1967) *Phytochem.* **6,** 373, 259, 275, 845

Hillis, W. E. and Banks, J. C. G. (1968) Personal communication

Hillis, W. E. and Hasegawa, M. (1962) *Biochem. J.* **83,** 503

Hillis, W. E. and Isoi, K. (1965) *Phytochem.* **4,** 541

Hills, K. L., Bottomley, W. and Mortimer, P. I. (1954) *Austral. J. Appl. Sci.* **5,** 258

Hirota, N. (1951–53) *Mem. of Ehine Univ. Sci. Sect.* II, **1,** 65, **2,** 99

Hirota, N. (1953) *Perf. Ess. Oil Rec.* **44,** 4, 167, 201, 236

Hirsjärvi, P. and Pirila, L. (1964) *Suomen Kemistilehti* 37B, 13

Hofmann, A. W. (1888) *Ber. Dtsch. Chem. Ges.* **13,** 1732

Hogg, R. and Beal, J. L. (1963) *Lloydia* **24,** 45

(Holmov, V. P. and Afanasiev, N. M.) Гольмов, В. П., Афанасьиев, Н. М. (1957) *Ж. Общ. Хим.* (J. Gen. Chem.) **27,** 1698

(Holmov, V. P., Trofimov, V. I. and Afanasiev, N. M.) Гольнов, В. П., Трофимов, В. И., Афанасьиев, Н. М. (1948) *Ж. Общ. Хим.* (J. Gen. Chem.) **18,** 175

Holt, W. L. and Costello, H. C. (1954) *J. Am. Pharm. Assoc.* **43,** 144

Holzach, O. and Flück, M. (1950) *Pharm. Acta Helv.* **25,** 299

Hörhammer, L., Hamidi, A. E. and Richter, G. (1964) *J. Pharm. Sci.* **53,** 1033

Hörhammer, L. and Hänsel, R. (1953) *Arch. Pharm.* **286,** 425

Hörhammer, L. and Hänsel, R. (1954) *Arch. Pharm.* **287,** 189

Hörhammer, L. and Hänsel, R. (1955) *Arch. Pharm.* **288,** 153

Hörhammer, L. and Rao, S. B. (1954) *Arch. Pharm.* **287,** 34

Hörhammer, L. and Volz, E. (1955) *Arch. Pharm.* **288,** 58

Hörhammer, L. and Wagner, R. (1962) In: Gore T. S. et al., *Chemistry of Natural and Synthetic Colouring Matters.* Acad. Press, New York and London

Horii, Z. Saitos, S. and Kodera, K. (1964) *Chem. Pharm. Bull.* **12,** 1118

Howard, G. A. and Slater, C. A. (1957) *Chem. and Ind.* 495

(Hrimlian, A. I.) Хримлян, А. И. (1948) *Бюл. Бот. Сада. Арм. ССР* (Bull. Bot. Garden Arm. SSR) 47

(Hrimlian, A. I.) Хримлян, А. И. (1951) *Бюл. Бот. Сада Арм. ССР* (Bull. Bot. Garden Arm. SSR) 93

(Hrim'ian, A. I.) Хримлян, А. И. (1957) *Бюл. Бот. Саба Арм. ССР* (Bull. Bot. Garden Arm. SSR) 107

(Hrimlian, A. I.) Хримлян, А. И. (1959) *Изд. АН Арм. ССР* (Rec. Acad. Sci. Arm. SSR) **12**, 83

(Hrimlian, A. I.) Хримлян, А. И. (1965a) *Изв. АН Арм. ССР* (Rec. Acad. Sci. Arm. SSR) **18**, 33

(Hrimlian, A. I.) Хримлян, А. И. (1965b) *Пробл. современный Биол. Бот.* (Probl. Modern Biol. Bot.) **1**, 85

(Hrimlian, A. I. and Minasian, S. A.) Хримлян, А. И., Минасян, С. А. (1955) *Изд. АН Арм. ССР* (Rec. Acad. Sci. Arm. SSR) **8**, 131

Hrimlian, A. I. and Tétényi, P. (1965) *Herba Hung.* **4**, 19

(Hrimlian, A. I., Vasserman, I. S. and Sepetchan, A. O.) Хримлян, А. И., Вассерман, И. С., Сепетчан, А. О. (1941) *Бюл. Бот. Сад. АН Арм. Фил.* (Bul. Bot. Garden Arm. Fil. Acad. Sci. USSR) 47

Hulssen, van C. J. and Meijer, Th. H. (1940) *Chem. Weekbl.* **37**, 274

Hummel, K. (1958) *Planta Med.* **6**, 454

Huneck, S. (1966) *Z. Naturforschung* **21b** 79, 199

Igolen, M. G. (1958) *Parf. Cosm. Savons* **1**, 51

Igolen, M. G. (1963) Personal communication

Ikeda, N., Shimizu, S. and Udo, S. (1960) *Sci. Rep. Fac. Agr. Okoyama Univ.* 1

Ikeda, N., Udo, S. and Nakamura, M. (1960) *Jap. J. Plant Breed.* **10**, 89

Ilieva, S. (1965) *III. Congr. Int. E – O* Sophia 272

Ilinskaya, T. N. and Yosifova, M. G. (1956) *Bull. Narcot.* **8**, 38

Iloff, P. M. and Mirov, N. T. (1953) *J. Am. Pharm. Ass.* **42**, 464

Iloff, P. M. and Mirov, N. T. (1954) *J. Am. Pharm. Ass.* **43**, 373, 742

Imshaug, A. A. and Brodo, I. M. (1966) *Nova Hedwigia* **12**, 1

Irk, K. (1911) *Pharm. Zentralhalle*, Dtschl. 1111

Isaacs, B. F. and Tyler, V. E. (1963) *Mycologia* **55**, 124

Ito, H. (1964) *Yakugaku Zasshi* **84**, 1123

Ivanov, D. and Ivanov, N. (1949) *C. R. Acad. Bulg. Sci.* **2**, 41

(Ivanov, N. N.) Иванов, Н. Н. (1937) *Изд. АН СССР, сер. биол.* (Rec. Acad. Sci. USSR, ser. biol.) **6**, 1801

(Ivanov, S. L.) Иванов, С. Л. (1961) *Климатическая теория образования органических веществ.* Изд. АН СССР Мсскеа (Climatic theory of the production of organic compounds). Ed. Acad. Sci. USSR, Moscow

(Ivanov, V. and Tomova, M.) Иванов, В., Томова, И. (1957) *Труды Н.—И. Инст. Фарм. № 1 (София)* (Works of Pharm. Inst.) (Sophia)

Janackovic, B. (1957) *Matières Médic.* **3**, 143

Janaki-Ammal, E. K., Sobti, S. N. and Handa, K. L. (1964) *Curr. Sci.* **33**, 500

(Janashevski, N. K. and Stepanov, N. V.) Янашевский, Н. К., Степанов, Н. В. (1964) *Ж. Общ. Хим.* (J. Gen. Chem.) **16**, 141

Janot, M. and Le Men, J. (1954) *C. R. Ac. Sci. France* **238**, 2550

Janot, M. M., Goutarel, R., Perezmador, M. C. and Barron, Y. (1953) *Ann. Pharm. France* **11**, 602

Jaretzky, R. and Axer, B. (1934) *Arch. Pharm.* **272**, 152

Jasperson-Schib, R. and Flück, H. (1961) *Pharm. Acta Helv.* **36**, 461

(Jaunsila, V.) Яунсила, В. (1961) *Тр. Ленингр. Хим. Фарм. Инст.* (Works of Leningrad. Chem. Pharm. Inst.) **12**, 197

Jay, M. (1968) *Taxon* **17**, 136

Jensen, K. A., Conti, J. and Kjaer, A. (1953) *Acta Chim. Scand.* **7**, 1267

Johnston, T. D. and Jones, D. I. H. (966) *J. Sci. Food Agric.* **17**, 70

Jones T. G. H. (1937) *Proc. Roy. Soc.* Queensland **48**, 48

Jones, T. G. H., Lahey, G. and Sutherland, M. D. (1949) *Univ. Queensl. Papers.* Dep. of Chem. 1, No. 37

Jong, De A. W. K. (1913) *C. R. XI. Congr. Int. Pharm.* vol. **2**, 979

Josefsson, E. (1966) *Qual. Plant. Mat. Veg.* **13**, 190

Joseph, A. P. and Whitefield, B. W. (1922) *J. Soc. Chem. Ind.* **41**, 172

Joseph-Nathan, P. and Romo, J. (1966) *Tetrahedron* **23**, 529

Joshi, M. G. and Joshi, A. B. (1963) *Curr. Sci.* **32**, 371

Joubert, T. G. and Enslin, P. R. (1954) *J. S.-Afr. Chem. Inst.* **7**, 131

Juhász, A. and Tyihák, E. (1968) *Acta Agronomica* **18**, 113

Juillet, A., Susplugas, J. and Courp, J. (1955) *Les oléagineux et leurs tourteaux* Paris

Juvonen, S. (1966) *Acta Bot. Fenn.* **71**, 1

Juvonen, S. (1967) *Farm. Notisblad* **76**, 167

(Kachuhashvily, T. N.) Качухашвили, Т. Н. (1965) *Мед. Промышл.* (Med. Indust.) **19**, 46

Kaczmarek, F. (1957) *Planta Med.* **5**, 51

Kafuku, K. (1917) *J. Chem. Soc. Ind.* **36**, 905

Kafuku, K. and Nozoe, T. (1931) *Bull. Jap. Chem. Soc.* **6**, 111

Kagan, H. B., Miller, H. E., Renold, W., Lakshimikantam, M. V. et al. (1966) *J. Org. Chem.* **31**, 1629

Kaku, T. and Kondo, T. (1931) *J. Pharm. Soc. Jap.* **51**, 3

Kapur, K. K., Vashist, V. N. and Atal, C. K. (1967) *Ess. Oil. Rec.* **58**, 148

(Karpenko, I. S., Pahomova, A. N. and Gudoshnikova, V. S.) Карпенко, И. С., Пахомова, А. Н., Гудошникова, В. С. (1953) *Новые лекарственные раст. Сибери* (New medicinal plants in Siberia) Tomsk, **4**, 124

Karrer, P., Eugster, C. H. and Patel, C. V. (1949) *Helv. Chim. Acta* **32**, 2397

Kartha, A. R. S. and Kidwai, M. A. (1965) *Ind. J. Chem.* **3**, 131

Kaul, J. L. and Trojánek, J. (1966) *Lloydia* **29**, 26

Kawaguchi, R. and Kim, K. U. (1937) *J. Pharm. Soc. Japan* **57**, 108

Kawamura, J. (1937) *Rep. Japan. Sci. Assoc.* **12**, 377

Kawamura, T. (1931) *Bull. Imp. Forest,* Exp. Sta. No. **31**, 97

Kawatani, T. (1955) *J. Pharm. Soc. Jap.* **73**, 783

Kawatani, T. (1959) *J. Pharm. Soc. Jap.* **79**, 392

Kawatani, T., Fujita, S. and Ohno, T. (1958) *J. Pharm. Soc. Jap.* **78**, 50

(Kazakovich, L. I. and Sobolievskaia, O. Yu.) Казакович, Л. И., Собольевская, О. Ю. (1928) *Ж. Опытн. Агрон. Юго-Восток СССР.* (J. Exp. Agron. South-East USSR) vol. **5/2**, 57 Saratov

Kerdiles, R. (1967) *L'Essence de Thymus vulgaris L.* These. Univ. Montpellier. Fac. Pharm.

Kesterson, J. W., Pieringer, A. P., Edwards, G. J. and Hendrickson, R. (1963) *Proc. Amer. Hort. Sci.* **84**, 199

Khafagy, S., El-Moghazy, A. M. and Sandberg, F. (1963) *Sv. Farm. Tidsk.* **66**, 481

Khanna, K. L., Schwarting, A. E. and Bobbit, J. M. (1962) *J. Pharm. Sci.* **51**, 1194

Kidd, D. A. A. (1955) *Chem. and Ind.* 1481

Kimura, Y. and Ohtani, M. (1928) *J. Pharm. Soc. Jap.* **48**, 128

(Kiryalov, N. P. and Konovalov, I. N.) Кирялов, Н. П., Коновалов, И. Н. (1959) *Интрод. Рас. Зел. Строит.* (Introd. Horticult. Building) **7**, 40

(Kiseliov, A. and Konovalova, R. A.) Кисельев, А., Коновалова, Р. А. (1948) *Ж. Общ. Хим.* (J. Gen. Chem.) **18**, 142

Kjaer, A. (1962) Private communication

Kjaer, A. and Fiis, P. (1962) *Acta Chem. Scand.* **16**, 936

Kjaer, A. and Hansen, S. E. (1958) *Bot. Tiddskr.* **54**, 374

Kjaer, A. and Thomson, N. (1962) *Acta Chem. Scand.* **16**, 591

Klee, J. (1914) *Arch. Pharm.* **252**, 211

Klein, G. (1921) *Sitzungsber. Akad. Wiss.* Wien, 295

Klein, G. (1932) *Handbuch. d. Pflanzenanalyse* Wien

Klein, G. and Farkas, I. (1930) *Öster. Bot. Ztg.* **79**, 107

Kleinschmidt, G. (1961) *Arch. Pharm.* **294**, 254

Kleinschmidt, G. and Mothes, K. (1958) *Pharmazie* **13**, 357

Klemperer, von M. E. and Warren, F. L. (1955) *Chem. and Ind.* 1553

(Klishchev, L. K.) Клищев, Л. К. (1961) *V. Biochem. Congr. (Moscow) Ref. Sect. Comm.* vol. **2**, 199

Klohs, M. W., Arons, R., Draper, M. D., Keller, F. et al. (1952) *J. Am. Chem. Soc.* **74**, 5107

Kobel, M., Schmeier, E. and Rutschmann, J. (1964) *Helv. Chim. Acta* **47**, 1052

Koch, K. (1942) *Archiv. Pharm.* **280**, 424

Kögl, F. and Sparenburg, van J. (1940) *Rec. Trav. Chim.* Pays-Bas **59**, 1180

Kohli, J. M., Zaman, A. and Kidwai, A. R. (1966) *IV. Int. Symp. IUPAC* Stockholm Abst. Book: 192

Kohlmünzer, S. (1964) *Diss. Pharm.* **16**, 393

(Kolesnikov, D. G. and Shvarcman, A. G.) Колесников, Д. Г., Шварцман, А. Г. (1939) *Ж. Общ. Хим.* (J. Gen. Chem.) **9**, 2156

Kolšek, J., Kornhauser, A. and Perpar, M. (1957) *Pharmazie* **12**, 101

(Konovalova, R. A.) Коновалова, Р. А. (1951) *Докл. АН ССР* (Rep. Acad. Sci. USSR) 78

Konovalova, R. A., Yunussoff, S. S. and Orechoff, A. P. (1935) *Ber. Dtsch. Chem. Ges.* (Comm. German Chem. Soc.) **68B**, 2158

Koolhaas, D. R. and Rowaan, M. (1937) *Parf. France* **15**, 245

Kopp, E., Kotilla, E., Csedő, K. and Mátyás, S. (1961) *Pharmazie* **16**, 224

(Koroleva, A. S.) Корольева, А. С. (1948) *Сообщ. Тадж. Фил. АН СССР* (Comm. Tadzh. Fil. Acad. Sci. USSR) **10**, 38

Korte, F. and Bechmann, G. (1958) *Naturwiss.* **45**, 390

Korte, F. and Sieper, H. (1964) *J. Chromatogr.* **13**, 90

Korzun, B. P., St.-André, A. F. and Ulshafer, P. R. (1957) *J. Am. Pharm. Ass.* **46**, 720

Kosova, V. (1959) *Act. Fac. Pharm.* Brunensis **2**, 71

Kosova, V. Chládek, M. and Petrik, F. (1958) *Pharmazie* **13**, 631

Kostka, K. and Pijewska, L. (1961) *Diss. Pharm.* **13**, 37

Kotilla, E. (1959) *Orvosi Szemle* (Medical Review) 308

Kovacic, K., Bozin, Z. and Ladanji, N. (1956) *Farm. Glasn.* 419

Kovacic, K., Bozin, Z. and Ladanji, N. (1958) *Farm. Glasn.* 267

(Koverga, A. S.) Коверга, А. С. (1959) *Тр. Гос. Никитск. Бот. Сад* (Works of St. Nikitsk. Bot. Garden). **29**, 3

Kozlowski, J. (1960) *Biul. Inst. Roslin Leczn.* **6**, 65

(Krachkovskaya, L. P.) Крачковская, Л. П. (1958) *Краткий отчет ВНИИМЕМК за 1957* (Short report of St. Sci. Res. Inst. of Oil and Aromatic Plants for 1957) 74, 83

Kremers, R. E. (1922) *J. Biol. Chem.* **52**, 439

Kremers, R. E. (1925) *J. Am. Pharm. Ass.* **14**, 32

Krynske, H. P. (1935) *Wiadomisc. farm.* **62**, 215

Kubitzki, K. and Reznik, H. (1966) *Beitr. Biol. Pflanzen.* **42**, 445

Kucera, M. and Mackova, E. (1955) *Ceskosl. Farm.* **4**, 78

Küchler, E., Büchi, J. and Oconomov, N. (1956) *Pharm. Acta Helv.* **40**, 85

(Kuchuloria, T. L.) Кучулория, Т. Л. (1964) *Тр. Сухумск. Опыт. Ст.* (Works of Suchumsk. Exp. St.) **5**, 13

(Kuchumova, L. P.) Кучумова, Л. П. (1959) *Сборн. Работ. Аспирантов. Ленинград* (Coll. of Aspirants works. Leningrad) 110

Kühn, L. and Pfeifer, S. (1965) *Pharmazie* **20**, 520

Kulesza, J., Cybulska, N. and Gora, J. (1964) *Chem. Abstr.* **61**, 17

Kulesza, J., Roth, Z. and Jaworski, T. (1961) Zestyty naukowe Politechn. Lodzkiej, Chem. Spozywoza No. **5**, 49

Kupchan, S. M., Cassady, J. M., Bailey, J. and Knox, J. R. (1965) *J. Pharm. Sci.* **54**, 1703

Kupchan, S. M., Chakravarti, K. K. and Yokoyama, N. (1963) *J. Pharm. Soc.* **52**, 985

Kupchan, S. M., Yokoyama, N. and Beal, J. L. (1960) *J. Amer. Pharm. Assoc. Sc.* **49**, 727

Kuroda, T. (1962) *J. Pharm. Soc. Jap.* **82**, 164, 171, 199

Kuroda, T. and Kawatani, T. (1965) *J. Pharm. Soc. Jap.* **76**, 1446

Kurokawa, S. and Jinzenji, V. (1965) *Bull. Nat. Sci. Mus.* **8**, 369

Kurokawa, S., Jinzenji, Y., Shibata, S. and Chiang, H. C. (1966) *Bull. Nat. Sci. Mus.* **9**, 101

Kurup, P. A. (1956) *Curr. Sci.* (India) **25**, 57
(Kusner, T. S. and Grinberg, F. L.) Куснер, Т. С., Гринберг, Ф. Л. (1935) *Ж. Прикл. хим. СССР* (J. Appl. Chem. USSR) **8**, 1221
Küssner, W. (1939) *Merck's Jahresbericht* **52**, 39
Küssner, W. (1940) *Merck's Jahresbericht* **54**, 29
Küssner, W. (1950) *Pharmazie* **5**, 76
(Kusuvkov, A. D. and Massagetov, P. S.) Кузувков, А. Д., Массагетов, П. С. (1956) *Ж. Общ. Хим.* (J. Gen. Chem.) **26**, 281
Kybal, J. and Brejcha, V. (1955) *Pharmazie* **10**, 752
Laakso, P. V. (1965) *Symp. Res. Trav. XXV. Congr. Int. FIP*, Abstr. Pap. Suppl. Prague
La Face, D. (1955) *Ess. Deriv. Agrum.* **23**, 111
Langerfeldt, J. (1954) *Planta Med.* **2**, 58
Laorga, R. and Pinar, M. (1960) *An. real. soc. esp. fys. y quim.* **56**B, 797
Lapin, H. (1957) *C. R. Acad. Sci. France* **224**, 3065
(Lapunova, P. M. and Borisiuk, Yu. G.) Лапунова, П. М., Борисьюк, Ю. Г. (1961) *Фарм. Ж.* (Pharm. J.). Kiev, **16**, 48
Leenhouts, P. W. (1962) *Flora Malesiana* **6**, 343
Leifertová, I. (1966) *Preslia.* **38**, 386
Lenkey, K. B. (1961) *Pharm. Acta Helv.* **36**, 43
Leprestre, L. (1927) *Quebrecho-Blanco, étude pharmacologique.* Thèse Université de Paris
Lewis, Y. S., Sankaran-Nambudiri, E. and Philip, T. (1966) *Perf. Ess. Oil Rec.* **57**, 623
Liberalli, C. H. and Sharovsky, C. A. (1957/1958) *An. Far. Odont.* Univ. S. Paolo **15**, 135
(Libizov, N. I.) Либизов, Н. И. (1938a) *Биохимия* (Biochemistry) **3**, 33
(Libizov, N. I.) Либизов, Н. И. (1938b) *Фарм. и Фармакол.* (Pharm. and Pharmacol.) **3**, 27
(Libizov, N. I.) Либизов, Н. И. (1939) *Фармация* (Pharmacy) **2**, 17
Liem Song Go and Hegnauer, R. (1955) *Pharm. Weekbl.* **90**, 513
Ligeti, G. (1959) *Pharmazie* **14**, 164
(Linjuchev, V. P. and Bankovski, A. I) Линючев, В. П., Банковский, А. И. (1959) *Тр. ВИЛАР* (Works of St. Inst. Med. and Aromatic Plants) **11**, 65
Liotta, N. (1923) *Riv. Ital. Ess. Prof.* **5**, 140
(Liu Jun-Lun) Лиу Юн-Лун (1962) *Мед. Промышл.* (Med. Industr.) **16**, 4, 7
Lorencz, H. and Schulz-Schaeffer, J. (1964) *Z. Pflanzenzüchtg.* **52**, 13
Lőrincz, K. (1962) *Herba Hung.* **1**, 73
(Loshkariov, P. M. and Bondarchuk, L. S.) Лошкарьёв, П. М., Бондарчук, Л. С. (1964) *Мед. Промышл.* (Med. Industr.) **18**, 10,16
Lossner, G. (1967a) *Pharmazie* **22**, 51
Lossner, G. (1967b) *Pharmazie.* In Press
Lossner, G. (1968) *Planta Med.* **16**, 54
Lucas, R. A., Rovinski, S., Kiesel, R. J., Dorfman, L. and MacPhilbey, H. B. (1964a) *J. Org. Chem.* **29**, 1549
Lucas, R. A., Smith, R. G. and Dorfmann, L. (1964b) *J. Org. Chem.* **29**, 2101
(Lukianov, I. A.) Лукьянов, И. А. (1963) *Агробиология* (Agrobiology) 936
(Lutkov, A. N.) Лутков, А. Н. (1955) *Краткий отчет ВНИИМЕМК* (Short report of St. Sci. Res. Inst. of Oil and Aromatic Plants) for 1954, 115
(Lutkov, A. N.) Лутков, А. Н. (1960) *Растительное сырье* (Raw material of plants origin) **6**, 226
Mabry, T. J. (1968) *Recent advances in Phytochemistry* vol. 1. Appleton-Century. Crofts New York
Mabry, T. J., Miller, M. E., Kagan, M. B., Renold, W. and Fischer, N. M. (1966) *IV. Int. Symp. IUPAC* Stockholm Abstr. Book: 60
Mackenzie-Lamb, I. (1951) *Can. J. Bot.* **29**, 522
Madaeva, O. S. (1958) *Chem. Abstr.* **52**, 12321
Maisit, J. (1935) *Latvijas Univ. Praksti, Chem. Ser.* **2**, 401

Maizite, J. (1942) *Arch. Pharm.* **52,** 173

Majumdar, N. D. (1955) *J. Ind. Pharm.* **17,** 158

(Makarova, G. V. and Borisiuk, Yu. G.) Макарова, Г. В., Борисюк. Ю. Г. (1957) *Тр. Фарм. Инст.* Works Pharm. Inst. Kharkov 244

Makleit, S. and Bognár, R. (1959) *Természetes és gyógyhatású szervesanyagok kémiája. Szimpozium* (Chemism of naturally occurring and medicinal organic materials. Symposium), Budapest, mimeographed

Makleit, S., Bognár, R. and Dobos, L. (1963) *Herba Hung.* **2,** 19

Makleit, S., Gaál, Gy. D. and Bognár, R. (1962) *Acta Chim. Ac. Sci. Hung.* **33,** 407

(Makovkina, A. I.) Маковкина, А. И. (1962) *Краткий отчет ВНИИМЕМК за 1959–60* (Short report of St. Sci. Res. Inst. of Oil and Aromatic Plants)

(Maksiutina, N. P. and Kolesnikov, D. G.) Максютина, Н. П., Колесников, Д. Г. (1962) *Мед. Промышл.*(Med. Industr.) **16,** 11

Malone, H. M., Robichaud, R. C., Tyler, V. E. and Brady, L. R. (1962) *Lloydia* **25,** 231

Malaviya, B. K. and Dutt, S. (1939) *J. Ind. Acad. Sci.* **25,** 1

Manjarrez, A. and Guzmán, A. (1964) *Bol. Inst. Quim. Univ. Mex.* **16,** 20

Mansfeld, R. (1959) *Vorläufiges Verzeichnis landwirtschaftlich oder gärtnerisch kultivierter Pflanzenarten-Kulturpflanze.* Beiheft 2. Akademie Verlag, Berlin

Manske, F. (1939) *Canad. J. Res.* **17**B, 399

Manske, F. (1942) *Canad. J. Res.* **20**B, 255

Manske, R. H. F. and Marion, L. (1942) *Can. J. Res.* **20**B, 153

Manske, R. H. F. and Marion, L. (1943) *Can. J. Res.* **21**B, 92

Manske, R. H. F. and Marion, L. (1947) *J. Am. Chem. Soc.* **69,** 2126

Marini-Bettolo, G. B. and Carvalho-Pereira, P. (1959) *Ann. Chim.* **48,** 869

Marion, L. (1945) *Can. J. Res.* **23**B, 165

Marion, L. and Manske, R. H. F. (1944) *Can. J. Res.* **22**B, 137

Marker, R. E. and Lopez, J. (1947) *J. Am. Chem. Soc.* **69,** 2383

Marker, R. E., Wagner, R. B., Elshafer, E. R., Witthecker, E. L. et al. (1943) *J. Am. Chem. Soc.* **65,** 1199

(Markov, V. V.) Марков, В. В. (1940) *Тр. ВИЕМ Промышл.* (Works of St. Inst. Ess. Oil Industr.) **8,** 97

Markovic, S., Benzinger, F., Porges, M. and Sropel, B. (1952) *Acta Pharm. Jugos.* **2,** 39

Martin, J. T. (1960) *Ann. Appl. Biol.* **48,** 837

(Maslova, T. A.) Маслова, Т. А. (1957) *Тр. Сухумск. зон. станц. эфиромасл. культур.* (Suhumsk. St. of Ess. Oil Plants) **2,** 19

Masón, L. M., Puschett, E. R. and Wildmann, W. C. (1955) *J. Am. Chem. Soc.* **77,** 1255

(Massagetov, P. S.) Массагетов, П. С. (1938) *Фарм. м Фармакол.* (Pharm. and Pharmacol.) **6,** 17

(Massagetov, P. S.) Массагетов, П. С. (1947) *Тр. ВИЛАР вып. 9, Медгиз* (Works of St. Inst. Medicinal and Aromatic Plants). Moscow. **9,** Medgiz

(Massagetov, P. S. and Kuzuvkov, A. D.) Массагетов, П. С., Кузувков, А. Д. (1953) *Ж. Общ. Хим.* (J. Gen. Chem.) **23,** 158

Máthé, I. and Held, G. (1965) *Bot. Közl.* (Bot. Rec.) **52,** 87

Máthé, I. and Szabó, E. (1963) *Herba Hung.* **2,** 84

Máthé, I. and Tyihák, E. (1960) *Gyógyszerészet* (Pharmacy) **4,** 269

Mather, M. and Dyer, F. J. (1944) *Quart. J. Pharm. Pharmacol.* **17,** 102

Mathews, W. S. A. and Pickering, G. B. (1958) *C. R. Congr. Int. Chim. Ind.* 31

Maturova, M., Parlaskova, D. and Santávy, F. (1966) *Planta Med.* **14,** 22

Maturova, M. and Preininger, V. (1962) *Abstr. of Comm. II. Int. Symp. of Nat. Prod.* 136

(Matveiev, N. D.) Матвеев, Н. Д. (1959) *Основы сортоводно семенного дела по лекарственным культурам. Сельхозгиз* (Bases of variety-breeding and seed-growing in the case of medicinal plants). Ed. Sel'hozgiz. Moscow

McCarthy, T. J. and Rheede van Oudtshoorn, M. C. B. (1966) *Planta Med.* **14,** 63

McClure, J. W. and Alston, R. E. (1964) *Nature* **201,** 311

McClure, J. W. and Alston, R. E. (1966) *Am. J. Bot.* **53**, 849

McGimpsey, J. R. and Murray, J . (1960) *J. Appl. Chem.* **6**, 180

McKenzie, A. W. and Proce. J. R. (1953) *Austral. J. Chem.* **6**, 180

McKern, H. H. C. (1965) *J. Proc. Roy. Soc. N.S.W.* **98**, 1

McKern, H. H. G. and Willis, J. L. (1957) *Perfum Rec.* **48**, 17

Meijer, M. Th. (1946) *Rec. Trav. Chim.* Pays-Bas **65**, 843

Melchert, T. E. (1966) *Am. J. Bot.* **53**, 1015

Mentzer, C. (1960) *Bull. Soc. Chim. France.* **203**

Mentzer, C. (1966) Biogenetic Classification of Plant Constituents. In: *Comparative Phyto-chem.* Ed. T. Swain, Academic Press London and New York. 21

Messerschmidt, W. (1965) *Planta Med.* **13**, 56

Michaluk, A. and Oswiecimska, M. (1959) *Diss. Pharm.* **11**, 191

(Michelson, L. A.) Михельсон, Л. А. (1938) *Биох. Культури. Раст.* (Biochem. Cult. Plants). vol. **6**, 108, 173

Miller, E. R. (1902) *Arch. Pharm.* **240**, 481

Miller, R. W., Daxanbichler, M. E. and Earle, R. R. (1964) *J. Am. Oil Chem. Soc.* **41**, 167

Miller, H. E., Mabry, T. J. and Turner, B. L. (1968) *Am. J. Bot.* **55**, 316

(Minasian, S. M.) Минасьян, С. М. (1947) *Биохимия* (Biochemistry) **12**, 298

Minato, H. and Horibe, I. (1965) *J. Chem. Soc.* 1009

Mingrone, L. V. and Ownbey, M. (1968) *Am. J. Bot.* **55**, 734

Mirov, N. T. (1956) *Canad. J. Bot.* **34**, 443

Mirov, N. T. (1958) *J. Amer. Pharm. Ass.* **47**, 404

Mirov, N. T. (1963) *Lloydia* **26**, 117

Mirov, N. T., Frank, E. and Zavarin, E. (1965) *Phytochem.* **4**, 564

Mirov, N. T., Zavarin, E., Snajberk, K. and Costello, K. (1966) *Phytochem.* **5**, 343

(Mishurova, S. S.) Мишурова, С. С. (1966) *Изв. АН Азерб. ССР. Сер. биол.* No 2 (Rec. Acad. Sci. Azerb. SSR, Ser. biol. No 2)

Mitra, G. (1957) *J. Sci. Ind. Res.* **16**B, 120, 167

Mittal, O. P. and Seshadri, T. R. (1956) *J. Chem. Soc.* 2176

Moens, J. C. B. (1882) *De Kinacultur in Asia.* Evans and Co. Batavia

Molisch, H. (1933) *Pflanzenchemie und Pflanzenverwandtschaft.* Fischer Verlag, Jena

Molisch, H. and Goldschmiedt, G. (1901) *Sitz. der Akad. Wiss.* Wien. Naturwiss. Kl. Abt. 1, **110**, 185

Mollan, T. R. M. (1961) *Perf. Record* **52**, 41, 284, 349

Montesionos, Q. F. F. (1949) *Bol. Soc. Quim.* Peru **5**, 99

Mooney, K. and Emboden, W. A. (1968) *Brittonia* **20**, 44

Moritz, O. (1962) *Allgemeine Pharmakognosie* VEB G. Fischer Verlag, Jena

Mors, W. B., Magalhaes, M. T. and Gottlieb, O. R. (1959) *Perf. Ess. Oil. Rec.* **50**, 26

Mors, W. B., Magalhaes, M. T. and Gottlieb, O. R. (1962) *Fortschr. Chem. Org. Nat. Stoffe* **20**, 131

Mortimer, P. I. and Wilkinson, S. (1957) *J. Chem. Soc.* 3967

Moschini, E. (1960) *Riv. Ortoflorofrutticult. Ital.* **44**, 249

Mothes, K. (1958) Arbeit der physiologischen Abteilung. *Kulturpflanze VI.* Akademie Verlag, Berlin

Mothes, K. (1960) Alkaloids in the plant. In: *The Alkaloids.* By Manske-Holmes, Acad. Press Publ. vol. VI, Ch. 1, 1—30

Mothes, K. (1961) *Wiss. Z. Univ.* Halle, Math. - Nat. Reihe **10**, 1153

Mothes, K. (1962) *Lecture on the biogenesis of alkaloids,* in the Ins. Stereochem Hung. Ac. Sci. Budapest

Mudgill, K. L. and Vridhachalam, P. N. (1922) *Perf. Record.* **13**, 172

Müller, J. M. (1957) *Experientia* **13**, 479

Murakami, K. and Fukuda, J. (1955) *J. Pharm. Soc. Jap.* **75**, 603

Muraveva, V. I. and Kuzuvkov, A. D.) Муравьева, В. И., Кузувков, А. Д. (1963) *Ж. Общ. Хим.* (J. Gen. Chem.) **33**, 693

Murray, M. J. (1960a) *J. Appl. Chem.* **10**, 366

Murray, M. J. (1960b) *Genetics* **45**, 925

Murray, M. J. and Reitsema, R. H. (1954) *J. Am. Pharm. Ass.* **43**, 612

(Murri, I. K.) Мурри, И. К. (1961) *Биохимия моркови. Биохим. овощных культур* (Biochemistry of carrot in Biochemistry of Vegetables) Moscow—Leningrad, 420

Myers, G. S., Glen, W. L., Morozovits, P., Barber, R. and Grant, G. A. (1952) *J. Am. Chem. Soc.* **74**, 3198

Nagasawa, M. (1961) *J. Pharm. Soc. Japan* **81**, 129

Nair, A. G. R. and Subramanian, S. S. (1962) *Curr. Sci.* **31**, 60

Nair, A. G. R. and Subramanian, S. S. (1964) *Ind. J. Pharm.* **26**, 140

Nakamura, H. and Ohta, T. (1933'34) *Proc. Imp. Acad.* Tokyo **9**, 91, **10**, 215

Nakano, T., Yang, T. H., Terao, L. and Durham, L. J. (1963) *Chem. and Ind.* 1034, 1763

Nakano, T., Saoki, Y. and Terao, L. (1966) *IV. Int. Symp. IUPAC* Stockholm Abstr. Book: 91

Nakaoki, T. and Morita, N. (1958) *J. Pharm. Soc. Jap.* **78**, 521

Narayanan, C. S., Kulkarni, K. S., Vaidya, A. S., Kanthamani, S. et al. (1964) *Tetrahedron* **20**, 963

Narbonne, G. (1940) *Ephedra Nord-Africaines et leurs alcaloïdes.* Thèse Pharm. Univ. Alger

(Naugolnaya, T. N.) Наугольная, Т. Н. (1963) *Раст. сырие* (Raw material of plant origin **9**, 167

Naves, Y. R. (1943) *Helv. Chim. Acta* **26**, 162

Naves, Y. R. (1948) *Helv. Chim. Acta* **31**, 932

Naves, Y. R. (1950) *Perf. Ess. Oil. Rec.* **41**, 286

Naves, Y. R. (1960) *Perf. Ess. Oil. Rec.* **51**, 242

Naves, Y. R. and Grampoloff, A. V. (1959) *C. R. Acad. Sci.* **249**, 306

Naves, Y. R. and Grampoloff, A. V. (1961) *Bull. Soc. Chim. France.* **37**

Naves, Y. R. and Marcovici, D. (1963) *Helv. Chim. Acta* **46**, 2139

Naves, Y. R. and Ochsner, P. (1960) *Helv. Chim. Acta* **43**, 406

Naves, Y. R. and Tucakov, J. (1959) *C. R. Acad. Sci.* **249**, 843

Nayak, U. G. and Guha, F. C. (1952) *J. Indian Chem. Soc.* **29**, 203, 205

Nazarenko, M. V. (1965) *III. Cong. Int. E/O* Sophia 214

Neczypor, W. (1958) *Kühn Arch.* **72**, 444

Neczypor, W. (1965) *Pharmazie* **20**, 735

(Nesterenko, P. A.) Нестеренко, П. А. (1934) *Базилик камфорный* (Camphoric basil.) Ex Burns-Runge, G. (1948) *Pharmazie* **3**, 262

(Nesterenko, P. A.) Нестеренко, П. А. (1935) *Тр. Гос. Никитск. Бот. Сада* (Works of St. Nikitsk. Bot. Garden) **18**, 127

Neubauer, D. and Mothes, K. (1961) *Planta Med.* **9**, 466

Neubauer, D. and Mothes, K. (1963) *Planta Med.* **11**, 387

Neybergh, A. G. (1953) *Bull. Agr. Congo Belge* **44**, 27

Nicoletti, R. and Baiocchi, L. (1961) *Ann. Chim.* **51**, 1265

Nigam, S. S. and Dutt, S. (1944) *Indian Soap J.* **10**, 19

Nigam, S. S. and Dutt, S. (1946) *Indian Soap J.* **11**, 210, **12**, 77

Nigam, S. S. and Purohit, R. M. (1961) *Perf. Ess. Oil Record.* **52**, 3, 153, 643

Nigam, S. S. and Purohit, R. M. (1962) *Riechst. Arom.* **12**, 185

Nigam, S. S. and Purohit, R. M. (1966) *Riechst. Arom.* **16**, 117

Nigam, S. S. and Radhakrishnan, S. (1963) *Perf. Ess. Oil Rec.* **54**, 86

Nigam, S. S. and Radhakrishnan, C. (1963) *Riechst. Arom.* **13**, 293

Nigam, M. C., Nigam, I. C., Handa, L. K. and Levi, L. (1965) *J. Pharm. Sci.* **54**, 799

Nijland, M. M. (1962) *Einige Resultate van papierchrom. Onderzoek van Hydrastis Wurtel.* Diss. Utrecht

(Nikolaev, A. G.) Николаев, А. Г. (1960) *Кишиневск. Унив. Тр. по Химии Прир. Соед.* (Kishinev Univ. Works in the field of chemistry of natural compounds) **3**, 11

(Nikolaev, A. G. and Nerevjanchenko, S. A.) Николаев, А. Г., Неревянченко, С. А. (1961) *Кишиневск. Унив. Тр. по Химии Прир. Соед.* (Kishinevs. Univ. Works on the field of the chemistry of natural compounds) **4**, 63

(Nikonov, G. K.) Никонов, Г. К. (1965) *Мед. Промышл.* (Med. Industr.) **19,** 21

(Nilov, V. I.) Нилов, В. И. (1934) *Соц. Раст.* (Socialist plant-growing) **11,** 21

(Nilov, V. I.) Нилов, В. И. (1936) *Тр. по прикл. Бот. Ген. Сел. Сер. 3* (Works on Appl. Bot. Gen. Sel. ser. 3) vol. **3,** 5

(Nilov, V. I.) Нилов, В. И. (1937) *Изв. АН СССР Сер. Биол.* (Rec. Acad. Sci. USSR, ser. biol.) **6,** 1709

(Nilov, V. I.) Нилов, В. И. (1938) *Биох. Культ. Раст.* (Biochem. Cult. Plants) **6,** 5, 145

Nishida, K. and Uota, H. (1931) *J. Agr. Chem. Soc. Jap.* **7,** 157

Nooteboom, R. P. (1966) *Blumea* **14,** 309

Novák, I., Buzás, G. and Tóth, L. (1962) *Pharmazie* **17,** 95, 166

Novák, I. and Háznagy, A. (1962) *Pharmazie* **17,** 533

Novotny, L., Jizba, J. and Herout, V. (1962) *Coll. Chem.* **27,** 1393, 2462

Novotny, L., Toman, J., Stary, F., Marquez, A. D. Herout, V. and Sorm. F. (1966) *Phytochem.* **5,** 1261

Nozoe, T., Yasue, A. and Yamane, K. (1951) *Proc. Jap. Acad.* **27,** 15

(Obuhov, A. N. and Kondratzki, A. P.) Обухов, А. Н., Кондрацкий, А. П. (1946) *Технология продукции эфиромасл* (Technology of the production of essential oil) Pyshchepromizdat, Moscow

Oelssner, W. (1951) *Pharmazie* **6,** 515

Ogawa, J. and Natori, S. (1968) *Phytochem.* **7,** 773

Ohno, S., Manki, K. and Ohmoto, T. (1959) *J. Pharm. Soc. Japan* **79,** 117

Ollis, W. D. (1968) *Rec. Adv. Phytochem.* vol. 1, 340

Ondetti, M. A. and Deulofeu, V. (1959) *Tetrahedron Letters* (7), 1

Orazi, O. O. (1946) *Ann. Assoc. Quim. Argent.* **34,** 158

(Orehov, A. P.) Орехов, А. П. (1955) *Химия алкалоидов* (Chem. of Alkaloids). 2. Ed., Acad. Sci. USSR, Moscow

Os van, F. H. L. (1950) *Pharm. Weekbl.* **85,** 732

Os van, F. H. L. (1957) *Pharm. Weekbl.* **92,** 846

Os van, F. H. L., Galenkamp, G. H. and Kliphuis, A. R. (1954) *Pharm. Weekbl.* **89,** 429

Os van, F. H. L. and Stehouwer, J. H. (1956) *Pharm. Weekbl.* **91,** 942

(Ostrovsky, N. I. and Bankovskaya, A. N.) Островский, Н. И., Банковская, А. Н. (1961) *Тезисы Докл. Научн. Фармацевт. Конф. Изучение Лекарст. Раст. Ресурсов.* (Theses of Lectures on the Sci. Pharmaceutical Conf. Studying of Medicinal Plants). Baku, 72

(Ostrovsky, N. I., Bankovskaia, A. N. and Kriukov, M. A.) Островский, Н. И., Банковская, А. Н., Крюков, М. А. (1964) *Апт. Дело* (Pharm. Affairs) **13,** 2, 26

Oswiecimska, M. (1963) *Diss. Pharm.* **15,** 471

Oswiecimska, M. (1968) *Planta Med.* **16,** 201

Oudin, A. (1939) *Ass. Fr. Avanc. Sci. Rapp. Comm.* **62,** Congr. 123

Paech, K. and Tracey, M. V. (1955) *Modern Methods of Plant Analysis.* vol. VI. Berlin

Paknikar, S. K. and Bhattacharryya, S. C. (1961) *Perfum. Rec.* **52,** 233

Palazzo, F. C., Palazzo, M. and Azarello, E. (1917) *Ann. Chim. Appl.* **7,** 88

Panova, D. and Tomova, M. (1963) *Planta Med.* **11,** 198

Parczewski, A. and Rajkowski, Z. (1962) *Dissert. Pharm.* **14,** 83

Parello, J. (1963) *Bull. Soc. Chim. (France)* 2787

Parello, J. and Munavalli, S. (1955) *C. R. Ac. Sci.* **260,** 337

Parihar, D. E. and Dutt, S. (1947) *Proc. Ind. Acad. Sci.* **25A,** 153, **26A,** 93

Paris, R. (1943) *Ann. Pharm. France* **1,** 138

Paris, R. (1949) *Ann. Pharm. France* **7,** 21

Paris, R. (1965) Personal communication

Paris, R., Moyse H. and Le Men, J. (1955) *Ann. Pharm. France* **13,** 245

Pascher, A. (1959) *Flora* **148,** 84

Pasich, B. and Kovalevski, Z. (1960) *Diss. Pharm.* **18,** 280

Patel, P. N., Hack, R., Tye, A. and Beal, J. L. (1965) *J. Pharm. Soc.* **54,** 1387

Páter, B. (1923) *Heil- und Gewürzflanz.* **5,** 86

Páter, B. (1924/25) *Heil- und Gewürzpflanz.* **7**, 137

Paul, V. and Handa, K. L. (1960) *Indian Oil Soap J.* **25**, 246

Pavanaram, S. K. and Row, L. R. (1956) *Austral. J. Chem.* **9**, 132

Peckolt, T. (1929) *Ber. d. Dtsch. Pharm. Ges.* **19**, 529

Pellini, G. and Morani, V. (1923) *Annali Chim. Appl.* **7**, 97

Penfold, A. R. (1922) *Perfum. Ess. Oil Rec.* **13**, 273

Penfold, A. R. (1925) *J. Proc. Roy. Soc. N.S.W.* **58**, 37

Penfold, A. R. (1926) *J. Proc. Roy. Soc. N.S.W.* **59**, 230, 351

Penfold, A. R. (1929) *J. Proc. Roy. Soc. N. S. W.* **62**, 225

Penfold, A. R. (1950) *Perf. Ess. Oil Rec.* **41**, 359

Penfold, A. R. (1959) *Perf. Oil Rec.* **50**, spec. number 16

Penfold, A. R., McKern, H. H. G. and Spies, M. C. (1953) *J. Proc. Roy. Soc. N. S. W.* **87**, 102

Penfold, A. R., McKern, H. H. G. and Willis, J. L. (1953) *Res. Ess. Oils. Austral Flora* **3**, 15

Penfold, A. R. and Morrison, F. R. (1950) "Tea Tree" oils. In: Guenther *The essential oils* (1953). vol. IV, 437, 525, 548

Penfold, A. R. and Morrison, F. R. (1953) *Perf. Ess. Oil Res.* **44**, 80, 121

Penfold, A. R., Morrison, F. R. and McKern, H. H. G. (1948) *Res. on Ess. Oils, Austral. Flora* **1**, 12, 18

Penfold, A. R., Morrison, F. R., McKern, H. H. G. and Willis, J. (1950) *Res. Ess. Oils Austral. Flora* **2**, 5, 8

Penfold, A. R., Morrison, F. R. and Smith-White, S. (1943) *Perf. Ess. Oil Rec.* **34**, 6

Penfold, A. R., Morrison, F. R., Willis, J. L., McKern, H. H. G. and Spies, M. C. (1951) *J. Proc. Roy. Soc. N. S. W.* **85**, 120, 123

Penfold, A. R., Ramage, S. R. and Simonsen, J. L. (1936) *J. Proc. Roy. Soc. N. S. W.* **68**, 80

Penfold, A. R. and Welch, M. B. (1921) *J. Proc. Roy. Soc. N.S.W.* **55**, 196

Pentilla, A. (1955) *Farmazeuttinen Aikakaus* **64**, 63

Pereira, A. M. (1957/58) *An. Fac. Farm. Odont. Univ.* S. Paolo **15**, 125

Pérez-Medina, L. A., Travacedo, E. and Deria, J. E. (1964) *Planta Med.* **12**, 478

Pfeifer, S. (1956) *Pharmazie* **11**, 387

Pfeifer, S. and Heydenreich, K. (1961) *Naturwiss.* **48**, 431

Pfeifer, S. and Mann, I. (1965) *Pharmazie* **20**, 643

Phillipson, J. D. and Melville, C. (1960) *J. Pharm. Pharmacol.* **12**, 506

Phokas, G. and Steinegger, E. (1956) *Pharmazie* **11**, 652

Piatrelli, M., Minale, L. and Proba, G. (1965) *Phytochem.* **4**, 121

(Pigulevsky, G. V.) Пигулевский, Г. В. (1943) *Ж. Общ. Хим.* (J. Gen. Chem.) **13**, 148

(Pigulevsky, G. V.) Пигулевский, Г. В. (1955) *Раст. Сырье* (Raw material of plant origin) **5**, 120

Pigulevsky, G. V. and Bakina, L. A. (1965) *III. Cong. Intern. E – O* Sophia 210

Pigulevsky, G. V., Kovaleva, V. I. and Motskuss, D. V. (1964) *III. Cong. Int. Ess. Oil* Sophia 121

(Pigulevsky, G. V. and Kovaleva, V. I.) Пигулевский, Г. В., Ковалева, В. И (1955a) *Раст. Сырье* (Raw material of plant origin) **5**, 7

(Pigulevsky, G. V. and Kovaleva, V. I.) Пигулевский, Г. В., Ковалева, В. И. (1955б) *Ж. Прикл. Хим.* (J. Appl. Chem.) **28**, 1355

(Pigulevsky, G. V. and Kovaleva, V. I.) Пигулевский, Г. В., Ковалева, В. И. (1959) *Ж. Прикл. Хим.* (J. Appl. Chem.) **32**, 2703

(Pigulevsky, G. V. and Kovaleva, V. I.) Пигулевский, Г. В., Ковалева, В. И. (1961) *Раст. Сырье* (Raw material of plant origin) **8**, 15

(Pigulevsky, G. V. and Maksimova, A. M.) Пигулевский, Г. В., Максимова, А. М. (1960) *Труды Ленинград Лесотехн. Акад. им. С. М. Кирова* (Works of Leningrad Acad. Forestechn. S. M. Kirova) No. 91, 2, 347

(Pigulevsky, G. V., Nazarenko, M. V. and Ramzaev, F. S.) Пигулевский, Г. В., Назаренко, М. В., Рамзаев, Ф. С. (1965) *Раст. Ресурс.* (Resources of plant origin) **1**, 219, 227

Pillay, D. P., Rao, B. A. and Simonsen, J. L. (1928) *J. Soc. Chem. Ind.* **47**, 52

Ping-Hsien, Y. (1960) *Perf. Ess. Oil Rec.* **51,** 293

Ping-Hsien, Y. (1961) *Perf. Ess. Oil Rec.* **53,** 371, 454

Ping-Hsien, Y. (1964) *Chin. Chem. Soc.* **11,** 41

(Pivnenko, G. P., Chagovec, R. K. and Lohvickaia, M. I.) Пивненко, Г. П., Чаговец, Р. К., Лохвицкая, М. И. (1957) *Тр. Харковск. Гос. Фарм. Инст.* (Works of Harkov St. Pharm. Inst.) **1,** 294

Pkheidze, T. A. and Madaeva, O. S. (1961) *Chem. Abstr.* **55,** 8459

(Platonova, T. F., Massagetov, P. S., Kuzuvkov, A. D. and Utkin, L. A.) Платонова, Т. Ф., Массагетов, П. С., Кузувков, А. Д., Уткин, Л. А. (1956) *Ж. Общ. Хим.* (J. Gen. Chem.) **26,** 173

Poelt, O. and Ullrich, H. (1964) *Öst. Bot. Z.* **111,** 257

Poethke, W. and Kerstan, W. (1958) *Planta Med.* **6,** 430

Poisson, J. (1959) *Recherches sur les alcaloïdes de Rauvolfia vomitoria Afz.* Thèse Doct. Sci. Paris

Poisson, J., Berjoeing, R., Chauveau, N., Sharma, M. and Goutarel, R. (1964) *Bull. Soc. Chim. France* 2853

Polonsky, J. (1957) *Bull. Soc. Chim. (France)* 1079

Porter, T. H. and Mabry, T. J. (1969) *Phytochem.* **8,** 793

Power, F. B. and Salway, A. H. (1911) *J. Chem. Soc.* **99,** 490

(Pravdoljubova, A. A.) Правдолюбова, А. А. (1936) *Тр. по Прикл. Бот. Ген. Сел.* (Works on Appl. Bot.) **3,** 87

(Pravdoljubova, A. A.) Правдолюбова, А. А. (1938) *Биох. Культ. Раст.* (Biochem. Cult. Plants) **6,** 51

Preininger, V., Vácha, P., Sula, B. and Santavy, F. (1962) *Planta Med.* **10,** 124

Prista, L. N. et al. (1964) *Garcia de Orta* **12,** 277

Priszter, Sz. and Tétényi, P. (1963) *Bot. Közl.* (Bot. Rec.) **51,** 67

Prohorova, O. A. and Lebedev, I. M. (1932) *Душистые раст. Алтая, 1931* (Aromatic plants of the Altai) Тр. Совета по изучению производ. сер. Сибирия. вып. 3.

(Proskurnina, N. F.) Проскурнина, Н. Ф. (1955) *Ж. Общ. Хим.* (J. Gen. Chem.) **25,** 834

(Proskurnina, N. F.) Проскурнина, Н. Ф. (1957) *Ж. Общ. Хим.* (J. Gen. Chem.) **27,** 3365

Pufahl, K. and Schreiber, K. (1964) *Züchter* **33,** 287

Puisieux, F., Patel, M. B., Rowson, J. M. and Poisson, J. (1965) *Ann. Pharm. France* **23,** 33

Puntambekar, S. V. (1950) *Proc. Ind. Ac. Sci.* **32**A, 114

Qazilbash N. A. (1948) Quart J. Pharm-Pharmacol **21,** 475

Qazilbash, N. A. (1951) *Ind. Pharm.* **8,** 505

Qazilbash, N. A. (1954) *Ind. Pharm.* **9,** 297

Qazilbash, N. A. (1960) *Pharm. J.* **185,** 497

Quilici, V. (1958) *Nouvo G. Bot. Ital.* **65,** 16

Rabak, F. (1912) *US Dept. Agr. Bur. Plant. Industr.* No. 235

(Rabinin, A. A. and Ilina, E. M.) Рябинин, А. А., Ильина, Е. М. (1955) *Ж. Прикл. Хим.* (J. Appl. Chem.) **26,** 633

Rajkowski, Z. (1962) *Act. Polon. Pharm.* **19,** 383

Rakshit, N. J. (1938) *Perf. Ess. Oil Rec.* **29,** 402

Ramachandra, R. L. and Anjaneyulu, S. A. R. (1962) *J. Sci. Ind. Res.* **21**B, 581

Ramaut, J. Schumacker, R., Lambinar, J. and Badouin, C. (1966) *Bull. Jard. Bot. Bruxelles* **36,** 398

Rangashwami, S. (1962) *Curr. Sci.* **31,** 495

Rao, B. S. (1923) *Ess. Oil Rec.* **14,** 271

Rao, B. S. and Simonsen, L. J. (1925) *J. Ind. Inst. Sci.* **9**A, 145

Rao, B. S., Watson, H. E. and Sudborough, J. J. (1925) *J. Ind. Inst. Sci.* **8**A, 174

Rao, K. M. and Bhave, V. M. (1959) *Ind. Perfumer.* **3,** 99

Rao, P. S. and Sood, V. K. (1962) *Soap. Perfum. Cosmet.* **35,** 253

Rastogi, R. P., Sarkar, B. and Dhar, M. L. (1960) *Res. India,* **19B,** 252

Rattu, A. and Falqui, M. T. (1953) *Rend. Sci. Univ. Cagliari* **23,** 69

Rattu, A. and Maccioni, A. (1953) *Rend. Sci. Univ. Cagliari* **23,** 91

Rau, M. G. and Simonsen, J. L. (1922) *Ind. For. Rech.* **9,** 25

Read, B. E. and Feng, T. C. (1928) *J. Am. Pharm. Assoc.* **17,** 1189

Regnier, F. E., Valler, G. R. and Eisenbraun, E. J. (1967) *Phytochem.* **6,** 1281

Rehm, S. (1960) *Ergebnisse d. Biol.* **22,** 108

Reichstein, T. (1963) *Planta Med.* **11,** 293

Reichstein, T. (1965) *Planta Med.* **13,** 382

Reifer, J. and Bathurst, N. O. (1943) *N. Z. J. Sci. Techn.* **24B,** 17

Reitsema, R. H. (1954) *J. Am. Pharm. Ass.* **43,** 414

Reitsema, R. H. (1956) *J. Am. Chem. Soc.* **78,** 5022

Reitsema, R. H. (1958) *J. Am. Pharm. Ass.* **47,** 267

Reitsema, R. H. and Varnis, V. J. (1956) *J. Am. Chem. Soc.* **78,** 3792

Rennie, E. H. (1886) *J. Chem. Soc.* 857

(Reuter, G.) Райтер, Г. (1961) *V. Biochem. Conf. Moscow Abstr.* vol. 2, 127

Reznik, H. (1955) *Ztschr. Bot.* **43,** 499

Rheede van Outshoorn, M. C. B. and Gerritsma, K. W. (1965) *Naturwiss.* **52,** 186

(Ribalko, K. S. and Bankovski, A. N.) Рыбалко, К. С., Банковский, А. Н. (1959) *Тр. ВИЛАР* (Works of St. Inst. Medicinal and Aromatic Plants) **11,** 106

(Ribalko, K. S., Massagetov, P. S. and Eshatan, R. I.) Рыбалко, К. С., Массагетов, П. С., Эшатан, Р. И. (1963) *Мед. промышл.* (Med. Industr.) **17** (6), 41

Ribas, I. and Basanta, J. L. (1952) *Anal. Fis. y Quim. ser. B,* **43,** 161

Ribas, I. and Seoane, M. C. (1953) *An. Edafol. y Fisiol. Veg.* **12,** 695

Ricardi, M. (1958) *Bol. Soc. Biol. (Concepcion)* **33,** 29

Richter, R., Mohr, K. and Reichstein, T. (1935) *Helv. Chim. Acta* **36,** 1073

Richter, R. and Wolff, K. (1927) *Berichte der Chemischen Gesellschaft* **60,** 477

Riedl, H. (1962) *Taxon* **11,** 65

Rimpler, H., Langhauer, L. and Frenzel, H. S. (1963) *Planta Med.* **11,** 325

Roberts, E. A. M., Wight, W. and Wood, J. (1958) *New Phytologist* **57,** 211

Roberts, J. B. (1962) *Ann. Rep. Det. Hop. Res. 1961* Wye College 21

Rochelmeyer, H. (1949) *Pharmazie* **4,** 326

Romeike, A. (1958) *Planta Med.* **6,** 426

Romeike, A. (1961) *Kulturpflanze* **9,** 171

Romo de Vivar, A. and Romo, J. (1959) *Chem. Ind.* 882

Romo de Vivar, A. and Romo, J. (1961) *J. Am. Chem. Soc.* **83,** 2326

Romo de Vivar, A. and Jimenez, H. (1965) *Tetrahedron* **21,** 1741

Romo, J., Romo de Vivar, A., Velez, A. and Urbina, E. (1968) *Can. J. Chem.* **46,** 1535

Rönsch, H., Schreiber, K. and Stubbe, H. (1968) *Naturwiss.* **55,** 182

Rooth, A. G. and Hegnauer, R. (1955) *Pharm. Weekbl.* **90,** 36

Rosenthal, C. (1941) *Arch. Pharm.* **279,** 344

Rosenthal, C. (1954) *Züchter* **24,** 40

Rosenthaler, L. (1929) *Pharm. Acta Helv.* **4,** 55

(Rostocki, B. K. and Bankovski, A. N.) Ростоцкий, Б. К., Банковский, А. Н. (1950) *Тр. ВИЛАР* (Works of St. Inst. Medicinal and Aromatic Plants). 10. Ed. Medgiz. Moscow

Rother, A., Atal, C. K., Gold, D. and Schwarting, A. E. (1961) *J. of Chrom.* **5,** 178

Rovesti, P. (1925) *Profumi italici* **3,** 180

Rovesti, P. (1927) *Ann. Chim. Applicata* **17,** 561

Rovesti, P. (1952) *Riv. Ital.* **34,** 247

Rovesti, P. (1957) *Pharm. Weekbl.* **92,** 792, 843

Rovesti, P. (1959) *Parf. Cosm. Savon* **2,** 270

Rowson, J. M. (1945) *Quart. J.* **18,** 175

Rowson, J. M. (1960) *J. Pharm. Pharmacol.* **12,** 66T

Rudloff, von E. (1962) *Tappi* **45,** 181

Rudloff, von E. (1964) *Can. J. Chem.* **42,** 1057

Rudloff, E. and Underhill, E. W. (1965) *Phytochem.* **4,** 11

Ruijgrok, H. W. L. (1966) The distribution of Ranunculin and Cyanogenetic Compounds in the Ranunculaceae. In: *Comparative Phytochemistry* Ed. T. Swain

Runeberg, J. (1960) *Acta Chem. Scand.* **14**, 1288

Saber, H., Balbaa, S. L. and Zaky, Y. A. (1965) *Planta Med.* **13**, 104

Sacco, T. (1953) *Ind. Parfum.* **8**, 449

Sacco, T. (1955) *Boll. Inst. Orto. Bot. Univ.* Torino **2**, 419

Sacco, T. (1959) *Alliona* **5**, 185

Sacco, T. (1960) *Alliona* **6**, 227

Sacco, T. and Shimizu, S. (1965) *Perf. Ess. Oil Rec.* **56**, 211

Sadgopal, S. R. C. (1960) *Soap. Perf. Cosm.* **33**, 293

Sadgopal, S. R. C. and Gulati, B. C. (1956) *Soap. Perfum. Cosmet.* **29**, 1129

Saghir, A. R. B., Mann, K. L., Ownbey, M. and Berg, Y. R. (1966) *Am. J. Bot.* **53**, 477

Saha, S. K. (1969) *Sci. Cult.* Calcutta **24**, 572

Saito, S., Shigematsu, N. and Horri, Z. (1963) *Yakugaku Zasshi* **83**, 800

Saito, S., Tanaka, T., Kotera, K., Nakai, N., Sugimatu, N. and Horri, Z. (1965) *Chem. Pharm. Bull.* **13**, 786

Salgues, R. (1945) *Chem. Abstr.* 5398

Salgues, R. (1953) *Mat. végét.* **1**, 144

Salgues, R. (1954) *83. Congr. des Sociétés savantes* 401

(Samatcov, A. S., Ahramov, S. T., and Junussov, C. J.) Саматцов, А. С., Ахрамов, С. Т., Юнуссов, Ц. Й. (1965) *Докл. АН Узбек. ССР 21* (Rec. Acad. Sci. Uzbek. SSR, 21)

Sandberg, F. and Agurell, J. (1959) *Svensk. Farm. Tidsk.* **63**, 657

Sandberg, F. and Michel, N. (1963) *Lloydia* **26**, 78

Sander, H. (1963) *Planta Med.* **11**, 23

Sander, H., Alkemeyer, M. and Hänsel, R. (1962) *Arch. Pharm.* **295**, 6

Sandermann, W. (1962a) Terpenoids: Structure and distribution. In: *Comparative Biochemistry*. Ed. Florkin-Mason. Academic Press, New York-London, vol. **3**, 502

Sandermann, W. (1962b) *Holzforschung* **16**, 65

San Martin, R. (1953) *Farmacognosia* **13**, 357

Sannié, C. and Lapin, H. (1952) *Bull. Soc. Chim. France* **19**, 1080

Sannié, C., Lapin, H., Eloy, F. and Sanchez, L. C. (1957) *Bull. Soc. Chim. Biol.* **39**, 301

Santavy, F. (1963) *Abhdlgen d. Dtsch. Akad.* No. **4**, 235

Santavy, F., Maturova, M., Nemeckova, A., Schröter, H. B. et al. (1960) *Planta Med.* **8**, 167

(Saraeva, P. I.) Сараева, П. И. (1952) *Культура лекарственных растений* (Culture of medicinal plants) Moscow

Sárkány, S., Dános, B. and Sárkány–Kiss, I. (1959) *Ann. Univ. Sci.*, Budapest *Sect. Biol.* **2**, 211

Sárkány-Kiss, I. (1962) *Herba Hung.* **1**, 155

Sárkány-Kiss, I., Szabó-Nagy, E. and Tyihák, E. (1960) *Acta Pharm. Hung.* **30**, 35

Sawicka, M. (1956) *Dissert. Pharm.* **8**, 231

Scarpati, M. L. and Oriente, G. (1958) *Ricerca sci.* **28**, 2329

Schäfer, J. and Stein, M. (1967) *Naturwiss.* **54**, 205

Schantz, M. (1958) *Acta Bot. Fennica* **59**, 1

Schantz, M. (1962) *Planta Med.* **10**, 98

Schantz, M. and Ivars, L. (1964) *Ann. Univ. Turku* A. **2**, 32

Schantz, M. and Järvi, M. (1965) *XXV. Congr. Int. Sci. FIP* Prague Abstr. Papers 73

Schantz, M., Järvi, M. and Kaartinen R. (1966) *Planta Med.* **14**, 421

Schantz, M. and Juvonen, S. (1966) *Acta Bot. Fennica* **73**, 28

Schantz, M. and Widén, C. J. (1967) *Sci. Pharm.* **35**, 197

Schaub, F., Kaufmann, H., Stöcklin, W. and Reichstein, T. (1968) *Helv. Chim Acta* **51**, 738

Schenker, E., Hunger, A. and Reichstein, T. (1954) *Helv. Chim. Acta* **37**, 1004

Scheuble, R. (1953) *Mitt. Forstl. Bdsversuchsanstalt* Mariabrunn, **49**, 5

Schick, E. R., Reimann-Philipp, R. (1957) *Züchter* **27**, 300

Schinler, H. (1957) *Arzneimittelforschung* **7**, 69

Schlittler, E., Schwarz, H. and Bader, F. (1952) *Helv. Chim. Acta* **35**, 271

Schmutz, J. (1961) *Pharm. Acta Helv.* **36**, 103

Schmutz, J. and Hunziker, F. (1958) *Pharm. Acta Helv.* **33**, 341

Schöpf, C. and Unger, R. (1956) *Experientia* **12**, 19

Schratz, E. (1947) *Pharmazie* **2**, 177

Schratz, E. (1949) *Arzneipflanzenanbau*, Hannover

Schratz, E. (1959) *Planta Med.* **7**, 495

Schratz, E. (1960a) *Planta Med.* **8**, 282–896

Schratz, E. (1960b) *Hdbch. d. Pflanzenzüchtung V, Arzneipflanzen.* 383

Schratz, E. and Egels, W. (1958) *Planta Med.* **6**, 148

Schratz, E. and Ragoonwala, R. (1965) *XXV. Cong. Int. FIP (Prague) Res. Trav.* 85

Schratz, E., Sckenelle, F. J. and Qédan, S. (1968) *Sci. Pharm.* **36**, 13

Schratz, E. and Vethacke, H. J. (1958) *Planta Med.* **6**, 45

Schreiber, K. (1963) *Kulturpflanze* **51**

Schreiber, K. (1958) *Planta med.* **6**, 94, 435

Schreiber, K., Hammer, U., Ithal, E., Ripperger, H. et al. (1961) *Tagungsber. Dtsch. Akad. Wiss.*, Berlin No. **27**, 47

Schreiber, K. and Rönsch, H. (1963) *Tetrahedron letters* (5), 329

Schreiber, K. and Rönsch, H. (1965) *Arch. Pharm.* **298**, 285

Schrčck, O. (1941) *Züchter* **13**, 145, 151

Schrčter, H. B. (1965) *XXV. Cong. Int. Sci. Pharm. FIP (Prague) Res. Trav.* 81

Schwerdtfeger, G. (1961) *Züchter* **31**, 202

Sckrypczakowa, L. (1961) *Acta Polon. Pharm.* **18**, 39

Sckrypczakowa, L. (1962) *Acta Polon. Pharm.* **19**, 491

Scora, R. W. (1966) *Plant and Soil* **24**, 145

Scora, R. W. (1967) *Am. J. Bot.* **54**, 446

Scora, R. W., England, B. A. and Bitters, W. P. (1966) *Phytochem.* **5**, 1139

Scora, R. W. and Torrisi, S. (1965) *Proc. Amer. Hort. Sci.* **88**, 262.

Sebe, J. (1943) *J. Chem. Soc. Jap.* **64**, 130

Seeligmann, P. and Alston, R. E. (1967) *Brittonia* **19**, 205

Seiferle, E. J., Johns, I. B. and Richardson, C. H. (1942) *J. Econ. Entom.* **35**, 35

Scikel, M. A., Hall, S. S., Feldman, L. C. and Koeppen, R. C. (1965) *Am. J. Bot.* **52**, 1046

Seshadri, T. R. and Vashista, K. (1963) *Curr. Sci.* **32**, 499

Sethi, M. L. and Atal, C. K. (1964) *Planta Med.* **12**, 173

Sfiras, J. (1952) *Recherches (Roure-Bertrand Fils)* No. 2, 39

Shah, C. S. and Khanna, P. V. (1965) *Lloydia* **28**, 71

Shah, C. S. and Sadji, A. N. (1966) *Planta Med.* **14**, 465

Sharma, R. G., Vardhan, C. and Shastry, S. G. (1953) *J. Sci. Industr. Res.* **12**b, 243

Shellard, E. J., Philipson, J. D. and Gupta, D. (1967) *Progr. Sci.* 27, *Congr. Int. FIP. Montpellier*, 100

Shellard, E. J. and Alam, M. Z. (1968) *Planta Med.* **16**, 127

Shibata, S. (1965) *Beiträge z. Biochemie Phys. Naturstoffen.* Ed. VEB Fischer, Jena

Shibata, S. and Hsön-Ching, G. (1965) *Phytochem.* **4**, 133

Shimizu, S. (1966) *Agr. Biol. Chem.* Tokyo **30**, 26

Shimizu, S. and Ikeda, N. (1958) *Bull. Agr. Chem. Soc.* **22**

Shimizu, S. and Ueda, H. (1962) *Perf. Record* **53**, 14

Shimizu, S., Ueda, H. and Ikeda, N. (1961) *Agr. Biol. Chem.* **25**, 263

(Shinkarenko, A. L. and Bondarenko, N. V.) Шинкаренко, А. Л., Бондаренко, Н. В. (1966) *Раст. Рес.* (Resources of plant origin) **8**, 368

Shinosaki, Y. and Nagasawa, T. (1929) *Rep. Imp. Ind. Res. Inst. (Osaka)* **10**, No. 9

(Shostenko, N. A., Dosjatkova, N. A. and Klokov, M. V.) Шостенко, Н. А., Досяткова, Н. А. и Клоков, М. В. (1936) *Тр. Бот. Инст. АзФАН* 2 (Works of Bot. Inst. Azerb. Fil. Acad. Sci.) **2**, 281

(Shtale, L. Zh.) Штале, Л. Ж. (1956) *Сбор. Научн. Работ. Рижск. Мед. Инст.* (Coll. Sci. Works of Rizhsk. Med. Inst.) **6**, 41

Siddiqui, S. (1939) *J. Indian Chem. Soc.* **16,** 421
Siddiqui, S. and Siddiqui, R. H. (1931) *J. Indian Chem. Soc.* **8,** 667
Sievers, A. F. (1913) *J. Agric. Res.* **1,** 129
Silber, A. (1952) *Pharmazie* **7,** 854
Silber, A. and Bischoff, W. (1954) *Pharmazie* **9,** 46
Silva, F. (1966) *Planta Med.* **14,** 302
Silva, M., Mancinelli, P. and Cheul, M. (1962) *J. Pharm. Sci.* **51,** 289
Simes, J. J. H, Tracey, J. G., Webb, L. J. and Dunston, W. J. (1959) *Commonw. Sci. Ind. Res. Org. Bull.* No. 208
Simonsen, J. L. (1922) *Indian Forest Rec.* **8,** 368
Singh, D. P. (1950) *Ind. Forest.* **76,** 288
Singh, J. and Rao, B. S. (1933) *J. Ind. Inst. Sci.* **15,** 79
Singh, G., Singh, T. and Handa, K. L. (1959) *Ind. Soap J.* **24,** 305
Slater, C. A. (1961) *J. Sci. Food Agric.* **12,** 257, 732
Slavik, B. (1950) *Stud. Bot. Czechoslov.* **11,** 226
Slavik, J. (1958) *Chem. Listy* **52,** 1957
Slavik, J. (1959) *Coll. Czech. Chem. Comm.* **24,** 2506
Slavik, J. (1960) *Coll. Czech. Chem. Comm.* **25,** 1738
Slavik, J. (1964) *Coll. Czech. Chem. Comm.* **29,** 1314
Slavik, J. and Appelt, J. (1965) *Coll. Czech. Chem. Comm.* **30,** 3687
Slavik, J. and Slavikova, L. (1954) *Coll. Czech. Chem. Comm.* **19,** 27
Slavik, J. and Slavikova, L. (1955) *Coll. Czech. Chem. Comm.* **20,** 31
Slavik, J. and Slavikova, L. (1959) *Coll. Czech. Chem. Comm.* **24,** 3141
Slavik, J. and Slavikova, L. (1963) *Coll. Czech. Chem. Comm.* **28,** 1728
Slavik, J., Slavikova, L. and Brabenec, J. (1965) *Coll. Czech. Chem. Comm.* **30,** 3697
Smith, D. M. (1968) *Am. J. Bot.* **55,** 739
Smith, D. M., Skakom, W. and Levi, L. (1963) *Agr. Food. Chem.* **11,** 268
Smith, D. M. and Levin, A. (1963) *Am. J. Bot.* **50,** 952
Smith, H. G. (1922) *J. Proc. Roy. Soc. N. S. W.* **56,** 181
Smith, R. H. (1964a) *Nature* **202,** 107
Smith, R. H. (1964b) *Phytochem.* **3,** 259
Smith, R. H. (1964c) *US Forest Serv. Res. Paper PSW* 15
Soine, O. T. and Willette, R. E. (1960) *J. Am. Pharm. Ass.* **49,** 368
(Sokolov, V. S.) Соколов, В. С. (1952) *Алкалоидоносные растения СССР* (Alkaloid containing plants in the USSR). Ed. Acad. Sci. (Moscow—Leningrad)
Sokolov, V. S. (1957) *Biochemie und Physiologie der Alkaloide*. Akademie Verlag, Berlin, 18
Sokolov, V. S. (1959) *Symp. Soc. Exp. Biol.* **13,** 230
Soldatovic, M. (1957) *Leukovite Sirie* **2,** 1. (Mat. Med.)
Soó, R. (1953) *Fejlődéstörténeti növényrendszertan* (Phylogenetical taxonomy). Tankönyvkiadó, Budapest
Soó, R. (1961) *Bot. Közl.* (Bot. Rec.) **49,** 145
Soó, R. (1963/64) *Bot. Közl.* (Bot. Rec.) **50,** 189, **51,** 227
Soó, R. (1964–1966) *A magyar flóra és vegetáció növényföldrajzi kézikönyve*. (Phytogeographic manual of Hungarian flora and vegetation) vols. I and II, Akadémiai Kiadó, Budapest
Soó, R. (1967) *Acta Bot. Sci. Hung.* **13,** 201
Soó, R. and Jávorka, S. (1951) *A magyar flóra kézikönyve* (Handbook of the Hungarian flora). Akadémiai Kiadó, Budapest
Sorm, F., Zaoral, M., Arient, J., Pliva, J. et al. (1951) *Coll. Czech. Chem. Comm.* **16,** 47
Sosa, A. (1951) *Bull. Soc. Chim. Biol.* **33,** 1679
Soucek, M., Herout, V. and Sorm, F. (1961) *Coll. Czech. Chem. Comm.* **26,** 803
(Sova, Z. V.) Сова, З. В. (1946) *Фармация* (Pharmacy) **9,** 27
Spehr, P. (1890) *Pharmakognostisch-chemische Untersuchung Ephedra monostachya*. Diss. (Dorpat)
Spoon, W. and Spruit, D. (1956) *Chem. Weekbl.* **52,** 580

Sprecher, E. (1958) *Pharmazie* **13,** 151

Srinath, K. V. and Ramaswamy, M. N. (1964) *Curr. Sci.* **33,** 346

Stahl, E. (1952) *Pharmazie* **7,** 863

Stahl, E. (1953) *Dtsch. Apoth. Ztg.* **93,** 487

Stahl, E. (1957) *Pharm. Weekbl.* **92,** 829

Stahl, E. (1964) *Arch. Pharm.* **297,** 500

Stahl, E. (1968) *Somm. Compt. Rend. IV. Cong. Int. Huiles Ess.* 208

Stahl, E. and Jork, H. (1964) *Arch. Pharm.* 297 273

Stahl, E. and Jork, H. (1966) *Arch. Pharm.* 299, 670

Stahl, E. and Scheu, D. (1966) *IV. Int. Symp. IUPAC* Stockholm Abstr. Books. 191

Stahl, E. and Schmitt, H. (1964) *Arch. Pharm.* **297,** 386

Staicov, V. and Tchigova, B. (1965) *III. Congr. Int. Ess. Oil* Sophia 294

Stapf, O. (1906) *Kew. Bull.* **8,** 297

Stary, F. (1960) *II. Congr. Biochemie und Physiol. d. Alkaloide* Jena

Stary, F. (1963) *Abhdg. Dtsch. Akad. Naturwiss.* No 4. Biochem. u. Physiol. Alkaloide, **175**

Steinegger, E. (1957) *Pharm. Weekbl.* **92,** 820

Steinegger, E., Bernasconi, R. and Ottaviano, G. (1963) *Pharm. Acta Helv.* **38,** 379

Steinegger, E., Bernasconi, R. and Ottaviano, G. (1963) *Pharm. Acta Helv.* **38,** 379

Steinegger, E. and Hänsel, R. (1963) *Lehrbuch d. allgemeine Pharmacognosie.* Springer Verlag (Berlin–Göttingen–Heidelberg)

Steinegger, E. and Peters, K. (1966) *Pharm. Acta Helv.* **40,** 385

Stermitz, F. R. (1967) *J. Pharm. Sci.* **56,** 760

Stermitz, F. R. (1968) *Rec. Adv. Phytochem.* vol. 1. 161

Sticher, O. and Flück, H. (1968) *Pharm. Acta. Helv.* **43,** 411

Stockmann, R. (1912) *Pharm. J.* **89,** 676

Stojanov, N., Panov, I., Ognianova, E. and Dimitrova, E. (1963) *III. Congr. Int. E/O* Sophia Abstr. 95

(Stojanov, N. and Savchev, P.) Стоянов, Н., Савчев, П (1964) *Фармация* (Pharmacy) **14,** 54

Stoll, A. (1942) *Schweiz. Pharm.* **45,** 53

Stoll, A. (1950) *Pharmazie* **5,** 328

Stoll, A. and Kreis, W. (1951) *Helv. Chim. Acta* **34,** 1431

Stoll, A. and Renz, J. (1956) *Verhandlungen Naturforsch. Ges.,* Basel **67,** 392

Stoll, A., Renz, J. and Brack, A. (1947) *Experientia* **3,** 115

Stuart, K. L. and Chambers, C. (1967) *Tetrahedron Letters* 2879

Suarez, L. R. (1952) *An. Ass. Quim. Uruguay* **52,** 48

Suominen, J. and Ahti, T. (1966) *Ann. Bot. Fenn.* **3,** 418

Sutherland, M. D. and Parks, R. (1967) In: *Terpenoids in Plants.* Ed. Pridham, Acad. Press, London

Svoboda, G. H., Shakovsky, G., Oliver, A. T., Diller, E. et al. (1954) *J. Am. Pharm. Ass.* **43,** 257

Swain, T. (Ed.) (1966) *Comparative Phytochemistry.* Academic Press, London and New York

Swalek, M., Bhasnan, B. and Sidhi, G. S. (1963) *Perf. Ess. Oil Rec.* **54,** 295

Swisher, H. E. (1966) *Perf. Ess. Oil Record* **57,** 771

Szász, K. and Márk, G. (1962) *Analysis of the Vinca minor alkaloids* (Manuscript)

Szendey, G. L., Renneberg, K. A. and Narborn, P. (1961) *Naturwiss.* **48,** 223

Tackie, A. N. (1959) *W.-Afric. Pharmacist* **1,** 10

Takeda, K. et al. (1954) *Pharm. Bull.* Tokyo **2,** 78

Takemoto, T. and Inagaki, N. (1958) *J. Pharm. Soc. Jap.* **78,** 289

Takemoto, T., Takahashi, N. and Nakajima, T. (1953) *J. Pharm. Soc. Japan* **73,** 1021, 1383

Talwar, Y. P., Nigam, M. C., Dutta, A. K. and Handa, K. L. (1961) *Ind. Perfum* **5,** 110

Talwar, Y. P., Nigam, M. C. and Handa, K. L. (1963) *Ind. Soap J.* **28,** 249

Talwar, Y. P., Nigam, M. C., Handa, K. L. and Kapoor, L. D. (1964) *Riechst. Arom.* **14,** 1

Tamm, Ch. (1957) *Fortschr. Chem. Org. Naturstoffe* **14,** 71

Tanhico, S. S. and West, A. P. (1933) *Philipp, J. Sci.* **52,** 263

Tardy, E. (1872) *Bull. Soc. Chim. France* **17,** 661

Targé, A. and Lambinon, J. (1965) *Bull. Soc. Roy. Bot. Belge* **98**, 295

Tatsuta, H. (1195) *Chem. Abstr.* **49**, 9634

Tayal, J. N. and Dutt, S. (1938) *Proc. Nat. Acad. Sci. India* **8**, 120

Tétényi, P. (1959) *Pharmazie* **14**, 696

Tétényi, P. (1961) *Pharmazie* **16**, 273

Tétényi, P. (1962) *Herba Hung.* **1**, 267

Tétényi, P. (1963) *Infraspecific chemical taxa and the breeding of medicinal plants.* Doct. Diss. Budapest

Tétényi, P. (1965) *Kísérl. Közl.* (Exper. Rec.) **53**C, 35

Tétényi, P. and Lőrincz, C. (1964) *Kísérl. Közl.* **57**C, 75

Tétényi, P., Tyihák, E., Máthé, I. and Sváb, J. (1962) *Pharmazie* **17**, 463

Tétényi, P., Tyihák, E., Máthé, I. and Sváb, J. (1964) *Pharmazie* **19**, 56

Tétényi, P. and Vágújfalvi, D. (1962) *Herba Hung.* **1**, 189

Tétényi, P. and Vágújfalvi, D. (1963) *Herba Hung.* **2**, 183

Tétényi, P. and Vágújfalvi, D. (1965) *Pharmazie* **20**, 731

Thoms, E. H. (1908) *Ber. Dtsch. Chem. Ges.* **41**, 2753

Thudim, F., Mohr, K., Schittler, O. and Reichstein, T. (1958) *Helv. Chim. Acta* **41**, 604

(Tomingas, A. J) Томингас, А. Й. (1958) *Сост. Раст. Ресс. СССР* (Situation of Plant Resources in the USSR) 312

Tomita, M. and Sugamoto, M. (1961) *J. Pharm. Soc. Jap.* **81**, 1090

Tomita, M. and Cang-Hsiung, Y. (1960) *J. Pharm. Soc. Jap.* **80**, 845

Tomko, J., Bendik, I. and Bauer, S. (1962) *Planta Med.* **10**, 138

Tomko, J., Bendik, I., Bauer, S. and Mokry, J. (1963) *Abhandlung. Dtsch. Akad. Wiss.* No **4**, 409

Tomova, M. (1955) *Bull. Inst. Bot. Acad. Bulg. Sci.* **4**, 277

Tomowa, M. (1962) *Planta Med.* **10**, 450

Tomowa, M. and Panowa, D. (1963) *Arch. Pharm.* **296**, 553

Toshiaki, T., Vorperian, E., Beal, J. L. and Cava, M. R. (1965) *J. Pharm. Soc.* **54**, 1389

Towers, G. H. N. and Maass, W. S. G. (1965) *Phytochem.* **4**, 57

Trautner, E. M. (1947) *Austr. Chem. Inst. J. Proc.* **14**, 411

Trojánek, J., Hodkova, J. and Cekán, Z. (1961) *Planta Med.* **9**, 200

Trzebny, W. (1967) *Pamietnik Pulawski* **25**, 45

Tschirch, A. (1917) *Handbuch der Pharmakognosie* **2**. *Aufl. Tauchnitz* Leipzig

Tsukamoto, T. and Yagi, A. (1959) *J. Pharm. Soc. Jap.* **79**, 1102

Tsukida, K. (1957) *Planta Med.* **5**, 97

Tucakov, J. (1960) *Parf. Cosm. Savon* **3**, 41

Tucakov, J. and Savin, K. (1960) *Mat. Med.* **5**, 19

Tunmann, P. and Racher, J. (1960) *Naturwissenschaften* **47**, 471

Turowska, I., Olesinski, A., Tym-Smajda, K. I. and Cybura, R. (1956) *Diss. Pharm.* **7**, 36

Turowska, I. and Skwara, J. (1959) *Acta Biol. Cracov.* **1**, 79

Turowska, I., Stepien, J., Tomczyk, H. and Liszkowska, M. (1940) *Prace Kom. Nauk Farm,* **1**, 117

Tuzson, P. and Kiss Z. (1957) *Acta Chim. Acad. Sci. Hung.* **12**, 31

Tuzson, P., Magyar, Gy. and Kiss, Z. (1958) *Acta Pharm. Hung.* **28**, 151

Tyihák, E. (1964) *Herba Hung.* **3**, 468

Tyihák, E. (1965) *Naturwiss.* **52**, 209

Tyihák, E. and Máthé, I. (1963) *Herba Hung.* **2**, 157

Tyihák, E., Máthé, I., Sváb, J. and Tétényi, P. (1963) *Pharmazie* **18**, 566

Tyihák, E., Sárkány, I. and Máthé, I. (1963) *Pharm. Zentralhalle* **102**, 128

Tyler, V. E. and Stuntz, D. E. (1963) *Lloydia* **26**, 158

Uchida, S. (1928) *J. Soc. Chem. Ind. Jap.* **31**, 650

Ueda, T. (1960) *Nippon Kagaku Zasshi* **81**, 1308, 1751

Ueda, T. and Fujita, Y. (1959) *Nippon Kagaku Zasshi* **80**, 1495

Ultée, A. K. (1937) *Rec. Trav. Chim. Pays-Bas* **56**, 409

Uota, H. (1937) *J. Dep. Agric.*, *Japan* **5**, 117
Uota, H. and Kondo, T. (1943) *J. Agr. Chem. Soc. Jap.* **19**, 355
Uota, H. and Nishida, K. (1935) *J. Agr. Chem. Soc. Jap.* **11**, 388
Uskert, A. (1960) In: *A Magyar Gyógyszeripari Kutató Intézet 10 éve* (10 years of the Hungarian Research Institute for Pharmaceutical Industry). Műszaki Kiadó, Budapest, 180
Utkin, L. A. (1959) Personal communication
Vágújfalvi, D. and Tétényi, P. (1965) *Pharmazie* **20**, 731
Vágújfalvi, D., Held, G. and Tétényi, P. (1966) *Arch. Pharm.* **299**, 812
Vale, de J. V. (1963) *Garcia de Orta* **11**, 107
Valentin, A. and Wagner, G. (1953) *Pharm. Zentralhalle* **92**, 354
Variati, G. (1954) *Ind. Perf.* **9**, 45
Varier, J. (1946) *J. Indian Chem. Soc.* **6**, 40, 48
Vashista, V. N. and Handa, K. L. (1964) *Soap Perfum. Cosm.* **37**, 135
Vashista, V. N., Nigam, M. C. and Handa, K. L. (1963) *Riechst. Arom.* **13**, 61
Vashista, S. K. and Siddiqui, S. (1914) *J. Indian Chem. Soc.* **18**, 641
Vaughan, J. G., Hemingway, H J. S. and Schofield, H. J. (1963) *J. Linn. Soc.* **58**, 435
Verghese, J. (1966) *Perf. Ess. Oil Rec.* **57**, 767
Vernazza, N. (1959) *Acta Pharm. Jugosl.* **9**, 9
Verzár-Petri, G. and Sárkány, S. (1961) *Planta Med.* **9**, 15
(Vetchinina, M. P.) Ветчинина, М. П. (1948) Разведение далматской ромашки (Cultivation of pyrethrum). In: Saraeva, Culture of medicinal plants, 1952, 45
Villalba, A. M. B., Medina, M. and Albarracin, L. (1945) *An. Soc. Biol. Bogota*, **1**, 189
Vodopivec, A., Sivec, S. and Tomasic, G. (1952) *Acta Pharm. Jugosl.* **2**, 41
Voight, R. (1958) *Scientia Pharm.* **26**, 83
Voigt, R. (1962) *Pharmazie* **17**, 101
Voskerusa, J. (1960) *Pharmazie* **15**, 552
(Voskresenskaya, G. S.) Воскресенская, Г. С. (1958) *Краткий Отчет ВНИИМЕМК* (Short Rec. of St. Sci. Res. Inst. Oil and Essential Oil Plants) for 1957, 37
Waal, de H. L., Neethling, L. P. and Perold, G. W. (1960) *J. S. Afr. Chem. Inst.* **13**, 45
Wall, M. E., Eddy,R. C., Willaman, J. J. and Correl, D. S. (1954) *J. Am. Pharm. Ass.* **43**, 503
Wall, M. E., Fenske, C. S., Garvin, J. M., Willaman, J. J. et al. (1959) *J. Am. Pharm. Ass.* **48**, 695
Wall, M. E., Fenske, C. S., Kenney, M. E., Correl, D. S. et al. (1957) *J. Am. Pharm. Ass.* **45**, 653
Wall, M. E., Fenske, C. S., Willaman, J. J., Correl, D. S. et al. (1955) *J. Am. Pharm. Ass.* **44**, 438
Wall, M. E., Willaman, J. J., Schubert, B. G., Garvin, J. W. et al. (1961) *J. Am. Pharm. Ass.* **50**, 1001
Wallach, A. (1941) *Arch. Pharm.* **272**, 393
Waller, G. R. and Regnier, F. E. (1966) *IV. Int. Symp. IUPAC* Stockholm Abstr. Book 170
Warnhoff, E. W. (1957) *Chem. and Ind.* 1385
Wasiczky, R. (1929) *Lehrbuch der Physiopharmakognosie der Pharmazeuten*
Webb, L. J. (1949) *Austral. Phytochem. Survey, C S I R O Bull.* 241
Webb, L. J. (1952) *Austral. Phytochem. Survey, C S I R O Bull.* 263
Wehmer, C. (1931) *Die Pflanzenstoffe*. 2 *Aufl.* Fischer Verlag, Jena
Wehrli, W., Schindler, C. and Reichstein, T. (1962) *Helv. Chim. Acta* **45**, 1183
Weizmann, A. (1952) *Bull. Res. Counc. Israel* **1**, 92
Werny, F. and Scheuer, P. J. (1963) *Tetrahedron* **19**, 1293
Wet, de J. M. S. and Scott, B. D. (1965) *Bot. Gaz.* **126**, 209
Wetter, L. R. (1955) *J. of Biochem. Physiol.* **33**, 980
Wetter, L. R. (1955) *J. of Biochem. Physiol.* **35**, 292
White, E. P. (1943) *N. Z. J. Sci. Techn.* **25**, 93
White, E. P. (1944) *N. Z. J. Sci. Techn.* **25**B, 146
White, E. P. (1946) *N. Z. J. Sci. Techn.* **27**B, 474
Wichmann, G. (1958) *Pharmazie* **13**, 487, 562, 718
Wichtl, A. and Fuchs, N. (1962) *Arch. Pharm.* **295**, 361
Widén, C. J. (1967a) *Farm. Notisblad* **76**, 185

Widén, C. J. (1967b) *Farm. Notisblad* **76,** 233
Widén, C. J. and Sorsa, V. (1966) *Hereditas* **56,** 377
Wieffering, J. H. (1966) *Phytochem.* **5,** 1053
Wieffering, J. H., Fikenscher, L. H. and Hegnauer, R. (1965) *Pharm. Weekbl.* **100,** 737
Wieland, T. and Wieland, O. (1959) *Pharmacol. Revs.* **11,** 87
Wight, W. (1958) *Nature* **181,** 893, 1355
Wight, W. and Barua, N. D. (1954) *Current Sci.* **23,** 78
Wilkinson, S. (1958) *J. Chem. Soc.* 2079
Williams, A. H. (1959) In: *Pharmacology of Plant Phenolics*, Academic Press, London
Williams, A. H. (1964) *Nature* **202,** 824
Williams, A. H. (1966) In: *Comparative Phytochemistry*. Ed. T. Swain. Academic Press, London and New York
Williams, A. L. and Bannister, M. H. (1962) *J. Pharm. Sci.* **51,** 970
Willis, J. L., McKern, H. H. G. and Hellyer, R. O. (1963) *J. Proc. Roy. Soc. N.S.W.* **96,** 59
Willuhn, G. (1966) *Planta Med.* **14,** 408
Winterfeld, K. and Bernsmann, G. (1960) *Arch. Pharm.* **293,** 991
Wirth, H. (1961) *Der rote Fingerhut*. Ziemsen Verlag, Wittenberg
Wong, E. and Francis, C. M. (1968) *Phytochem.* **7,** 2131, 2139
Woodward, E. F. and Smith, E. (1962) *Lloydia* **25,** 281
Wright, D. E. and Schofield, K. (1960) *Nature* **188,** 233
Wulff, H. D. (1954) *Arch. Pharm.* **59,** 529
Wulff, H. D. and Fritz, E. (1958) *Flora* **146,** 328
Wulff, H. D. and Stahl, E. (1960) *Naturwiss.* **47,** 114
Yasue, M., Itaya, M., Kaiya, T. and Wada, A. (1965) *Jakugaku Zasshi* **85,** 1090
(Yermakov, A. I.) Ермаков, А. И. (1960) *Зерновые и крупянные культуры, УАГН* (In: Cereals and crops) Ed. UAGN Kiev, 51
(Yermakov, A. I.) Ермаков, А. И. (1961) *Физиол. Раст.* (Plant Physiology) **7,** 447
Yones, T. G. H. (1937) *J. Proc. Roy. Soc. Queensland* **48,** 48
Yoshikosi, A. (1960) *Nippon Kagaku Zasshi* **81,** 981
Youngmann, B. J. (1952) *Kew. Bull.* **61**
(Yunusov, S. J. and Progressov, N.) Юнусов, С. Й., Прогрессов, Н. (1950) *Ж. Общ. Хим.* (J. Gen. Chem) **20,** 1151
(Yunusov, S. J.) Юнусов, С. Й. (1948) *Ж. Общ. Хим.* (J. Gen. Chem.) **18,** 515
(Yunusov, S. J.) Юнусов, С. Й. (1961) *Докл. АН ССР Узбек.* (Rep. Acad. Sci. Uzbek. SSR) **8,** 43
(Zabolotnaya, E. S.) Заболотная, Е. С. (1950) *Тр. ВИЛАР* (Works of St. Inst. Medicinal and Aromatic Plants) **10,** 129
(Zabolotnaya, E. S.) Заболотная, Е. С. (1959) *Тр. ВИЛАР* (Works of St. Inst. Medicinal and Aromatic Plants) **11,** 254, 387
Zaidi, S. and Gupta, G. (1962) *Ind. Oil Soap J.* **27,** 103
Zalkow, L. H., Park, M. K. and Ellis, J. W. (1963) *Perf. Rec.* **55,** 507
(Zaraiskaya, E. N. and Borisiuk, Yu. G.) Зарайская, Е. Н., Борисьюк, Ю. Г. (1957) *Тр. Харковск. Гос. Фарм. Инст.* (Works of Kharkov St. Pharm. Inst.) **1,** 105
Zavarin, E. (1966) *Chem. Engineering News* **44,** 5, 27
Zavarin, E. (1968) *Phytochem.* **7,** 92
Zavarin, E., Mirov, T. N. and Snajberk, K. (1966) *Phytochem.* **5,** 91
Zavarin, E. and Snajberk, K. (1965) *Phytochem.* **4,** 141
Zechner, L. (1966) *Die Glykoside*. Verlag Cramer, Weinheim
Zeijlemaker, F. C. J. and Mackenzie, A. M. (1965–66) *Rep. Wattle Res. Inst.* 57
Zellner, J. (1926) *Monatsch. Chem.* **46,** 309
(Zhukovski, P. M.) Жуковский, П. М. (1950) *Культурные растения и их сородичи. Советская Наука* (Cultivated plants and their relationship) Moscow
Zopf, W. (1907) *Die Flechtenstoffe*. Fischer Verlag, Jena
Zoschke, M. (1962) *Angew. Bot.* **36,** 185